BEAUTY FOR ASHES

BY CHRISTOPHER LA FARGE

▣▣▣▣▣▣

Beauty for Ashes

□□□□□□□□□□□□□□□□□□□□□□□□□□□□

CHRISTOPHER LA FARGE

". . . to give unto them beauty for ashes, the oil of joy for mourning, the garment of praise for the spirit of heaviness . . ."   Isaiah, 61:3

Coward-McCann, Inc.   New York

Prologue

FIRST look down from on high, it is all below you.
Seen from the air it's all seen: viewed in little,
sharp in October's whetting light. And time's
to bed with space to give her pregnancy
of new dimensions. Now three thousand feet
make maps of living and the devouring speed
is motionless. You see the shadowed dog's
sequence unmoving behind the shadowed horse
whose trot is undiscernible. The speeding
car's but the moveless symbol on a chart,
its noise absorbed in littleness. They're all fixed
in the long afternoon by house and house
on the unleading road that's but a thin stripe
between topographies. This Rhode Island village
is miniature in dwellings.
                          They're not less large
because you view them thus, down-looking, steep:
the microscope lends great stature to the germ
under the multiplication of so many watts,
but (knowing now how the cells branch and grow,
how multiply in the brilliance) who shall say
they are less in fact? The aggrandisement of the lens
lent but to you, not them: it made your eye
at last percipient.
                   This four-square base below you,
this stony relic of a once present house,
contained and harbored life in all the things
one man had gathered to sell. These many houses,

each lifted by its shadow toward the sun,
the unobtainable, and toward you, partly
obtainable, holds all the irrationals
of man's existence. Line on hard autumn line
they group together in the village pattern,
for fear, for hate, for love and its affection,
for sheer need and its goad, or because time
ordered the pattern, arbitrary, loose:
for springs, for contours, for the wayward sea.

Arm of the sea: a bay: that's vast enough
even from on high. Even the clouds propose
their time for its deep passage. But the sea,
it's not the independent thing the village is,
set in the small, close countryside.
                                        Sea waters
are tended by the wind, combed by the gale,
their shape is the moon's shape, they're nursed by dark
        clouds;
pale sun and lavender rain, the sounding fog,
the greens of night and double twilight's rose:
these are their dressers. Beauty of the sea
belongs to every vagrant weather tramp
that embraces it. Mountains and oceans both
are feminine in this.
                            The little village
close held in small land, all the growth of it,
all its environs, these are always same.
Arbutus, brier-rose, blood-red tupelo,
white house or red barn or grey shingled shed,
the elm in summer's lovelies, winter's bare grace,
the yellowing birch and sassafras, the line
of small, precise hills, granite's hard reminder
in the smooth ledge that's outcropped, these, all these
need neither sun nor rain nor dusk nor dawn
nor moon to be themselves, season on season,
perpetual, masculine.
                            Now from the evening air,
the place of absent clouds, in the long shadows,
there's pattern seen: village and land and bay,

x

ocean beyond, islands, the coloring woods,
and always trace of man.
                    Man.
                    It's the same trick
the lens played with the microbe (but reversed now):
you see what you did not see, the pattern's there
you did not realize: man in his little dwellings
forever in a pattern. Perception's granted,
briefly and swiftly, but half understood:
it is too wide to grasp.
Cling to it now though earth moves up to meet you,
though trees block trees from sight, this hill devours
house after house, these bushes hide all lovers,
the neat, thin ribbon of the air-viewed road
is soon invisible by its pretty slopes,
and the heard car's speed carries not to the eye.

But the pattern's always there: as God is there.
As fear and hate and greed and dread of night,
as envy, bitterness, or lust and sloth
lie ever within man's unshaken hope
(within his dignity as the child of God),
so is the female, variable sea
held in the land's perpetual, virile arms,
and all within a scheme so high and vast,
so small, so miniscule, that our dull eyes
are troubled to see it.
                    But the pattern's there.

BOOK ONE

Theme

LONELINESS is a garment you must wear:
it clothes you fully and intact from birth,
and all the years you gasp for needed air
it covers you, until again in earth
your nakedness companions naked ground
and makes a pact with the bold colder soil
to let you lie in harmony without sound,
become at last the fellow of time's toil.
Then do not mend that garment, let it fray,
leave rent and rip and ragged rough-fringed hole,
let ravelled threads that living wore away
give entrance to your over-covered soul,
for if you mend or if you buy anew,
through all eternity loneliness is you.

ROCHESTER MALLIN dried himself in the thick
warmth of the big towel, put on his gown
of the grey silk with the yellow silk lining,
and left the bathroom. His dressing room felt chilly
after the steamy heat. Out of his window
he saw the lights of the village of Chogs Cove
make darts of gold in the harbor's stilly surface,
and a few stars, polished toward winter's brilliance,
hung in the green and vanishing afterglow
of the western evening.
                    "October," he said, "already.
The time's gone fast. Too little to show. Too much
extraneous doing, like this damn trip today
up to New York and back for nothing. I wonder

3

if I am doing these things because I'm afraid
that I'm running dry?"
                                He felt the weight of the day,
that had made so little, drag at his back and shoulders.
"The bath," he thought, "it has almost lost its magic.
I need a good day, a flowing, a gushing day—
or perhaps a little bit less than fifty years
to weigh me down—and a little less self-indulgence
in the scatter of effort."
                                He flicked the lights on then
in the two Wedgwood urns now candelabras,
and he brushed his thick grey hair.
                                "Not bald," he said.
"Not fat. Still fit. I wish to the very devil
this Hearing wasn't tonight, a cursed nuisance."
He went to the other door and he knocked.
                                                "Serena,"
he called out loudly. He heard his wife's clear voice
say, "Just a minute, please."
                                To himself he said,
you needn't worry. I don't want to come in.
You can cover your body in layer on layer of silk
and hide what you've got, for all of me, my girl.
Aloud he said, "I simply wanted to know,
what the hell do we wear?"
                                Faintly and through the wood
he heard her say, "Oh, wear a tweed, grey flannels,
something like that. It's no place to be dressy."
"Thanks," he called.
                        "You can come in, Roche," she said.
"It's all right now."
                        "Never mind," he said. "Don't bother.
That's all I wanted to know." And he turned away
thinking, 'to know' was added for pure politeness.
How rarely I do want more!
                                But it wasn't quite true
and he knew it wasn't. The 'more,' he thought, I want
from somebody else, some nameless somebody else.
I've got a block in me that makes it, keeps it
nameless. The work. It ought to go better. It would

4

if the somebody had a name.
                              He heard the familiar
sound of the motor, saw the green light moving
double over the mirror of the harbor.
"Late for lobstering. Might be Walter Hoxsie.
Will he come to the Hearing?"
                              He picked out a brown
            tweed jacket,
a pair of dark grey, heavy flannel trousers,
a pair of brown shoes with their thick crepe soles,
and he started to dress.
                         "If I wear a flannel shirt
I'll sweat at the meeting. Well, it's good to be hot,
but not that sort of heat."
                         He chose blue cotton,
with a handsome foulard tie. He was almost dressed
when he heard Serena's knock.
                         "Come in," he said.
He looked at his wife when she came into the room
because he was used to looking. Her soft grey hair
was neat as always. She wore a dark green skirt
with a plaid pattern and a grey green blouse
with a yellow jersey. Whatever else you might say,
she was well got up, she was always well got up.

"You'd better hurry, Roche, if you want a cocktail.
I've ordered supper ready for sharp six-thirty."
"Why," he said, "do you say, 'if I want a cocktail'?
I always want one. We speak in a sort of empty
set of formulae."
                  "Did you have a poor day, dear?"
He put on his jacket.
                  "No worse than usual.
I kidded myself, I'm awfully good at that.
I took my work along, it had a nice trip
all the way to New York, all the way home—
and nothing done. I'd thought—or pretended to think—
I'd work on the plane. I didn't. I should have known
better than that."
                  "Oh, I am sorry," she said.

5

"Yes, so am I. I let myself be seduced
by the view from the plane window. It flew well east.
I recognized Naius River, I could see
the old Standeven place. It's curious, too,
you could still see the formal pattern of gardens
abandoned—how many years?"

                          "Long time," she said.
"Six or seven at least."

                    "I guess," he said.
"It was so clear I could see the village too,
and I think I spotted the pattern of the foundations
of the Ben Sweet house. It's little things like that
seduce the mind and get between me and work.
Do we have to go to this wretched thing this evening?"
"You don't," she said. "For myself, I wouldn't miss it.
There'll be some sort of a row—the sort of cold
New England row, quiet, bitter, and full
of remarkable phrases. I couldn't bear to miss it.
Don't go if you'd rather not."

                              "Will your mother go?"
"I promised we'd pick her up." She ran her hand
a little nervously over her well-waved hair.
"You know Mother."

                  "God, yes," he said. "She'd feel
she was letting the whole community down with a bang
if she didn't show."

                    "Perhaps in fact she would be,"
Serena said.

            He laughed and he said, "Let's go.
Let's get that cocktail."

                        "Cocktails," she said. "Remember
your formulas."

              Mallin went over to the door
that led to the hall and he opened it for his wife.
"Who will be there?" he asked as they walked downstairs.
"Who engineered this thing?"

                            "I guess it was Mother,"
Serena answered. "I know she talked to Jerome,
and Jerome talked about it to Quintus Lamy.
Then Mother began to move."

6

"I'll bet she did.
Then Quintus will surely be there. I guess Virginia
will lie at home?"
                    "She's sick again," said Serena.
"A cold or something. She's grown so terribly thin,
it leaves her vulnerable."
                    "It does," he said.
"But she makes it happen, a little. They've got a word
for that sort of thing now. Psychosomatic.
It fits her well."
                    "Oh, no!" Serena said.
"Oh, yes," he said, and he added without a pause,
"Hard on Lamy. And used to be hard on Messler.
Maybe that's why he left her."
                    "Cruel," she said.
Mallin smiled and he poured gin and vermouth
into the silver shaker and added ice.
"Will Jennifer be there?" He began to shake
the cocktail skilfully. Serena waited
till he was done.
                    "I suppose she will," she said.
"She's turned a corner. She's a young woman now."
"I've noticed," Mallin said with his back to his wife,
dryly. "If I were Lamy I think I'd show
less—well, affection for a grown young woman
who wasn't my proper daughter."
                    "Oh?" said Serena.
She took the cocktail he gave her, said, "Happy days,"
and drank. "Well, she'd better be your inducement,
you can look at her, it'll pay you back for coming."
"It'll take more than that," he said. "Great God,
even in this small, narrow, out-of-the-way
backwater of living there always seem to be
demands, demands. Will you do this or that,
will you attend this, serve on that committee,
see that the wheels go round, help raise a fund—
oh, Lord knows what! How shall I keep my mind
fallow and fertile for the enriching thoughts
that make a book, in the end, more than some pages
with words impressed on them? Isn't the poor subconscious

7

drowned in the waters of these trivial things?
That's why I'm empty, that's why the damned page
stares back at me."

"May I have another martini?"
Serena said. She watched her husband's face
as he filled her glass again. His expression showed
gloom and dissatisfaction.

"Let these things
fill up your reservoir then," she said. "But even
if they deplete you, how shall you then be you,
Rochester Mallin, man of the earned distinction,
and avoid the fruits, the tokens, of your position?"
"Position, hell," he said. "If I have a position
it's because I'm well-to-do and married a Gosford
in Gosfordville which is usually called Chogs Cove.
Who reads my books?"

"Everyone here," she said.
"With admiration. Indeed, if you come to that,
even the Gosfords."

He looked at her keenly then
and he said, "You do it well, damn well, Serena.
Oil on the troubled waters. But it is still
a formula. Empty."

"Nonsense," she said. "Let's eat,
if you're ready now."

"I'm ready," he said. "I'm hungry."
"Good," said Serena. She rose then from her chair
and moved ahead to the dining room. He followed,
thinking, it's an odd form of hunger, though,
more than for food, and God himself alone knows
how one can satisfy it.

◻◻◻◻◻◻

WILL YOU be part of the whole rhythm of life,
richer for poorer, the gain or the loss forgotten?
Will you take love and its sister hate to wife,
and the health that's glory, the sickness that turns you
        rotten?
Will you make something fresh of the rancid day,
and spice the flat dull measure of common hours?
Will you seek wisdom all the long, groping way,
even while ignorance innocence deflowers?
Look in the pit, then, where the fires of hell
melt the bright metals to dull residues,
look at the dayspring's promise and know it well,
its punctual renewal your love renews,
and in the end through even the bitter pain
you shall be whole in all of your parts again.

NOW AT THE END of the day, the day's work done.
(that is never done, that waits for the near tomorrow,
the drawings pinned to the boards, the blueprints rolling
into fat tubes of white, the tracing linen
color of dusk, invisible in the evening,
under the night light, needing you and light
to make a meaning),
Quintus Lamy drove to his house. It lay
halfway along the narrow and winding road
from Chogs Cove village to Hoxsies Cove, where the little
bungalows (perched as though they might all take off
at a loud noise) made their straight close rows
dark in October darkness, autumn depriving
them of their meaning, as the extinguished green-shaded
lamps set drawings at rest: into night's nothing.
The drawings would live tomorrow. The little houses
must wait in the winter months and the chilly spring
for the summer's living.
                        The mind, he thought, my mind,
once it gets going, revolves too fast. And now
it must go again tonight. I shouldn't have let it

run so hard in the day with night to follow.
He parked the car by the door and he went inside.
"Hallo!" he called. "Is there anyone in this place?"
What odd, repetitive things one said! What curious
hopes persist in the heart!
                              "Hello," his wife called,
her deep and husky voice from the living room,
and the warm light came from the room to the darker hall
and the voice had light. "This house is bulging full.
Be joyful, you."
                    He hadn't expected this,
and it took him aback. It ought to have been his daughter
who called from the room.
                              He threw his coat and hat
on the hall bench, seeing and hardly seeing the coats,
the gloves, the sweaters, the school bags and the pencils,
the red hat and the blue cap and the football,
the leather handbag, that told him his son Edwardus
was home, and Jennifer too.
                              And Jennifer too . . .
the thought came and was brushed aside, too quickly.
Why should I brush it aside?
                              He walked directly
into the living room. A fire was burning,
its flames said comfort and welcome and this is home,
the table by the sofa was set with tea things,
the copper kettle, the silver pot, and the glinting
of silver spoons in the pale blue saucers holding
the fluted cups. The smell of tea was pungent
in the warm air.
                    "But this is great!" said Lamy.
"Tea and a fire—and you downstairs!" He stood
and looked for a moment, still moved by his surprise.
"How did you get down here?"
                              "Isn't it lovely?
Jennifer helped me. Darling, I felt I had to,
sick of the bed, and I felt better too,
no pain at all today. Not all day long!
Isn't that wonderful?"
                        "Wonderful," he said.

10

"Guinevere Lovelace came, she's free now, darling,
she's going to come each day. So I thought how good
to have tea for you for a change. I knew you'd be
weary with all the work and the Hearing early.
High tea instead of supper—is that O.K.?"
"Perfect," he said. "Too tired now to be hungry.
If I ate a full meal now, why, I'd sleep at the Hearing,
and that would never do."
                         "I know," she said.
"Oh, it's good to be here! So good to feel
almost human once more!" But suddenly then
she began to weep, not sobbing, a silent weeping,
the large tears falling. "Oh, God!" she said, "it's hell
to be so useless, a weight!"
                         A weight, he thought,
and felt it descend. The effort, now, make the effort.
He crossed the room and he came to her and bent
and kissed her. She did not move, the easy tears
flowed still, were salty upon his lips. He said,
"Forget it now. You're here, and there's no pain,
a fine tea and a fire, and I am home
ready for both, and you."
                         "Oh, yes," she said.
"You're always ready, you're wonderful to me,
you try so hard—for what? What do you get?
My illness, my complaints, my uselessness—
what sort of wife is that? God, I can't move
even to pour your tea, I'm such a coward,
afraid of the movement that may start the pain,
and always, always so!"
                         "Come on," he said.
"I'll hoist you up, a pillow, you'll be all right,
you'll pour my tea and have some for yourself
and then, first thing you know, I'll have to be
firm with you to prevent your trying to go
up to the Hearing! So—like this."
                         He reached out,
lifted her gently, put a cushion behind her.
He felt her thinness enter his arms like pain.
"Isn't that better?"

11

He watched her face contort
into a smile. He took his handkerchief
and dried her eyes, her face.
                              "Now, tea!" he said.
"I'm famished for it."
                              "Oh," she said, her voice
clouded and husky, "oh, you are so sweet."
Then, with an effort. "Now. The tea. Oh, Q,
I'm sorry I made a scene!"
                              "Forget it now.
Where are the children?"
                              Gingerly she began
to pour his tea. "They're both upstairs," she said.
"Jenny's policing Eddie, he came home filthy.
Even that I can't do. It sometimes hurts me
to watch her move, so graceful, I remember
when I could move like that."
                              "Small boys," he said.
"They're always dirty." Within himself he knew
he couldn't bear any more of her troubles now.
"I guess it's just normal to their age and weight."
"I made him wash," she said.
                              "A trial, indeed,"
Quintus said, and he laughed. To his relief
his wife laughed too.
                              "They'll be right down," she said.
"Now have your tea, it's hot. And tell me, Q,
about your day. I feared that you'd be home late."
"I couldn't help it," he said. "The work piles up.
Rochester's Barn, and the scheme for the Ellett's house—
if ever they do make up their minds to build.
I was going good, I was knocking it off for fair.
I shouldn't have come at all, I'd have stayed right at it,
if it hadn't been for tonight."
                              "I'm glad you couldn't.
I needed you here—the tea, the voyage downstairs,
and all the rest of it. Quintus, who takes the· meeting?
Oh, God, I wish I really were up to going."
"Jacob Ledbetter," Quintus said, "for the Council,
he's head of the Zoning now. He's a damn good man.

12

They seem to think up Cottrellton way there'll be
a pretty good turnout, mostly folks from here.
Mrs. Gosford goes, of course, she really began it,
and Jerry Westen will be there, I'm glad of that."
"Good," she said. "Serena has said she's going,
and she's taking Rochester too."
                              "She's not!" said Quintus.
"I don't believe it. How in hell did she do it?"
"I don't know," Virginia replied. "She simply told me
he said he'd go. Just that—and just like that.
Being Serena, she didn't allow surprise
to show in her voice at all. She builds him up,
she always has. She's clever. In spite of the fact
that she's my cousin, I think Serena's ruthless
where Rochester is concerned."
                              "Only Rochester?"
"Don't be small," she said. "Henry Dexter's going,
I guess he'll take his wife. And they say that Jerry
has made the Hoxsies go because Walter knew
the Sweet house in the days when old Deborah's father
still was alive there."
                              "Good," said Lamy, "good.
That's what we need. I'll bet Jerry Westen got him.
It would be like him."
                              "Serena said lots of others,"
Virginia said. "There's going to be old Miss Hall,
and both the Congdons, and naturally Hetty Browne.
I guess she wouldn't miss it."
                              "The sparks will really
fly if she's there," he said, "with Walter Hoxsie.
It ought to be quite a meeting. I'm awfully glad
Jacob Ledbetter's in the chair. But it's a pity
to have to have this sort of a row at all.
It's going to rake up a lot of the old hatreds,
the ancient feuds, the bitterness. In some ways
I'd rather let Kellam build his store as he wants it,
instead of stopping him—if we still can stop him—
at such a cost."
                              "But Q," Virginia said,
"it'd hurt the village. You know it'd hurt the village."

13

"Yes," he said. "I know. And that's why I'm going.
But I hate to see it happen this way. It's funny—
there'll be Rochester—yes, and Serena too—
and all of us on the same side for different reasons!
For an immediate gain, we pay a high cost
in future effort. Well. More of the good tea, please,
it goes to the right spot."

        "Neat!" said a voice in the
      doorway.
"Look at that cake!" And a boy rushed into the room
and around the sofa, skidded the rug to wrinkles,
and seized on a cup-cake frosted with yellow icing.
"Put it down," said his father. "Put it straight back."
The boy looked at him and hesitated. "You heard me,
      Eddie."
"Why do I have to put it back? Jennifer said
if I got washed up and changed and my shirt tucked in,
I could have some cake to begin with."

        "Put it down,
put the cake in the plate, darling," Virginia said.
"Do that first."

        Reluctantly the boy did it.
"Good," said Quintus. "Now, child, just say good evening."
"Good evening, Pops. Can I have the cake now?"

            "Yes,
you can have the cake."

        The boy reached down at once
and took the cake and bit half into his mouth.
"That's good," he said, and his voice was clouded with
      crumbs.
"You don't make Jennifer always say good evening
and all that sort of junk."

        "Good evening, Q,"
said a girl's clear voice.

        "Oh, you!" her half-brother said.
"You heard me, Jenny. You did it just to be mean.
Angel Jenny."

        Quintus turned round and said,
"Good evening, love. And there just might be a shadow,
a faint suspicion of truth in what Eddie says."

She made a face at him and she said, "My manners
are mine, and yours and Mummy's are your generation's.
I'm sure it must be hard for you, at your age,
to adjust to the change."
                                Virginia frowned and said,
"Sit down and have your tea. You're nineteen, Jenny,
and you try to sound like thirty."
                                The girl just smiled,
and she moved a chair up close to the big tea table
and sat with her back to the fire.
                                My God, thought
        Quintus,
she's pretty, she moves well. I wonder if that's the way
Virginia looked when she married Jimmy Messler.
But she was twenty then, the girls were younger
than now they are. She doesn't look like her mother,
nor like her father. Throwback to somebody else.
"How did it go?" he said.
                                "Not bad," said Jennifer.
"Never really bad—or good. He's a stuffy teacher,
old Mensinger. He knows his stuff. He draws
like a crooked angel, he knows his paints and colors,
but, jeepers, he sees things through a sort of lens
he must have inherited from his great grandfather.
He can't take my kind of stuff, he just can't see it.
He lets me do it, it hurts him, he really twitches.
I know it hurts him and that upsets me too.
I can't go on forever with him."
                                "You study
forever with no one," Quintus said. "That's so.
But get what he has to teach before you leave him."
"I hope it won't corrupt me," she said. "I want
to be free soon, before he cramps me. I want to study
with people who see like me and paint like me.
If it wasn't for you and Mummy, I swear I'd die.
He's stuffy, that's the trouble." She giggled. "His painting
is like your manners."
                                They all laughed then. Virginia said,
"Q is right, though. Stick it a little longer.
She wants to go to the meeting, Q."

15

"Oh, does she?"
Quintus could feel a happy warmth run through him,
but he dared not look at his wife for fear he'd see
the expression her voice said was upon her face.
"Good enough," he said. "Is Harlow coming down here?
We could take him along if he were."

"No," Jennifer said.
"He's not coming down this week-end. Boston's charms.
And I want to go with you."

The boy said, "Mummy,
can I have some more sugar in this? Are you going to marry
Harlow Standeven, Jenny?"

"Oh, don't be a goon,
a little, precocious, nine-year-old little goon,
who's got to be helped to wash."

"I don't have to be
helped,"
Eddie said. "I just like some company, that's all,
it's lonely upstairs alone. Can I go to the meeting?
It's Friday night."

Funny, thought Quintus Lamy,
I ought to be pleased.

"Do you really want to go?
You're sure?"

"Sure," said the boy. "And Jennifer said
there might be a fight there."

Quintus laughed aloud.
"That sort of a fight would bore you, Eddie," he said.
"He'd be bored to tears," said Jennifer, "the poor lamb.
He'll twitch on the hard seats. Listen, Eddie, my love,
it'll be like church, only longer, and no singing,
and a very long sermon."

"Oh," said the boy. "That's
dumb.
I don't want that."

"I'll play you a game," said Virginia.
"You keep me company. Eat some sandwiches, Eddie,
no more cake till later. This is your supper, dear."
"O.K.," said the boy.

"Good, then," said Virginia.

Good, though Quintus. I really didn't want Eddie.
Because he is too little? Because I'm tired?
Because of his energy, or the young, incessant
demands of childhood? The question after question?
You shouldn't get tired like this, to the stupid point
where you can't cope with the sweet, the loving duty,
the good rewarding duty. Or is it that?
Or is it something else? Virginia is well—
well for the moment. Why isn't that enough,
why does one look ahead, always and always,
to a future trouble?
    "We had better be off now.
Have you eaten, Jennifer?"
        "Yes," she said, "I've eaten.
I'll get my coat." She rose and she left the room
as a shadow runs over a hill with the wind's urging
of the plentiful cloud.
        "Will you be late?" said Virginia.
"Yes," he said. "It'll drag on late, I guess,
and once we're there, we'd better not leave till the end.
We'll be quiet getting home."
        "Good. Remember
  everything,
I'll want to hear it."
     "I shall," he said. "Good night,
sleep well." He kissed her.
      A kiss, he thought, become
a hunger sated in sleep and the long awakening
ringed in friendship as Saturn is ringed in moons,
the embracing, untouching circle
of the dusty moons.
      "Good night, my son," he said.
"I'll see you tomorrow morning."
        He went to the hall
and he put on his coat and hat. As he waited there
he could hear the step, the delicate tap,
the light descending, the soft approaching,
the sound of Jennifer.

◻◻◻◻◻◻

BREATHE IN the daily air for body, not mind:
mind is the body's tool, instinct's true reason;
blood is for running in the long, designed
rivers of body, no matter mental season.
Hurry because you must or rest for good rest,
sleep's but the harvest of your waking hours,
passion's for simple having on receptive breast,
thought's hunger soon all fruit of love devours.
Goodness intends the nature of your whole man,
let the faults go, they're nothing more than faults,
failure was in you before ever thought began,
success is you that over failure now vaults.
Breathe in the daily air, the shared hot, the lone cold,
there's time for living before the flesh is grown old.

SUPPER to cook now. Children all in the parlor. I hope
        Edyth,
lovely, an eye on Freddie, to keep at four; adorable. How
did we not want him? Three girls then and the hot sun,
pine needles and mid-summer, never did get the pine gum
from the cotton, blue, pretty print gone.
Edyth ought to be done now, six o'clock,
all their homework. Supper early, Hearing. Sometimes
wish to be just alone, just me, sort out house and mind,
        easier
being alone. Butter now, ice-box. Jerry.
Jerry and Millicent, Millicent and Jerry, which
first now? Marriage is
love but the daily.

                "Tell me, Jerry,
why do they all gang up so? What have they got
against Sueton Kellam?"

Smokes too much, he always
has to clear his throat. That draught in the kitchen! Cool
air like fingers too light. His voice
always young.

18

"They're not ganging up, Millie.
Kellam bought this, he knew the zoning laws. He's tried
to get away with it—and they're just smarter than he is.
I'll say this, Millie, it makes me laugh, by God, it's funny,
the people who get together to move against him."

Second burner, back one, I wish I didn't always
turn on the front. So. Half a mind.
                              "What way funny?"
That draught! Being touched when you're only tired, like
cold drip in hot tub on ankle flesh. Smoke
in the eyes or finger of air on neck skin. Oh,
when the fan comes. Ventilator.
                              Love
his voice, warm.

"What way funny? Why, the combinations, ones on the
          one side,
the ones on the other. Nobody much in the middle.
Chogs Cove, Jesus! It gets together
only to fight. We're funny that way. There's Mrs. Gosford,
Serena, even the great man, Mister Rochester Mallin,
          author,
the Messlers—with Henry Dexter and, listen, Millie,
with Walter Hoxsie. You know
you got to giggle at that one. Walter! All in the same boat,
          all
lined up together against Sueton Kellam—and of course,
against Hetty Browne, too, and who is with her?
Anna J. Hall, my gosh!"

Loretta Messler. I wish . . . no, won't think
ever again. War. Having
Freddie, no, won't think. Listen.
                              "I hear
Rose Peckham is going. You know you got to laugh, Millie.
Clifford Peckham, that dope!
He's a cousin to Hetty Browne and I reckon they all
have a finger in Kellam's pie. What'll Rose do, Millie?

Stick with her folks, her father, with Henry Dexter?
Or be a good little, loyal, obedient wife
to dopey Clifford?"

When he laughs, I laugh too. God! glad
not married to Clifford then. What did I do
with the butter? Oh, yes. Laughter
wraps love warm and cozy.
                              Sound of faint music.
                                                "Listen!
Is that the radio, Jerry? I told them not. I know
they haven't finished their homework, not yet."
Goes to the door, shouts through, big voice, couldn't
sound fierce if he tried. Sweet.

"Who turned that radio on?"
                              Silence, music, the faint
          sound
stops. Bet it was Emily, loves her music, I love
music, love his grin now, sits
down again. Weary. Sometimes I'm
cross with the children, curious, nothing
ever can make him cross. Angry yes, not cross, goes
as clouds go, fair, storm,
wind of his own, his sun, his shadow
color my hours.
                    "But Walter Hoxsie, Jerry!
Who got Walter to go? Did you do that?"

"That's right, I did it. But actually it was old
Lady Gosford, she was the one remembered. By God,
she never forgets, the elephant. She had me come in,
she gave me tea. You know the method. She said,
'Now listen to me, Jerome, in the high and far-off days—'
the way that woman talks!—
'in the high and far-off days when Mr. Hoxsie's'—
she always calls him mister, though I'm Jerome to her, I
          guess
it's a sort of compliment—anyway, she said, 'When Mr.
          Hoxsie's

20

mother was still alive, he knew the family, he knew
old Benjamin Sweet. A mean and a close old man. I never
liked Mr. Sweet. Poor Deborah! What a tragic life
the poor thing lived in her youth! As bad, I believe,
as the sort of thing the Brontës wrote of, isn't it?' "

Laugh. Really
he makes me laugh, makes voice
sound so like Mrs. Gosford. Oh, dear,
nothing to wipe eyes, apron, yes. Wonder
what it's like to live so you talk like that, keep
cook and a maid, guests? Now salt.
And cover, where cover, the double boiler, oh, yes, there,
there you are, on. A cook,
mess up the kitchen not hers. Voice
his own now, sometimes
his voice at night the sound of strong swift water,
deep river, carries me
on its flowing, silver, silver. Be carried
lovely in darkness.

"Well, whether old Ben Sweet was
mean or not—but I guess the old girl's right,
he probably was—I was too young to know. But Walter
was in and out of that house before the days his cousin
Sarah came to live with him. He knew it. People say
he knew Deborah too well. There's no love lost, though,
between him and Hetty Browne or him and Sueton. The
        stories
they spread about Walter!"

Means to say Sarah? Poor thing. There,
about all, five minutes, table all set. Ah!
                                        "Jerry!
Don't put ashes on my clean plates."
                                "I'll wash it.
Do you want to go?"
                "Go where?"
"To the meeting, sweetie-pie, going to be quite a meeting.

Ledbetter takes it. Come along. You could learn
plenty tonight."

Wish I could, part. The night drive, cool
air of October, big stars, being
alone with Jerry, and people later.
                              "There's no one
to stay home. Edyth and Emily, both made dates
with the Lyttleton girls. And Justine, she's got
a cold now. I'd better stay. I don't want Freddie
running around the house in bare feet."
                              "Tell him not to.
Leave him. Come on! It's going to be something, Millie."
"I can't, Jerry, I can't, dear. Will you
be home late?"
                "Late, yes. I guess I will."
"Jerry, then wake me."

Yes, he says, whisper, you he says, rises. Not now!
"Call the kids now, Jerry."
                        Coming toward me.
                                        "Supper."
Not to the door but me. Ah, how simple
man's current! Complex the wanting
and the not wanting in me. Weary, to be alone
not lonely, ever the combination?
"Call them, Jerry. No more!"
                        "No more—now."
Laughs. Even his back, the wide
shoulders (goes to the door) mine, saying love, mine—
now supper! Bread in the oven, goodness, forgot it, I
can forget plenty sometimes. Deep tide
rose and falls, why always
tide or cloud, or long searching sun,
storm, cool stars, huge moon, soft grey
of before-dawn—thinking of him not thinking? Always
nature, colors of sweet lingered autumn, smell
of wilding apple in pasture, grapes,
spring rain touching
body of earth, my body, weary. The children. Now!

22

Supper! Later, Jerome, wake
softly later, later, this
is the sleep now, unknowing, unfeeling,
buried beneath of living.
                    "Hi, kids!

Supper's ready!"

So sweet. Love
has a thousand faces.

□□□□□□

OH, TELL ME, tell me, did you give too much
too soon, too suddenly, beyond your will?
Did war, fatigue, and boredom's wasting touch
empty your years before your years could fill?
Or did you find simplicity too soon,
all life revolved about a single point
as though the sun of hate should glare at noon
forever vertical in time's disjoint?
Can you not rest now? Or do day on day
pile up their constant hours in demands
for payments heaped beyond the means to pay,
deeper than drifts, more infinite than the sands?
Patience! Until the drifts of debt become
riches you cannot reckon up the sum.

"TURN OFF that God damned radio. How in hell can a man
        study
when that thing bleats and bleats?"
                        (Why do I, Harlow
        Standeven—
whoever that is other than a name once given—
sound so savage? Or feel so savage so often? What makes me
yell and be angry? And at a man like Fatso?)
                        "O.K., Harlow.
It bleats no more. It's little heart bleats
for you, Jack. Bleats blut, drip by drip, Jack. Now, Jack,

23

you happy, Jack?"
                    "Yes, Jack."
(You pick it up and play with it, throw it back, until guilt
is turned to laughter, laughter to love?)
                                        "That's good, Jack.
What you trying to do, become a scholar? Studying, Jack?"
"Yes, Jack. At eleven o'clock on Monday, in Room X
on the second floor of Sever, home of the brave,
you will present yourself, in person it says here, and
there will be served refreshments, Jack, all written out on paper."
"Ah, yes. The fun and games department, the little gambols
        laughingly
called Hour Exams, I know, Jack, I have heard of them. They're
very amusing. Well, Jack,
no more radio. Study, Jack. Even at our advanced age Jack
can jack himself up, Jack."
                        "Look, Fatso, jack yourself off."
"Tut, and again tut. Is this the sort of cross but rugged expression
you learnt when you were in the Service, grandpaw?"
                                            "Yes, son."
"You must of learnt a lot in the Service, grandpaw. Was it
in the Great Global War?"
                        "Yes, the Great Global War."
"Well, tell me, grandpaw,
will you agree that the great globular war could easily
be called the Globaldegook? Or, following out the idea
of Higher Warfare—that was a poem by Longfellow,
        Higherwarfare—
be just called War-war Tafu, little Firefly?"
                                        "The great
unbuttoned firefly?"
                    "Or perhaps unzippered.
The Fly in the Ointment, the Fly in Forever Amber. Tell me,
is this the war you mean?"
                        "I guess so, sonny."
"Tell me more, grandpaw. What sort of war was War-war?"
"I'll tell you, son, in just one phrase: Far Flung."
                                        "Ah, far flung.
Yes. I'll tell my grandchildren that I learned that phrase
at the knee of Lieutenant Commander Harlow Standeven,

24

U.S.N.R., retired. So it was far flung?"

"The farflungest
war yet, son. Yes, sir, by God, far flung. Even
the admirals were far flung where I came from. And the nurses."

"Tell me, grandpaw, were you far flung?"

"Well, yes and no, son.
There were a lot of wheels there in the Pacific. There were also
wheels within wheels. And there were also
heels within wheels."

"And you?"

"I was just a cog, son. Just a
cog."

"A cog? No! Mercy me, what far flung language!"

"Out in New
Guinea
cog is a word you must not ever say. It's tabu."

"Tabu, not tafu?"

"Tabu, son, the thing
you must not do at a piano, even
a baby grand."

"Well, tell me, grandpaw, cog,
what does it mean, if ever I should find myself
out in New Guinea?"

"You're bound to. Cog. It means a virgin
wedded to two men simultaneously but without
a requisition signed by the Main Wheel."

"I'll remember that.
If ever I get to New Guinea."

"Everyone gets to New Guinea, son.
The next war will be even more far flung."

"Far flung or maybe
fart flung?"

"Either. Have it your own way. Officially, in the Great Far Flung
War
only the Top Brass employed gas. Brass-gas."

"Thanks, Jack. Now
that we have completed our studies on this important topic,
shall we take up the matter of Lieutenant Commander Standeven
and how
he got moved into the other half of the Globaldegook?"

25

　　　　　　　　　　　　　　　　　　　　　　　　　　　　"No.
Let's not."
"But my curiosity is piqued, brother. What, for instance, is the
　　　synonym
for Cog in Italian?"
　　　　　　　　　　"Skip it, the whole damn thing."
"But weren't you involved in that great Eyetalian imbroglio—
as we Italians say—and am I to sit here
and be denied a briefing on this after the resourceful
reduction of the Pacific to terms any schoolboy
can write on a blank wall with chalk? Dear me, Harlow,
what reticence! Am I not to become, through you,
one of the Cog-noscenti?"
　　　　　　　　　　"Skip it, Fatso, skip it,
for Christ's sweet sake!"
　　　　　　　　　　"Ah! we need something soothing.
Shall we turn the bleat on again?"
　　　　　　　　　　　　"No, leave the bleat off.
I've got to study."
　　　　　　　　　　"It is too late. You have wasted
the best years of your life, either in the global Pacific
or the gobble of Italy's olio. Half past nine of a Friday!
Close up the books, roll up the old papyrus, Harlow.
We got to get dressed for the Big Bounce at the Somerset."
"Gawd, I'd forgotten that!"
　　　　　　　　　　"Sometimes I hate to think
what would happen to you if I weren't around to remind you
of your social obligations. Forget the Big Bounce? The first and
　　　foremost
Bounce of the season? The presentation
of the succulent Leftwell twins, virginal, so the story goes, shaped
exactly like pears, to the uninterested inspection
of four hundred and sixteen far flung Harvard undergraduates,
cousins, and eligible alcoholics not yet anonymous, drawn
at random from a stud-list—forget that? Harlow! Harlow!
What shall I do with you?"
　　　　　　　　　　"Stay me with flagons, bud,
comfort me with apples: for I am sick of love. I'm not going
to the Big Bloody Bounce, Fatso. I am going to go
down to Rhode Island."

26

(Jennifer, Jennifer! This is the pain, this the confusion,
this is the hunger that's all unfed.)

"Stay me with flagons, Fatso."
                              "Brother,
our only flagon is almost empty. But even so
we'll complete the process."

(What would I do without Fatso Levering? I hang
on his strength and his humor. Love. Love Jennifer and love him.
But his is returned. The whiskey
bites and warms. Telephone soon now. God, but I wish
I could stay at my own place. Often. I wish it often,
orphan Harlow. What would it do to me
to have a mother to love like Mrs. Lamy?)
                              "Listen, Harlow.
Go to the Big Bounce."
                    "Why?"
                              "Boy, let her miss you, let
time pass."
            "I don't like the Leftwells, they're too damn rich,
      they're
all over the place."
                    "For God's sake, doc, make sense, who cares
for the Leftwells? There will be champagne and Klingman's band
and Les Boys and—this is the point, Jack—dozens and dozens
of Les Girls. And you. And you not down in Rhode Island, not
this week-end. Why? she asks. Ah, because Harlow couldn't
resist the Leftwells' dance, a hell of a party, the best damn
party this season—everyone was there. Boy,
get on to yourself!"
                    "Look, Fatso, look. It isn't only that, see,
it really isn't. It's so damn hard to explain. It's
going down there, home. It's being
twenty-four, not seeing
all those childish faces, the childish drunks, the childish
middle-aged men drunk too, the silly, circular
insanity of a dance. I'm past it. Bored. I'm beyond it. I
grew outside it. It's all so damned confusing, how
do you get yourself unconfused?"

27

"You go
to the Leftwells' dance, bud. You let Jennifer
sweat it out for a week."

(God! I wish I could tell him the real reason. I wish
I could tell myself the reason, too. Well, know thyself. When
do you know yourself? So many
people here, so many demands and questions, you never
catch up with yourself. Rhode Island in October
is peace—except for Jennifer, Jennifer . . . lying
close in the dark, the devouring, the consuming,
the passionate had . . . not now? Not
ever again? This time?
                    Control, say nothing, be
just yourself and by yourself. I wonder
could I walk to the old place? The steady rhythm, the old,
the accustomed, steady, the time
of the unquestioning, recaptured. Being
the person you are to be.
                    I dream sweet dreams
that I let the day destroy.)

                    "No, Fatso. No. It isn't
only Jennifer. I am weary. I can't take
the apple-cheeked undergraduates, not this time, boy. I want
to collect myself. I'm scattered. I have been scattered
ever since V.E. day. It's so damn funny, you knew, you knew,
it was all so clear, the hates and the loves were clear, the knowing
was a bright light, you had only to come back home, the meaning
was all foreseen. But the home was not clear, it's
confusion. Why
do we stay here? To become what? To do what when?
Where do we go, in what world, when we're finished? When
Harvard says, Go, now, we're finished with you, go,
you're on your own now. What's my own? Well? Hell!
I can't think straight here. Too many points of view, too many
voices saying, 'There's this but then, you see, there's that, and you
must weigh them carefully.' No, Fatso, no,
I'm off to the country—if the Lamys will have me.
No Bounce."

28

        "O.K., Harlow. Have it your own way, boy. You're
        trying
to run away from yourself. You're going to run smack bang
into your Jennifer. Crunch. Me, my friend,
I'm off for the bath. The flagon
is yours, boy, stay yourself. I think you need lots of staying.
Now I shall dunk my beautiful white body and dream
of the pear-shaped twins. I wonder if they are ripe?
Ah, ripe for rape, oh tittering twins entwined!
Is that cog backwards without the wheel's requisition? Two
allegedly virgin twins who sing together, as they repose them,
now I lay me? Lamy. You'd better
call them before it gets too late."

(How does he manage to have such fun of life? Not being
in love? No. Well, the telephone. Long distance. I want
Chogs Cove 437. No, anybody. I'll talk to anyone. Fatso
can talk to anyone. Sound of the running water, like time
slipping away. Days bleed
their time away. All's insecurity and so
time's haemophilia. I should have put in the call
person to person to Mrs. Lamy. Now,
Jenny might answer. Want her and not want her, the weakness
of the undecided.)

        "Hello? Mrs. Lamy? Hi, there. It's Harlow."

(I thought it was Jennifer, their voices
ring to the same sound over the wire, it makes you
breathless.)

"I'm fine, I'm weary. I'd like to come down to you, if maybe
you've got a bed for me. Is Lanier at home or still
up at St. Paul's? Oh, good. I've got to study, I've got
Hour Exams on Monday, but here, well, here
too many distractions."

(Or Jennifer's not a distraction? Now the warm voice, husky
smoothing and comforting.)

29

"No, I'd leave soon. I'll drive the old Ford,
I'll be latish. I'll put
myself in Lanier's room, I'll be quiet. I'll breakfast
with Mr. Lamy? Good, I'll see you tomorrow. I'm so happy
you'll take me in. I need it. Good night and thanks. Is
Jennifer home? Oh. Then I'll see you all
in the morning. Thanks."

(What is it makes you able
to warm with a voice, to wrap the heart in a voice as though
it were a physical warmth?)

"Hey, Fatso, boy! I'm going.
The Lamys will have me. Get the hell out of that shower,
I want one too."

(The warm shower and the standing warm,
and the things foretasted. Jennifer? Must one always sorrow
to taste of joy? Or joy, must it always spring
from the exterior, never within, within?)

"Hey, Fatso, listen,
step on it, bud."
"I'm purifying my body. I'm cleansing
myself with rites in case I should be a cog, and mesh
with the Leftwell twins. Ah, baby, what a mesh!"

(He makes me laugh, and I love to laugh. Now pack—
and think of the dark miles, one by one disappearing, sweetly,
always nearer and nearer, the excitement
rising with the discarded miles, the white beam
of the lights probing happiness, on ahead, forever, always
on ahead . . . till you turn again and return? In the light
of the day, the miles that gather, that heap, that drift, like time
over you and between you and between laughter and . . . now,
put love in a brown bag. Put
a tourniquet on the day's deadly bleeding, the wasting.
The time for laughter is now.)

□□□□□□

30

(THERE IS no view now possible from the high air. The October
night permits but the impersonal brilliance
of the courant stars: this scene is witnessed
at ground level, neither magnified by the transitive
curve of the lens nor transformed into the little, comprehensible
        pattern
through the assumption of a cloud's prerogative. It is self-sized:
misted in the confusion of many persons: whose bodies
range in stiff, even rows, as though
they had given in to a mass conformity; whose minds
clash into incompatible figures of space, of time, of use.
Confusion is life-scaled, its resolution
striven for, hardly obtainable: truth now
is but the compromise of these irrationals: relative.)

(Big four-square building, glazed brick, its color yellow
positive in dissonance even under the timid, ameliorating light
of the remote street lamp. Here the sixty-year-old
focus of a community, the Town Hall, built
as the hopeful symbol, the fumbling practicality
of man's optimism made concrete.)
                                (Within,
drab corridor of grey with a dark brown dado of paint chipped
into whiteness; creaking, oiled board floors, a smell
familiar to all public buildings: the acrid, stale
odor of an unloved but a constant washing and cleaning;
men and cigars have scented this, there is here
little of women. Sweat and the disinfectant still
outrank the cosmetic.)

(People in the long, wide corridor: some stop to greet each other,
        some nod;
these push on toward the rectangular, ill-designed
steep stairs at the back. The elderly, the limping, take
grateful pause on the square landings. Above, dim lit, another
        corridor,
fellow in drabness to the one beneath it, showing
double door widely open; many little doors in dark brown, closed.
Light, bright and impersonal, flows from the double door, from
        the big

31

Meeting Room; large and naked electric bulbs under white tin
reflectors hung on dust-fluffed cords from the high grey ceiling.
Here are the rooms of the unwelcoming wooden benches, a centre
      aisle,
two narrow side aisles, and a low
platform at the head of the room, a long dark brown table,
six chairs behind it: it all awaits
man's indecision: his hope.)

(This room: filling now rapidly, the usual
drab of male and color of female seated, the peering
of the standing, the moving, the looking for place where
place will be welcome or not hateful, or will be
solitary, unregimented. The gestures
of greeting, the occasional low-voiced words spoken,
the accomplished public self-hiding of the New Englander,
the nudge and the half-pointing hand saying, there, there,
that's the place, there's so-and-so; the turned head
speaking impatience with a laggard, anticipation
of a position lost by vain chatter.
                   The clock on the wall
back of the dais ticks loudly unheard, the unmeasured shuffle and
whisper, the rasped cough
subdue its punctual rhythm.)

(This is no room to absorb or to diminish:
bare, ugly, hard used, it allows
the individual to persist, it gives scope
to the single spirit to add its singularity to the other digits
that are the unfused wills of the congregation. It says,
be yourself, I shall not coerce you nor charm you nor move you
into a fused will: there will be here no music
nor often the modes of eloquence.
                   It says,
too many minds have stood here obdurately alone:
I shall not alter that, my walls
reflect a number, a group, but not a mass; I harbor
the word of the most made into its size by units hardly
and singularly accreted.)

(Back of the dark brown table are three men seated. These
are the Zoning Board of Review, the responsible,
the civic-minded men.
                            On the right is Lester Parry,
plumber and heater, veteran of the first world war, commander
of the American Legion Post, sober and with a temper
his wife is most aware of.
                            On the left is seated
Willoughby Cross, he's forty, amiable, the manager of the A&P,
            his father
used to beat him so often when he was little that now
he needs to be kind to everyone.
                            Well known, respected, they are
            called
solid men. Solid? Yes, if one accepts,
half way toward liquid the weather-wise
bright mass of mercury.
                            In the centre is seated
Jacob Ledbetter. There's no mercury here. One should
know a little of Jacob, Yankee, whose seventy-nine years
look like sixty.
                            Black hair turned silver only at the temples,
close cut on neck and sides, thick on the crown.
Cropped moustache of grey over a strong mouth, the whole face
lined with humor, patience, and dignity: serenity
sits on this man, his heavy body rests in his chair in a pose
of comfort motionless.
                            Jacob Ledbetter, man of the many pasts:
owner now of the big hardware store at Cottrellton, trustee
of the Savings Bank, member of the Town Council. At seventeen
he joined the Navy and saw the slope of the world. At twenty
he killed a Frenchman at night in the streets of Shanghai
and disposed of the body neatly, successfully: his strength
was sharper than the sharp knife of the other. He can remember
the anxious seas, curved rivers, the fat bays of the merchant world,
            the use
of steam and sail, of the heavy-laden, tide-ruled schooners
he skippered along the coast of his native country, their gunwales
sluggish beneath the lumber. There are few ports or harbors

33

strange to Jacob. He knows them in peace and war, in
youth and in age. Home at last, settled down he has buried
the wife of his need and the son of his love; he houses
his grandchildren now. He is the man who captained
the local ferry back and forth, all weather, the man often
storm-caught on the island end of his run and rowing
little flat skiff cross gale, cross tide,
over the whited bay home, his left leg shackled to a short chain,
the chain to an anchor: knowing not how to swim, full willing
to elude the linger of death.

He rests now

within the complex, the restricted orbit of his community, loved
    and hated,
respected. He slept in his irresistible prime
with unnumbered women, with Chinese, Malays, New
    Englanders,
French and Dutch and Canuck and a Hopi squaw
(whose dress was aromatic with piñon smoke)
that he met by chance in the wilds of Arizona under
the sun and the mesquite. But he rests now, determined,
useful, admired, central, basking pleasantly, without tension,
in the tolerant light of his sins and his acts.
This the accomplished, dispassionate
chairman of many meetings.)

(Jacob raps now with a tin of tobacco on the wooden table.)

JACOB: If you'll jest be seated, we'll call the meeting to
          order.
      Find a seat. One seat's as hard as another.

      (to Willoughby Cross in a low voice)

      Clock don't wait for us so I guess it's better we
          don't try
      to wait for the clock.
CROSS: Yep. Better. Most of 'em's here.
JACOB: Give 'em a few more minutes to settle down.

      (Jacob thinking)

34

So the great man's come, Mr. Rochester Mallin.
        The great man's wife,
and the old lady Gosford. But she's not old, the
        old ones here,
Walter Hoxsie and Anna J. Hall
and Jacob Ledbetter. Funny combination. Looked
        in the mirror
and I seen my face and it said, you're old, but
        damn if I feel it,
or I do feel it, but it ain't what I thought
when I wasn't old and thought of being old.
Young Jerry Westen, there's an able feller left his
        wife to home,
lets her tend the children. But Mrs. Gosford now,
        let alone Serena,
bet they brought Mallin. Women in the saddle,
        Chogs Cove women,
Whales Head women to the north of the village.
Lamy brought his daughter or his daughter brought
        Lamy? Shucks,
a good man trying too hard to be good. Wear
        yourself out
with all that effort.
                        Sueton Kellam setting next to
        Mitchell Crane.
Mitchell, a talker, gabble till you stop him. Funny
        thing, lawyers,
I never did like them and I don't like Mitchell.
        But I won't show it.
No, sir, not Jacob.
Jacob is an old man, old man, old man,
Jacob is an old man setting in the chair. Well,
I guess the Almighty laughs—when He thinks it's
        funny. And it's
God damned funny Jacob setting in the chair. Ha!

JACOB: The meeting will now begin. Jest set down
        anywheres.
        There's plenty of seats. I'll commence by saying
        that

35

I'm a little bit hard of hearing. I'll take it kindly
if those that speaks will speak out. We're here to
        listen,
and we want to hear what's said. I reckon there
        are others
with the same affliction.

(Old Miss Anna Hall, seated next her cousin,
        Hetty Browne,
nods her head and the big, wrinkled wattles
that hang from her chin continue to nod and
        quiver after
the nodding head's at its stiff rest again.)

JACOB: This Board's got but two cases to come before it.
                First off
                we'll take the Lucas case, at Indigo Mill, it
                hasn't had opposition, leastways so far. This Board
                is inclined, on study, to grant the petitioner,
                Gerald Lucas, the change to a non-conforming
                        use from
                a Residential B. He aims to use it—well, maybe
                be quicker if we just read off the regular notice
                        printed
                in the Cottrellton Herald. You got it handy,
                        Willoughby?
CROSS: Got it right here.

(Reading, in his pleasant, amiable voice)

"On petition for reconsideration, Gerald S. Lucas,
        applying
for an exception or variation of the Zoning
        Ordinance so that
the use of property Residential B Zone, may be
        changed
from Residential to a non-conforming use, Farm
        Machinery
Sales and Service Station. Location:

36

Indigo Mill at the Intersection of Chogs Cove
Road
with the Cottrellton Highway on the west side of
Indigo Pond, Curtis Farm, so called, a frontage of
two hundred and fifteen feet, a depth of one
hundred and fifty feet.
A hearing will be given all interested persons
by the Zoning Board of Review at the Town Hall,
Cottrellton,
at seven-thirty p.m. on October 8, nineteen
hundred and forty-seven."
That's the end of it.

JACOB: Well, that's it, then. I guess you've all heard it.
Mr. Lucas is here, I see. Is there anyone
wants to speak about it?

(Big man, heavy-set, in a dark grey suit, his fingers
fumbling
with an old felt hat, gets up from his seat and
stands.
He does not look at Jacob: he looks out of a
window and his mouth
moves softly as though he were chewing.)

JACOB: It's Lyttleton Browning, ain't it?

(The big man nods, but he doesn't look at Jacob.)

You got something to say, Mr. Browning?
BROWNING: (clears his throat)
Well, yes. I have.

(He pauses, collecting his thoughts, his eyes still
searching
out the dark window: one sees
the image-intention clearer in the darkness.)

BROWNING: Yes, sir.
Spoke to Gerry Lucas and we agreed I was to sort
of canvass

37

at Indigo Mill. I done that.
There's no objection, seems so,
folks is glad to have him. But the opinion
was, wouldn't be no objection if he come out
and say, in meeting, he didn't have no intention
to cut down the hedge there. Sort of an arbor
                  vitae,
windbreak oncet, been growing a real long time,
high and handsome, sort of. Don't need no more
than just his say-so, we all know Gerry Lucas,
it's just for the record. An uncommon sort of a
                  hedge,
you might say. Well, I . . .

*(He sits down now, he rests the hat on his knees,
his mouth begins its chewing, his eyes look down.)*

JACOB: Mr. Lucas? You want to respond to that?

(A bright little man with a beak of a nose gets up.)

LUCAS: Yes, sir. I do. I'll state it in public meeting.
We got no intention to cut the hedge nor change
                  it,
mighty beautiful hedge, real thick and solid,
make our heating bills, come the winter season, the
                  north winds,
considerable less. No, we won't cut it.

(He sits)

JACOB: That satisfactory to you now, Mr. Browning?
BROWNING: Yes, sir.

*(Jacob glances at Cross and Parry; both nod to
                  him.)*

JACOB: The Board of Review
grants the request of Gerald Sigsbee Lucas,
classification changed as per petition. Now

we'll get on to the next case.
Where's the papers, Willoughby?

(*Willoughby Cross, with a shadow of a smile, a compromise*
smile halfway between amusement and conciliation,
shuffles his papers, and hands a sheaf, one by one,
to Jacob.
The rustle and crackle of each sheet is clearly audible in
the hush of the room. Tension
decrees a relevant silence; a cough
sounds loud and explosive. The clock makes audible now
the drip of time.
                    Miss Anna Hall's wattles
have ceased to quiver.
                    Rochester Mallin, publicly
at his ease, rolls up his overcoat into a cushion
to lean his elbow on.
                    The bright, glaring light
of the naked bulbs has almost a sound of its own.)

(*Jacob thinking*)

Makes me sort of think of lightning over water,
        off in the distance
over the horizon, seen in the greyness.
But you can't hear nothing but the slap of the
        water,
the whisper of the runnels that the ship's divided,
louder for the lightning that the ear can't hear,
        and you hear the thunder
in the ear of the mind.

JACOB: This here is the case of the building that Mr.
                Sueton Kellam
            aims to put up on the north side of Seldom Brook,
                on the site
            of the Benjamin Sweet house, used to be called so,

39

in the village of Chogs Cove, Whales Head area.
    I guess
everyone here is familiar with the notice published,
and we'll dispense with it, unless I hear an
    objection.

(The silence, that let go a part of itself, reluctantly,
    to the clear
syllables of Jacob's voice, draws taut again.)

JACOB: There being no objection, we'll proceed in this
    question.
Protest has been registered to the project by
    certain parties resident
in the village of Chogs Cove. This hearing
is to conclude the matter. So, following the usual
    method,
we'll just ask Mr. Sueton Kellam to say his say,
    telling
the Board his side of the case, the reasons
he thinks he should have the exception granted.
    Jest to be clear,
he wants to change from a Residential AA to
a non-conforming use, to include a store.
We'll hear from Mr. Kellam now, as I notice
he's here with us.

(The silence that tried to come again is soon
    broken by the loud creak
of the bench as Sueton Kellam rises. The bright
    light
shines from his bald crown. His thick, powerful
    shoulders
hunch forward in a quick gesture of effort, his
    hands
pull at his jacket. His eyes
look down once, briefly, at the thin man beside
    him and then
rise to Jacob's face, an aggressive look, saying,

40

I'll have my say and I'll have it in my own
   manner.)

KELLAM: If the Board don't object, I'll just let Mitchell
              Crane
           state the case for me. This case now,
           it was pretty simple, but now it's no longer simple.
              I figured
           it had got to the point where I'd need an attorney,
              a lawyer,
           to present my side, seeing the opposition
           has hired Mr. Cullen Ryan to represent them. But
              I'll just add,
           I never expected to have any sort of an argument
           requiring lawyers for just a matter of building
           something that's good and useful. Gets so a man,
              these days,
           can't make a living simple. Got to have law. Well,
           I'll let Mr. Crane talk, if it's all the same to the
              Board.
JACOB: No objection to that. Or I guess there isn't?

           (He looks at Willoughby Cross and Lester Parry,
              and both men shake their heads.)

           There's none. We'll hear Mr. Crane.
           You want to use the end of the table, Mitchell?
           All them papers?

           (Sueton Kellam sits down, but he doesn't look
           to right or to left: he keeps his big head faced
              straight
           to the front, his eyes on Jacob Ledbetter.)

           (Mitchell Crane gets up from beside Kellam. He
              holds
           a dark brown manila envelope, overflowing with
              papers,
           in his long, thin hands. His tall

41

lean body with the stooped shoulders seems to
                tower
over the room. His quick, intelligent dark eyes look
                carefully,
boldly around the room and go back to Jacob.
He smiles.)

CRANE: Yes. That'll be better. Thanks. I'll do that.

                (Edges his way past Sueton Kellam and another
                        man,
                Asa Congdon, to the centre aisle)

                Excuse me, Asa.

                (He walks up the aisle in the silence defined by his
                        own footfalls,
                goes to the left of the table and puts the papers
                        slowly
                and neatly in order there. He picks up one sheaf to
                        hold
                in his long and clever fingers, glances at it, looks
                        out
                over the audience, turns and nods his head
                to the three men on the dais.)

CRANE: Thank you. Now, Mr. Chairman, I'll try
                to give it briefly, but you'll have to be patient,
                there's quite a bit to it, better to have it clear, strip
                        it
                of the confusions that have grown up around it. As
                        my client
                said this moment, the thing is essentially simple.
                        I'd like
                to get back to that simplicity.

                (He lifts the paper up and reads it, apparently,
                for a matter of five long seconds. Then
                he places it on the table, clasps

42

his hands behind him, and addresses, in a most
                pleasant voice,
the audience before him. His manner
is a nice blend of the conciliatory, the amiable,
and a suppressed impatience that so many people
                of importance
should be wasting their good time in the
                determination
of so easy a matter.)

CRANE: I'll begin with just a little history, folks.
                You all know Sueton Kellam. He's been around
                these parts since he was a boy. He's worked for
                                years now
                in Hazlitt's Grocery store at Cottrellton, he's been
                                manager
                for the last two years. Now Sueton Kellam wants
                to start a store on his own. It's the sort of thing
                we all would like to do and we try to do:
                the American way. Now Mr. Kellam figures
                there's a place for another grocery store on this
                                site,
                something to help himself and to make the
                                community
                prosper more.
                                There are plenty of stores at
                                Cottrellton—
                but I'll call your attention now, and I'll repeat it,
                to the fact that there hasn't been one, not one
                                objection
                from Cottrellton people to this well-planned
                                project—
                and it isn't a new one. There are also stores
                in Chogs Cove village, west and south of the
                                Landing,
                but there's none at North Ferry, lying halfway
                                between
                Chogs Cove and Cottrellton. And what's more to
                                the point,

there's none for the growing colony, twenty
    houses,
at Hoxsies Cove. I see Mr. Walter Hoxsie's
here this evening, I daresay he'd be willing
to bear me out when I state the folks that inhabit
that summer colony are a long way from
    provisions.
Isn't that so, Mr. Hoxsie?

(A big man in a blue serge suit, patched neatly,
    his hair
long and unkempt and grey, needing a shave, a
    face
impassive, concealing,
nods his head once.)

HOXSIE: Need 'em, yes, but don't always pay for 'em, seems
            so.

(There is a little ripple of laughter, soft, controlled,
    uncomfortable,
as one laughs at an old hurt.)

CRANE: Mr. Kellam will sell for cash.

(The laughter now
breaks into a louder ripple, the people seated
move on the benches and settle again to silence.)

HOXSIE: Maybe they got some cash. Kinder hard to know.

(Once more the laughter, louder now, but divided,
    spotted
here and there: there are faces
refusing merriment.)

CRANE: (swiftly, making a quick, clever gesture that stops
            the laughter)

44

One way to find out is to let my client
build his store.
                    But the point I'm trying to make
is that there's need, the established need, for a
        store
halfway between the villages of Chogs Cove
and North Ferry. Now Mr. Kellam has carefully
        studied
this matter since nineteen hundred and
        thirty-seven
when the Sweet place was purchased. He's asked
        questions,
he's talked to his neighbors, he's . . .

JACOB: I don't like to interrupt you, Mitchell, I like to
        let a man
have his say out, but seems you're wide of the
        mark.
We're not discussing the wisdom of any business.
        We're here
to determine if it's proper to change a zoning
from residential to business.

CRANE: I don't agree, sir.
I claim there's animus here, that this opposition,
aroused long after the time of original purchase,
can have a competitive base. If I can show you
the need for a store, that it benefits the locality,
that it harms no one, then I have gone a long way
toward pointing the reasonableness of a change of
        zoning.
Isn't that so?

JACOB: I won't say yes and I won't say no. I reckon you
        got
the right to be heard. But I say what I said before:
this Board don't set to determine the possible
        profit
of a business venture. No. It sets to determine
        whether the place
is proper for business, whether a business located
in that particular spot is against the intention
of the original zoning or whether

45

it can't do any harm to allow an exception and
    maybe
to set a precedent. I don't know the answer. I'm
    here,
with these two gentlemen, to listen, to follow, to
    hear.
You jest present it
as you've a mind to. I guess it's your privilege.

CRANE: Thank you.
Now I'll get back to the facts. Mr. Kellam bought
    in
in 1937. The following year
the hurricane came and the house, that was old
    and rotten,
fell to pieces. I'm sure there's no argument
about that fact. He cleared up the place, he tore
    down
what remained of the house. He did it himself,
    his own hands,
Sundays and holidays, it took plenty of time.
In 1939 he applied for a permit,
he got it from Orville Creston, the building
    inspector.
Now Creston died in the following year, I think,
but we've got the permit here, signed, sealed, and
    delivered.
If he'd had the money to hire the help he wanted,
Kellam would then and there have commenced to
    build—
but he didn't have it.
               Well, then the war came.
You know about that, and about the question of
    building
in those dark days. Kellam went into the Navy,
he got out in forty-five. Now, two years later,
he has his money to build and he can get
the stuff he needs to build with—though you all
    know
how the costs have risen.
              Now, Mr. Chairman,

	before I go on, I'd like it if you'd enquire
	if anyone questions what I have just recounted,
	or if we can take it that this is true representation
	of the bare facts of the case.
JACOB:	Is there anyone here, and I guess in particular Mr.
	Ryan,
	who questions these facts as stated?

> (*Mr. Cullen Ryan, a fat little man with a cheerful,
> prosperous face,*
> *a dark brown tweed suit, well cut, moves*
> *to the edge of his seat and looks around him,
> catching*
> *the eyes of his friends, his clients. Some make
> negative*
> *motion of pouted lips, some shake their heads,
> none*
> *questions the statement made.*
> > Ryan turns back,
> > *he*
> *faces Jacob.)*

RYAN:	No, Mr. Chairman. No. We'll grant
	the facts so far, as facts, but barring
	agreement on any of the conclusions or
	implications
	in the earlier part of Mr. Crane's presentation.
	As far as history goes, we find no reason
	to quarrel with it. Perhaps we had better add
	that we believe Mr. Creston erred when he gave
	the permit to Mr. Kellam.
JACOB:	We can get to that, but get to it later, I reckon.
	Go ahead, Mitchell.
CRANE:	I thank you, Mr. Chairman.

> (*Crane looks down at the floor, then up at the
> ceiling, then*
> *suddenly at his audience. It is skilfully done,
> creating*

the atmosphere of thought bent toward sincerity
in a hard search for the truth.)

Very well, then. We come now, finally,
to the core of the matter.
                        What I mean to say is,
why pick out a house site already set in a zone
that's residential? Why not some other location?
The answer's easy and clear. The house was a
        store.
Mr. Ledbetter mentioned a precedent. Well, we
        have one.
Benjamin Sweet, its former owner, used it
for commercial purposes, precedent was
        established,
the zoning law that placed it as residential
with an AA rating was going against the grain
of its former history. Kellam was, is, returning
to the natural use. This is the crux of the matter.

(Crane pauses.
                As he does so
there is a stir in the room, the soft sound
of the rustle of clothes, the scrape of leather on
        wood floor,
the squeak of wood bench, the sibilant, indrawn
breath in many nostrils.
                        Miss Anna Hall nods
in a sort of affirmation as her old head turns slowly
toward her neighbor, Mrs. Ezra Browne.
                                        Jennifer
        Messler
looks up at Lamy beside her, a startled, expectant
look of surprise.
                Rochester Mallin turns
and smiles at Serena. The smile says, clear as
        words, well,
what about that?
                Jerome Westen grins.)

48

(*Cullen Ryan leans forward quickly on his bench,
his hands go
forward to grip the back of the bench before
him.*)

RYAN: We'll be obliged—not to speak of interested—
very interested, Mr. Chairman, if Mr. Crane
can adduce proof of this remarkable statement.

CRANE: That's what we're here for.

(*Ryan leans back in his seat, with a shake, slow, of
his head,
the trace of a smile; his hands
let go of the bench ahead, they rest on his knees.*)

CRANE: Yes, that's what we're here for.
I'm going to tell you about it, and then I'll ask
some people
who've been around Chogs Cove the bulk of their
lives,
the people who knew Ben Sweet and his wife and
daughter,
to substantiate what I've said.
                              Let's start with the
buckeys.
Ben Sweet fished for his living, his main living,
he followed his father's calling. They used to have
once
a fish shop out on the Landing, the west of the
Cove,
they sold the fresh fish there. But the spring-run
herrings,
what we call buckeys, they smoked in their own
smokehouse
and stored and sold them up at their own
dwelling,
in the shop in the ell of the house that ran to the
west.
It was obvious why they did it, why Ben Sweet
did it.

They netted the buckeys right out of Buckey Inlet,
and Seldom Brook.

As I've said, the place was a
store,
you went there to buy smoked herring. Well,
nowadays,
you buy your buckeys at Henry Dexter's store
in the middle of Chogs Cove.

But there's more
than that.
Ben Sweet used to pickle eels, or his wife did. Say
she learned
from an old Italian, Di Angelo, used to live
up at Dark Corner. Ben Sweet speared his eels
in Buckey Inlet, he pickled them at the house,
and he sold them there, and he sold the skins for
trolling,
for those who went after bluefish. He had a sign,
painted it was, stuck up on the old Town Road
just north of his house by the road in, it said,
"Fresh Mummies."
He seined the mummies, mummiechogs, those
little minnows,
in Buckey Inlet too, and he sold for bait,
for the run of the baby mackerel and the skipjacks
that ran up Seldom Brook in the late summer
and on to October. His daughter Deborah
sold live mummies, and shiners too, they tell me,
after her father's death. So there's three things—
buckeys and pickled eels, not to count the skins,
and mummiechogs—that were sold at Ben Sweet's
store,
in the ell of the house.

Now that isn't all he sold.
Ben Sweet made crabbing nets, they say he made
the best in South County, and a man could buy
them
up at the store, in the house. He cast lead sinkers
for fishing flounders. He manufactured also
eel-spears and cranberry rakes. He didn't sell them

down at the Landing, for you had to go
up to the shop in the house, where his women
      sold them
if he was away from home.
                              Well, there's your
      store—
if ever there was one. Buckeys and eels and live
      bait,
eel-spears and crabbing nets and big lead sinkers,
and cranberry rakes—and beautiful things they
      were.
I own one of Ben Sweet's rakes, though I must
      admit
I bought it after his death at the recent auction
of the Curtis Farm—the place that you gentlemen
have allowed to be changed from a Residential to
      Business
this very evening. Indeed, a most proper decision,
though the Curtis Farm, unless I am much
      mistaken,
was never a store like Ben Sweet's place.
                                      Well,

      now,
I think that's all for the moment, unless Mr.
      Kellam
thinks I've left anything out?

(*The big-shouldered Sueton Kellam removes his
      eyes from watching
the face of Jacob Ledbetter, looks at Crane and,
      with emphasis,
shakes his head.*)

KELLAM: No, those are the facts.
CRANE: That's good. We want to
      be clear,
and not leave any loose ends. Now, Mr. Chairman,
I'll ask again, as I asked you once before,
is there any contradiction to this as stated?
The historical facts of the case?

51

JACOB: Is there any objection?

RYAN: Yes, sir. Decidedly.

(Ryan stands up now, facing the men at the table, holding
his body erect and earnest.)

JACOB: Yes, Mr. Ryan?

RYAN: If you follow the usual method, perhaps I'd better
state the side for those who object to the change,
before we go any further. I take it for granted
Mr. Crane will call his witnesses later. I'll call
    mine,
and both can question, of course. If that's
    agreeable
to the gentlemen of the Board and to Mr. Crane?

CRANE: That's agreeable.

JACOB: That's what we usually do.
Go ahead, Mr. Ryan. Come up to the table, too,
if you've a mind to. You set right down there,
    Mitchell,
there's plenty of room for both.

CRANE: I will, I thank
you.

(He sits at the end of the table, his chair turned
a little to one side, so that he may observe, with
the least
moving, both Ledbetter and Ryan.)

(Ryan comes up to the dais and mounts it. He
carries
a briefcase in one hand, but he doesn't open it,
sets it
on the other end of the table. He places his hands
flat spread
on the table itself, leans forward on their support
and
begins at once.)

52

RYAN: Two things to say to begin with, Mr. Chairman,
and ladies and gentlemen.
Both I believe to be relevant to this issue
that now confronts us.
First:
if the Zoning Board of Review and the taxpayers
          of this township
grant Mr. Crane's contention that Benjamin Sweet
could have claimed a store in his dwelling place,
          why then
there's scarcely a native house in the village of
          Chogs Cove,
Indigo Mill, North Ferry, or even, I dare say,
at the settlement up at Hoxsies Cove that can't
          claim
a founded right to be so described.
Well! Store?
                    Why, yes, if you'll accept the word
in the sense of storage, or store-house: a building,
          or part
of a building where goods are placed for storage.
          Ben Sweet
stored his nets in the ell of his house, in winter.
          He used it
the way a farmer uses an ell or a barn or an
          out-building
to store his plow and his rake and his
          mowing-machine,
his harness and farm equipment. The definition
of a store in this country is this: a shop on a large
          scale,
one that deals in a great variety
of articles for sale.
                    But more than this, and
          speaking
to the same point, how many people hereabouts,
and in particular farmers, who don't put signs,
          painted ones,
like the one Mr. Crane described that said *Fresh
          Mummies,*

outside their places? They say *Fresh Eggs* or *Corn* or
Vegetables or *Setter Puppies* or *Annuals.*
Are all these stores?
If they are, then the designation of AA Residential
as a protection to property, a control of its use,
is about as much use to the community as a sick
        headache—
or maybe a sick Town Council, which God forbid!
Store? Ben Sweet had no store, he had
an ell to his house and he used it the way all local
people use their space. And like any other Yankee,
there wasn't too much that he had that he
        wouldn't sell
if he'd get his price.
Now. A second point.
Here's something Mr. Crane didn't care to
        mention.
I don't wonder.
                Ben Sweet sold liquor. Everyone
here in this room that's over the age
of fifty knows it. He didn't bother, not he,
to take out a license, no, indeed, licenses cost
        money.
He sold it first when the Town, by local option,
was dry as a bone. We used to call the sort
of thing he did, the place where you bought your
        liquor
in a dry town, a Blind Tiger. Remember? Yes, Ben
        Sweet,
he ran a Blind Tiger. Whiskey and gin.
Well, you might, you just might
call that a liquor store—if you don't care too much
for the legal aspect. But I don't reckon
this Board, or the taxpayers, or the residents, will
        wish
to set that sort of a precedent for the village.
Now.
Let's recognize—and deal with—one more fact.
Mr. Kellam knew, as everyone else there knew,

54

that the Sweet house and all the land it stood on
        and
in fact the whole acreage that was bought, when
        it was bought,
was zoned AA Residential. It wasn't a secret.
It had been zoned that way since the time the
        zoning laws
passed in the Council, after the residents—
including Mr. Kellam—had had their chance
to make an objection. There wasn't any objection.
Not from him, no, not from the residents
of Chogs Cove village. The area,
as Mr. Crane and your Chairman have pointed
        out,
was lumped together under the general name
of the Whales Head area, to distinguish it
from the village proper. Why was it so zoned?
Because it was residential, because the houses
        standing
already there were used for residence only, not for
        business.
So.
It's obvious that the introduction, at this point,
of a store in such a locality would have
the effect of lowering values. Make this exception,
and where does it end? Why should you then
        refuse
to allow, let's say, a garage for the same reason
as Mr. Kellam produces to justify
the location of his new store?
No, ladies and gentlemen, gentlemen of the
        Zoning Board,
that's a bad precedent, harmful. It was for this,
to prevent this, that the zoning was classified
as it was at the time. There is the precedent,
        firmly
established.

                I think it is fair to say at this point
that the late Mr. Orville Creston, who issued a
        permit

in 1939 to allow this building, exceeded
his authority, erred in fact.
I point out, too, that the record shows, you all
    know it,
that three of Creston's permits were challenged
    after
their issuance and that all three challenges
were subsequently sustained by the Zoning Board.
I'm sorry to bring this up of a gentleman
who isn't here to defend himself, and in particular
as I see his daughter is present, whom we all like,
Mrs. Sueton Kellam.
                    Now one more point.
Mr. Crane has rested his whole case, as I see it,
on the assumption that once on a time that house
was used as a store, by Ben Sweet and his
        daughter.
If we can show—as I have already begun to—
that that assumption is false and in fact
        unfounded,
then I suggest that the Zoning Board of Review
cannot do other than disallow Mr. Kellam
his claim to reclassification.
                    To this end,
I'll ask of some of the older residents
of the Whales Head area, their recollection
of the use of the Ben Sweet place.
                        It'll be better,
        quicker,
if they'll just stand up to speak, not come to the
        table.
If that's agreeable to Mr. Ledbetter here, and also
to Mr. Cross and to Mr. Parry?

JACOB: Yes, that's agreeable. Willoughby? You too,
        Lester?

(*Both Cross and Parry nod their heads.*)

(*The tension grows in the room now: this is the
        point, this*

the moment, the circumstance, the awaited
   thing.
            One hears it
in the sudden, subdued rustle of clothes in small
movement, the creak
of the wooden bench. One sees it
in the failure to glance aside or around, no eye
catching another, the attentive
focus of all eyes forward as though
to turn would be to betray, to count in advance,
to participate untimely, to lose the last
hope of avoidance: sweetest, most constant,
deadliest anodyne.)

(Jacob thinking)

A lot of rancor harbored for a long, long time:
funny how you feel it.
Now they got to speak, now they got to witness,
spill it to the neighbors and say it out in public.
Wonderful how long a hate will last when it's
        been buried.
If you plowed and if you planted,
if you cultivated ground
where the hate was buried, would the hate become
just a part of the rich earth?
I wish I wasn't here and I didn't have to listen.
Haven't we got more to do than dig up the old
        quarrels?
Get it over quickly.

RYAN: I'll start off first with Mr. Walter Hoxsie if
             he'll just be good enough to give us the benefit
             of his recollections.

(As Walter Hoxsie rises to his feet in the silence
    there is heard
the harsh breath of Mrs. Hetty Browne expelled
through contemptuous nostrils; her pleasant face

57

turns pink with emotion, the color spreads down
          slowly
over her neck, into
the hiding of her neat dress.)

RYAN: I think, Mr. Hoxsie, that you knew Benjamin
                  Sweet
              during his lifetime?
HOXSIE: Yes, sir. I knowed him.
RYAN: You knew his wife and his daughter, too?
HOXSIE: That's right. They was neighbors,
              in a manner of speaking.

(Again the contemptuous breath, a harsh
          combination
between a cough and a whistle, from Mrs. Browne,
          and
Hoxsie turns his head and looks full at her.)

HOXSIE: You ailin', Hetty?

(Mrs. Browne's soft lips close tight, the color
deepens again on her face and neck.
She must have been pretty once; but never did
          anger
sit comfortably on her face. But we are not
finished with Hetty Browne.)

RYAN: You knew the house too? The ell of the house
              where the nets were stored? You'd been there?
HOXSIE: I was in and out of that house all seasons, all
                  seasons.
              Bought his nets from his daughter when I took to
                  fishing.
              Knowed the house well.
RYAN: Would you say that
                  Sweet,
              or his wife, or his daughter Deborah, ran a store?
HOXSIE: No, sir. He ran no store.
RYAN: He sold things there?

HOXSIE: Sold as we all sell, like you said. He sold
the things he made, as he made 'em, or to your
order.
He was a man to sell. Sharp.

RYAN: Did he sell liquor?

HOXSIE: So it's reported.

(There is a light ripple of laughter, uneasy: it runs
through the audience so attentive.)

RYAN: You don't know of your own knowledge?

HOXSIE: It was a long time back. There might be some
can testify to it. Personal.

RYAN: Did Benjamin Sweet
sell
the things Mr. Mitchell Crane described to us this
evening?

HOXSIE: Jest about that. Sinkers and nets and rakes.
He made some winters, some years. He didn't
always have 'em.
As I said, he'd make them for you. He was a good
man
with the use of his hands.

RYAN: But surely, in your
opinion,
he hadn't a store there?

HOXSIE: No, sir. No. No store.
He sold his stuff to others that do run stores,
now and again, it's said.

RYAN: Did he advertise
the things that he made and sold?

HOXSIE: You mean in
the papers?

RYAN: Yes. Or a sign on the house?

HOXSIE: No sign on the
house.
Deborah Sweet put up the sign said Mummies,
I made it, painted it for her. She set it up.
She done that after Ben died. No, he didn't run
no piece in the paper, or I never got to see one.

59

People jest knew about him. He had a sign
on the shack on the Landing. Fish, it said, Fresh
    Fish,
and maybe lobsters too, but I disremember,
it was over the door to the shack.

RYAN: I see. I see.
The shack was really a store?

HOXSIE: I guess you'd call it
a store, a fish store.

RYAN: Well, now, Mr. Hoxsie,
just one more question. Do you think Mr. Sueton
    Kellam
has a right to a change of zoning? Do you think
a store has a place there, on the old Ben Sweet
    place?

HOXSIE: I wouldn't care to say.

RYAN: You have no opinion?

HOXSIE: Might have an opinion, but I don't care to say.

RYAN: I see. Well, thanks. Unless Mr. Mitchell Crane
wishes to say a word?

CRANE: Later, sir. Later.

RYAN: That's all, then. Thank you.

(*Hoxsie sits down again.*
                    Sueton Kellam heavily,
almost reluctantly turns in his seat and stares for
    a brief
moment at Hoxsie; then he returns his gaze to the
    dais,
to Jacob Ledbetter.
                    Mrs. Browne's fingers open
    her black handbag
and shut it again with a snap.)

RYAN: Mr. Henry Dexter?

(*A man of medium height, stout and thickset,*
    with white hair,
heavy-lensed eyeglasses framed in bright gold,
    comfortably

old fashioned, a dark grey suit, his empty left
        sleeve pinned
into the coat pocket neatly, rises now, slowly but
        steadily, without
apparent hesitation. A kind face,
wrinkled and pink, a short-clipped
white moustache, a well scrubbed look.
                                    He raises
his hand in a half salute to Jacob Ledbetter who
returns the gesture with a nod of the head.)

DEXTER: Yes, sir?

(It is the shopkeeper speaking, it implies,
what can I do for you today?)

RYAN: Good evening, Mr. Dexter.
            You knew Mr. Benjamin Sweet?
DEXTER: I knew him well. We grew up here together,
            though he was older. Maybe by fifteen years.
            I fished with his father, Abijah Sweet, when I
            was a young man, before I took over the work
            of my father's store.
RYAN: You fished with Ben Sweet as well as with his
                father?
DEXTER: Yes, sir. With both, for three years. It's how
            I come to lose my arm, in Abijah's schooner,
            off Brenton's Reef.
RYAN: Oh, I see. How did that happen?
DEXTER: I fouled in the anchor chain, and they cut it off
            to save me drowning. Ben Sweet did it. But that
            was a long while back, no odds now.
RYAN: No, but it
                goes
            to show your knowledge. Now, Mr. Dexter,
            I ask you this: you're a storekeeper, isn't that so?
DEXTER: I've run my store since I was a man of thirty.
            My father's store, and his father's it was before
                him.

61

RYAN: In the light, then, of such knowledge, and as you
                  knew
               Ben Sweet and his father—and his daughter,
                  Deborah?
DEXTER: Deborah? Surely.
RYAN: In the light of this knowledge,
               would you say that Sweet ran a store up at his
                  house,
               in the ell of his house?
DEXTER: No, sir. That was no
                  store.
               Or not as I use the word.
RYAN: Did Ben Sweet think
                  so?
DEXTER: Don't know as I'd care to say what another
                  thought,
               but he never said so. He never claimed it a store
               in all the good and the hard years that I knew
                  him.
               Nor nobody else I ever heard, till now.
RYAN: You knew the house, of course?
DEXTER: Why, surely,
                  surely,
               there was no mystery to it.
RYAN: He sold things to you?
DEXTER: I bought his buckeys. I ordered cranberry rakes,
               crab-nets, from Ben. I stocked them and I sold
                  them.
RYAN: Could anyone buy them? I mean, from Benjamin
                  Sweet?
DEXTER: I reckon they could, and did. He'd make to order,
               but in his own time, glory, yes, sir, his own time.
               You'd wait for a spell before you got your order.
               He wasn't a regular sort of a man, it seems so,
               not regular in his habits of work.
RYAN: The sort of
                  man
               who'd have been good in a store?
DEXTER: No, sir. No
                  good,

RYAN: not in a store. But a sharp man to trade.
I see. Well, I thank you, sir. I'll close
with the same question—the one
I asked Mr. Hoxsie: is it your considered opinion
that a store has a proper place to be situated
on the Ben Sweet place?

DEXTER: There's room for another
store
in this community. If there's another store
it'll take trade away from mine, at Chogs Cove.
I guess I'm prejudiced. But the community's
growing,
bigger each year, more people. North Ferry needs
one, too.
But granting my prejudice, seems like a poor idea
to invade a residential area when there's places
is zoned for business. I guess that that's about all
I'd care to say on the matter. Sueton Kellam's
a competent man.

RYAN: I thank you, Mr. Dexter,
that's all I wanted.

JACOB: Questions, Mitchell?

CRANE: You'd lose by the deal, Mr. Dexter, in your
opinion,
if Kellam erects a store on the site of the Sweet
house?

DEXTER: Could be I'd lose some trade, yes, sir, unless
the loss would be borne by Cottrellton.

CRANE: Then why
does Cottrellton not object?

DEXTER: I don't know. Maybe
they figger the loss would come out of Henry
Dexter,
and that don't pain them.

CRANE: I see. But you still
admit
your prejudice in the matter?

DEXTER: I stated it.

CRANE: You did, sir. Thank you, that's all.

RYAN: That's all, Mr. Dexter. Thank you again.

63

(Dexter sits down at once. His face now
is a little pinker, his mouth is more firmly closed,
        he
looks less amiable.)

RYAN: I'd like to hear now from Mr. Jerome Westen,
             if he'll be so kind.

(Beauty's a rare thing: here is masculine beauty as
        Jerome
Westen rises.
                Wide strong shoulders, narrow hips,
a flat stomach achieved without effort, small
waist, six feet of male. A well-shaped head, dark
        hair still thick
at the age of thirty-eight. Straight brows and dark
        brown eyes
with a woman's lashes, a mouth all ready for
        smiling
or perhaps for the flowers of kisses whose fruit is
        laughter.
No tension here: ease: and the pose of ease that
        says,
I know what you think of me but I never
think about it.)

(The audience settles softly, audibly,
more comfortably in its seats. The dissonance
        binding
their nerves to a pitch is less audible: the moment
speaks for itself, it is disconnected
from the stream in spate; the water of all emotions
turns to rest in the gentle pool.)

(Jennifer Messler, thinking and seeing,
wonders now if the taste of kisses, kisses given,
the touch of lips
could be sweeter—and being sweeter . . .
now she moves—her body, sensible,
suddenly sensible, near to Lamy.)

64

RYAN: I think, unless I am very much mistaken, I believe
you had something to do, Mr. Westen, with the
sale
of this property in the first instance, to Sueton
Kellam?
WESTEN: Well, in a manner of speaking, Mr. Ryan. Yes,
I had something to do with it.
A hand in the outset of the sale. But I didn't
conclude the deal, sell the property.

(He smiles.)

A frequent
enough experience
in real estate. You are the one begins it, you start
the ball a-rolling and then, in the end, somebody—
somebody else—concludes it. It's the end,
unfortunately,
that seems to pay off.

(Voice attuned to appearance: resonance that
resembles—
beyond reason or the close meaning of mere
words—
the bugles of regal lilies sprung in a June garden to
blow
passion over the air: a passion for things
willed or wanted, possessed or desired, positive or
negative;
the unconquered want
of the wisdom-serpent which in a whole circle
devours its own end, unending, perhaps insatiable.)

RYAN: But you began the job? You recall that?
WESTEN: I recall it. It's a funny thing
the way such failures stick in the memory longer
than the successes. Yes, I recall it well enough.
RYAN: Please tell about that, I believe it may have a
bearing.

WESTEN: All right. Mr. Kellam came into the office, my
office,
I guess it was late in the summer of '36, I think so,
asking
if I knew how to locate the heirs of the Sweets.
You see,
Deborah, Ben Sweet's daughter,
died without making a will. The property went
then
to the heirs, her cousins, there may have been all
told
ten or a dozen, don't recollect now, but
I did some asking around. I found the names, got
hold of
the addresses. They wanted to sell, there was but
one of them,
a woman in Minnesota, who made any trouble
and that
didn't amount to much. I reported all these things
to Mr. Kellam. I told him the price. It seemed
reasonable in those days—at least it seemed a
proper investment
if he aimed to subdivide, to sell it in good sized
parcels of land. I figured that all out too. He said
he might subdivide, but later. First off he wanted
to set up a store in the house, a grocery store, as
he says tonight.

RYAN: And how did you respond to that suggestion?

WESTEN: I told him he'd have trouble, that land was all
zoned, AA,
and he'd get no permit to build. He said then
he didn't have to build, just alter. This was before
the house
got hurt in the hurricane. Said if he had to build,
at that,
he reckoned he'd get his permit. Well, Creston,
he was his father-in-law, he had something there.
I had to
admit that. We talked of that problem, back and
forth, and

66

of developing later. He said he'd do it in small plots, like

it was done at Hoxsies Cove. I argued against it. But that is apart from the question, isn't it? None of my business.

He took the job to Melaney and Emerson. I didn't blame him.

That's about all I know.

RYAN: I see.

But the fact of the matter is, he had had an opinion

that he oughtn't to set up a business on that site?

WESTEN: He'd had my opinion. But then,

he did get his permit to build later on, at that.

RYAN: Did Mr. Kellam ever say anything to you—

while you were discussing this question, the permit—

about a precedent, anything about Benjamin Sweet

and his keeping store?

WESTEN: No. Nothing on that. Or not as I recall now, I think

I'd remember that. He did say

the house, the way it was then, way it was laid out, would alter

easily into a store. I agreed with him.

RYAN: But the word was alter?

WESTEN: Yes.

RYAN: So. Mr. Westen, one more question on that.

You spoke of development, the decision

between big lots and small lots. You said you advised

against the small lots, like the ones at Hoxsies Cove?

WESTEN: I did.

RYAN: Was your advice, then, based on a zoning question, or purely financial?

WESTEN: I didn't go into the question of zoning, though I thought of it.

	Mostly it was financial. But I guess you could say,
	I'd say,
	it was also social. It'd be dynamite
	to plat it out like that.

RYAN: In what way?

WESTEN: Like this . . .

CRANE: *(suddenly)*
If I may interrupt a moment, Mr. Ledbetter?
Isn't this exactly the sort of discussion
that you suggested I had better leave out?

JACOB: It might be, it might be. If it isn't a question
of zoning, Mr. Ryan, where does it fit?

RYAN: I'll respond to that. Mr. Crane very cleverly
introduced
into his presentation for Mr. Kellam, the idea
that Kellam was doing this—at least in part—
to better the neighborhood, the community—
Chogs Cove,
Hoxsies Cove, North Ferry. I'd like to show, if I
may,
that he and the others concerned with him—he's
not alone in this—
that they'd better with one hand, maybe, but
worsen
with the other. In brief, that the point, like others,
has no validity.

*(Suddenly now his voice
has taken on truculence, his pose has
hardened.)*

*(The room grows quiet, too quiet,
there is too much attention, the spell of the
beauty
is diminished now.)*

RYAN: Look, Mr. Chairman, gentlemen:
it is possible that the sort of development Mr.
Westen
indicates was the ultimate aim

68

of Mr. Kellam, could be protested in much the
         same
sort of proceeding as this one. That sort of platting
isn't within the intention, generally speaking,
of an AA Residential rating.
                              But grant this
               exception,
grant from an AA to Business—who
has a right to protest then? A legal ground for
         protest?
Very well, then.
We will make him a proposition.
Will Mr. Sueton Kellam
bind himself, in writing, to refuse to develop—
I use the word refuse advisedly now—
that land into lots of less than one-half acre?
Will he do that?
My clients, as I believe, will consider
withdrawing their protest to a grocery store
on the site of the Sweet house—granted the
         building
is not an eyesore, but is decently built
in a solid manner, no shack.
Will Mr. Kellam do this? Or can he do it, seeing
he is not a free agent wholly, not alone in this?
Well?
There is the nub of the matter.
We were bound to get to it.
How about it?

CRANE: I protest, Mr. Chairman.
My client is being asked now to strike a bargain,
to accept this pressure, to qualify future freedom,
as a price for something he claims as a perfect
         right.

RYAN: There's nothing unusual in a bargain, is there?
Wasn't there one just struck in the case preceding?
Nothing illegal. The use of land is determined
by the wishes of all concerned. If, now,
the adjacent owners wish to withdraw the one
         objection,

that's their right. They are only asking protection
against another menace, one that threatens
to knock the bottom out of property values—
values attained, maintained by them,
at long expense, investment.

CRANE: Mr. Chairman! Please!
I request, I request most urgently that we now
return to the point at issue. We are not here,
we're not called here, by notice duly printed,
to debate a future use that has here arisen
on the say-so of one witness, unsupported,
and wholly outside the intention of this Hearing.

JACOB: Well, now.

(He scratches his chin.)

It seems to me we'd ought to git back to the
question
of the business exception. I guess Mr. Crane is
right.
Leastways, he's right unless we can settle the
matter
offhand by Mr. Ryan's method. So, unless my
Board
objects, I'll say this. Now, Mr. Crane, or Mr.
Kellam,
are you willing to follow out Mr. Ryan's suggestion,
to agree to limit the sort of development that
may later be made of the land? On the
understanding
that the protest here, the one on the grocery store,
would be then withdrawn?

(Kellam, red in the face and angry,
stands up suddenly, opens his mouth to speak.
Crane waves him down—a hard, swift,
determined gesture.
                    The big man
sinks to his seat again, the redness
spreads to his neck now.)

70

CRANE: I know, I know, Mr. Kellam. I know how you feel.

But I'll say it for you. The answer, Mr. Chairman, is a decisive no. We wish our rights, we are not here to ask favors or strike bargains.

JACOB: Yes, sir. Now, Mr. Ryan. Will you go on?

RYAN: Yes, indeed, and thank you.

Now, Mr. Westen.

*(His manner
reverts to smoother tones, there is
a smile for Westen—the sort of smile
that includes both pleasure and
an understanding between them.)*

A little more history, please.
You would know, would you not, the details of the sale of this land
if and when it was sold?

WESTEN: I'd know if the deed was recorded, here in the Town Hall,
yes, sir. It's my business to follow up real estate transactions in this area.

RYAN: Did Mr. Kellam then buy this land from the heirs of Deborah Sweet?

WESTEN: No, he didn't. Not first off.

RYAN: Who bought it?

WESTEN: Mrs. Ezra Browne.

RYAN: And when did Mrs. Browne buy it?

WESTEN: I think it was February of '37. Yes. I remember.

CRANE: *(in a rather weary voice)*
Now, now, Mr. Chairman, Mr. Ledbetter!
What are you conducting a hearing into?
How can this sort of thing be relevant, please, to the case at hand?

JACOB: Well, I don't just know. Mr. Ryan?

RYAN: It's relevant. I've said before, sir,
I believe the application for a change of zoning
is not simply and essentially for the purpose of establishing

a store on the site, but to open the door, wide open,

to another change of use. I propose
to demonstrate this. Clearly, too. Now that
is certainly relevant. I can promise, though,
this will be brief and wholly to the point.
May I proceed?

JACOB: Yep. Go ahead.

RYAN: I thank you. Now, Mr. Westen,
was this sale recorded?

WESTEN: It was.

RYAN: Did Mr. Kellam attempt to buy the land again from Mrs. Browne?

WESTEN: Well, not right off, it seems, though I don't know that

from my own knowledge, only by guess.

RYAN: Did anyone try?

WESTEN: Yes. The School Board did.

RYAN: The School Board. What did they want it for and when

did they try to buy it?

WESTEN: They tried to buy it in March, 1937. They asked me

to sound Mrs. Browne out. They needed—well, everyone here

knows what they needed—a site for the new school,
the amalgamated one, the one we still
haven't got in the town. To take the place of the three

sites now used, and the old wooden
school buildings, antiquated. It was a nearly perfect
central location. The funds for the building were underwritten

if the Town would provide the land.

RYAN: No sale, though? A good price offered?

WESTEN: No sale. They offered a price that was higher
than what I could have bought it for for Sueton when

first he came to me. I don't know

what Mrs. Browne paid. That's none of my
business, either.

RYAN: No. I guess not. So.
Did Mrs. Browne make plans for its use?

WESTEN: I only know she got hold of Theodore Gross, he
works
for Melaney and Emerson, and Gross laid out
a plat of the property for its development and sale
in small lots. I know this because Ted Gross came
and showed me the plat and asked me questions
about it.

RYAN: The plat you saw, the lots on it were what size?

WESTEN: The property's about twenty acres in all, the plat
covered ten acres only, the rest is marsh, it would
be pretty costly to drain it to make it fit
for development. The plats ran
about eight to the acre, a hundred by fifty feet.

RYAN: Did you tell Mr. Gross this land
was zoned AA?

WESTEN: No. He knew that already.

RYAN: Did anyone, then, Mr. Gross, or Mrs. Browne,
apply for a permit to start such a project there?

WESTEN: No, sir. Or not to my knowledge.

(Suddenly Ryan turns now: he looks
away from Westen, he stares, hard, bright,
accusing,
at Mrs. Browne, who is seated
so near to Miss Anna Hall.)

RYAN: Mrs. Browne. You have heard Mr. Westen?
You have heard what he said
of your refusal to sell to the School Board,
and of Mr. Gross's plat of the land you bought.
Have you any comment to make?

(Small, plump, comfortable, a pink face, kindly,
brown eyes enlarged into softness by heavy lenses
in incongruous lavender plastic frames, uptilted,

73

a green dress and a green hat with a red flower:
anonymous;
Mrs. Ezra Browne sits quietly, her hands folded
on top of her black handbag on her cozy
lap, motionless.
Lips move softly, not rigidly.)

MRS. BROWNE: No, no comment, mister.

(Ryan nods once, emphatically, turns
instantly back to Westen.)

RYAN: And Mr. Kellam, when did he come into
this curious picture?

WESTEN: He bought into the property, or let's say the deed
was recorded in his and Mrs. Browne's names,
in September of that same year, 1937.

RYAN: I see. You say eight lots to the acre?

WESTEN: Yes, that's right. It was that way on Gross's plat.

RYAN: That's all, Mr. Westen. Unless
you have anything more to add?

(Westen laughs and the sound of the laugh runs
like the sound of the waves on a July beach in
the heat of the sun, inviting, promising coolness,
the
implication of all refreshment.)

WESTEN: No. No. I guess there are some here
will say I have said too much. I'd be glad to stop
now.

RYAN: But your opinion: this change
in the use of the land—it's proper?

WESTEN: Real estate's funny business. You learn, unless you
are stupid,
you can't stop change, in the long run, zoning
or no zoning. The pressures, financial or people,
when they
get too strong, the use changes, the times change
and use goes with them. Right now

74

	this might be too soon, too fast, sort of artificial,
	like forcing a plant. That's my opinion.
RYAN:	I see. Oh, and one more thing:
	where will the school site be?
WESTEN:	If I could answer that one, a whole lot of parents
	hereabouts
	would be tickled to death.

(*He laughs again.*)

RYAN:	(*smiling*)
	I see, sir. Thank you. Now, Mr. Crane,
	you may question.
CRANE:	Nothing, except to point out to Mr. Westen
	that he's prejudiced in the matter. Isn't that so?
WESTEN:	Can't afford that sort of prejudice in my business.
	And the circumstances, they're altogether too
	common.
CRANE:	Yet, if Mr. Kellam's claim is now disallowed,
	you might then hope for a profit?
WESTEN:	No, Mr. Crane, I'm not
	that sort of an optimist. Couldn't afford that
	either.
CRANE:	Very well. That's all then.

(*Westen sits down. He is still smiling.*)

(*The room—the bare room, with its bare lights, the
     chamber
furnished only with people—is still. The air
lies used and palpable, the sound
of a sigh is heard, but not one, many fused
into one soft and whispering sound. The clock
says time, time, time. A window rattles
tiny defiance against the oncoming of night air,
     the fresh
breeze of the open places, the unconfined
surrounding night.
                    A pause now, a gathering
against new conflict.*)

RYAN: I would like to hear now
from Mr. Quintus Lamy, the architect. Mr. Lamy,
will you be next, please?

LAMY: I will—but I hate to do it.

(He rises now, tall and a little stooped, a big man,
shaking his head, his voice, too loud,
echoing with a deep and a moving timbre
from the dry, unabsorbing walls.)

(The room-full stirs, uneasily. This
is what they don't want: it is
the unexpected, the unpredictable, the unease
of what you cannot foretell or foresee.
The unpleasant:
that can be faced, the known things, the sales and
        the
hard refusals, the accusations, the common
knowledge of man and his ways, his
pettiness, hatred, anger, greed, all these
are but the known factors.
                    The dread lies always
in the voice of the unknown, the new
factor added beyond
precomprehension: the guards are
never upraised in time.)

RYAN: I know, Mr. Lamy, I know and I sympathize.
When we first discussed this matter you made
your reluctance clear. Notwithstanding,
it will help now, help us to clarify,
if you'll give your opinion on this change, as an
        architect,
and also as a neighbor. I understand
your house and land border the old Sweet place?

LAMY: They do. The site of the Sweet house lies across
on the opposite side of the old Town Road from
        mine.
You will understand, you will all of you
        understand,

76

RYAN: if I say I'm prejudiced here.
             We understand. But we want
             your opinion, private as well as professional.
LAMY: Very well. I'll try to give it.

(The big man rubs
the back of his left forefinger across his forehead, a gesture
patent of his fatigue, his effort. His voice now
is clouded, muted.)

(The audience of the dividing room stirs,
disturbed, uneasy: weariness
is as contagious as laughter and
never is welcome.)

(Jennifer, Jennifer, are you cold?
Seated alone on the worn-smooth bench,
here in the hot room, are you cold?
What was the source of the heat you miss,
where is the source?)

LAMY: There is a clear intention in zoning laws,
             they are made to protect, and we count on their
                   protection,
             investing our money—indeed, investing lives
             because of a faith in them.
                          Mr. Westen's right:
             they don't protect forever. Times change forever,
             they must change, usage changes, the use of land,
             the type of person, their possible way of life.
             But they mustn't change too soon, or go too fast,
             or be arbitrary, for if they do, then many
             who sank their fortunes, I use the word in the
                   broadest
             sense I can think of, into a use of property,
             are cheated untimely out of that very use.
             Wars bring on violent changes. Now we're at
                   peace—
             or so we hope. We must act, at least, as though

the peace were real.
                                    A grocery store, that's
                    nothing.
It could do no great harm. For myself, I'll say
it couldn't be handier, the site of the new store
would lie but a hundred and fifty, two hundred
                    feet
from my own front door. The store under Mr.
                    Kellam
would indubitably be well run, a competent man,
I've dealt with him at Hazlitt's for many years.
It isn't the grocery store, it's the other matter:
the exception used as a wedge to plat the acres
into a different sort of community
at odds with the one that's grown, through the
                    many years,
because the growers, if I may use that word,
were confident they were safe in that sort of
                    growth.
Eighty potential houses on ten small acres:
the whole of the area zoned to be residential,
north of the Inlet, north of the village proper,
is a scant two hundred acres. It holds ten
                    dwellings,
and fourteen buildings in all. A violent change.
I don't say that it's right that ten families
should monopolize all that land. And I don't say
the Sweet place couldn't be platted into dwellings,
perhaps as many as twenty more—half-acres,
as Mr. Ryan proposed. But eighty houses
crowded together in lanes is itself a village
and those who would buy them and live in them
                    would differ
in habit and use—and the other owners
would be hurt financially, land would depreciate—
as it always does in a case like that—and all
would be angry and unhappy. The village proper
would suffer, for mark you, some would move
                    away,

and some would plat their land in the same small
        plats—
the precedent once established, who shall refuse
        them?
See what it comes to!

(*His voice has become strong, resonant, his*
pose is erect, his shoulders do not stoop now,
he is beyond
the weariness of the thought
of his own effort.)

                  What could I do—I—
I use myself as example since I don't know
what steps the others would take—what could I do
if the land were platted thus?
                  You heard tonight
of a hedge at Indigo Mill, a fine old hedge,
and the people who live there didn't want it cut,
they exacted a promise from Mr. Gerald Lucas
that he wouldn't take it down.
                  Well, here's the
        opposite:
I could plant a hedge, a high and a great thick
        hedge,
I could put it along the road, the entire southern
edge of the holding, and block off the little houses
clean from my view. Those trees, all rooted
in anger and in distrust, would shut off the whole
view of the ocean, the sweep of the lovely bay,
from the folk who bought the plots to be near the
        ocean,
to see the sun on the water, the glow of evening
as the western light declined and the waves took on
the color of dusk.
                  And I, who had done this thing,
I'd have lost the view to the southward, the subtle
        slope
of land to marsh and marsh to the perfect curves

of the sallywinder of Seldom Brook and the Inlet,
the incredible green of marsh grass in the autumn,
the green swept over with patches of lavender
            mist
where the rosemary grows—I could sit and stare
            and stare
at the thick green foliage of my enemy hedge
that grew two ways to hatred.
                        I do not say
I'd commit this cruelty, no. I tell you the thing
that leaps to the mind.
                    What sort of a village are
            we?
What is the matter with us that all such matters
are bounded north and south and east and west
by the old hates and quarrels and hurtful wants
of our competitions?
                    When the hurricane blew,
the village changed. The quarrels were buried,
            forgotten,
each housed other, for need and human kindness,
food and house and clothes, they were shared, all
            shared,
and the morning after, when all went out to reckon
the sum of this disaster, all men were working
together and for one end. And one heard only
the single comment, "It might have been worse, at
            least
no life was lost here." Why, in the daily run,
in the days of peace, of calm, is the sharp division
always aroused? No land for the common school—
that's but one instance. And now division fostered
over this scheme. Can we not move together,
work as one people for a communal purpose,
settle this peacefully, let in the grocery store,
give Mr. Kellam his chance for his independence,
plat the land in parcels that but improve
the whole of the village—and bring to many sweet
            pleasure

in the land God made so beautiful for such
     pleasure?
Let us make no new wounds in a wounded body.
That is all I have to say.

(The stillness now, as he ceases to speak, is too
     great:
it is a void of sound.
                    The many eyes—the windows
of hate and of love, the assessors
of man's meaning, the surveyors of all
clouded intention—they are turned off from
     Lamy, they look
at all other things. Such windows
would prove to be open doors, allowing
too much to escape.
                    Mrs. Ezra Browne
looks at her handbag, without seeing.
                              Anna Hall,
the loose skin of her neck twisted to a fine
     spiralled curve,
looks to Hetty Browne to discover
something she could not name, her mind
remembers the hot blue day stinking of fallen oak
     leaves
after the hurricane, the bare trees, winter
in summertime and the vision turns
to the wide fields of youth, recaptured now
by a voice, in age.
                    Sueton Kellam
looks at his clasped fingers, wishes
he could move his body witched now into
     unwanted stillness, knowing
that the feeblest motion would be a breeze
to scatter the mist of ridiculous guilt that hangs
like a fog on his mind.
                    Jacob Ledbetter thinks:
a good man trying too hard to be good. The spell
will break with the first word.
                              Jennifer Messler

81

watches the back of this standing man,
sees it sag, the effort expended, wishes within
                    her—
not with the mind but the emotions—
something could comfort, something support,
and something cherish and heal.
His fatigue is hers now.)

RYAN: I thank you, Mr. Lamy.
Most moving statement.

(Rustle all over the room. The individuals
have come back to themselves.)

(Lamy sits down, looks at the floor, then
swiftly turns his head and
smiles at Jennifer.
It is a shy smile: a small boy's
smile that says, I did it, it's all over.)

RYAN: I shall ask Mr. Rochester Mallin for his opinion,
if he'll be so good.

(Mallin pushes himself upright with his elbow
on the folded overcoat, pokes one finger swiftly,
                    secretly,
into the side of his wife Serena's thigh,
and rises slowly and gracefully
to his feet. A slight smile
bends the sharp cut of his full lips. His hands
go into his jacket pockets.)

MALLIN: What would you like my opinion on, Mr. Ryan?
RYAN: Did you know the house, in the days of Benjamin
            Sweet?
Was it ever a store to you?
MALLIN: It was never a store, not in the remotest sense
of the use of the word. I knew it very well
in the days of Ben Sweet, that cantankerous
            citizen,

and after his death, when Deborah lived there. I
    tell you
she wasn't cut out as a storekeeper, the Almighty
didn't intend that. She was much too fetching,
a wonder she never got married.

*(A ripple of laughter, subdued, a few
heads turn toward neighbors in acknowledgment
of a point made, a common knowledge
shared unspoken, richer for silence.)*

MALLIN: No, store is the
    wrong word.

RYAN: I see. So. As to the proposition
of the possible future development, will you speak
to that point, please?

MALLIN: Mr. Lamy was very moving. I won't pretend
I can do the same, I haven't his gift for words—
on such a subject. I fear my human rancor
would rise to block me. I haven't got—well, his
    Christian
attitude toward the deal. He has spoken of change,
of the naturalness of change, as times do change.
But there's nothing in this, I fear, to warrant a
    novel,
I'll say a destructive novelty such as threatens.
We've set a use now, haven't we?
                            I used to live
in Cottrellton here, on Chepaug Point, in the
    house
my father owned. I left it after the town built
the road to Chepaug Point, on the edge of the
    water
across South Harbor, and the land was developed
into a lot of cheap houses. Well, this is a town.
But Chogs Cove is a village, and so I came
and settled on Whales Head, near Mrs. Gosford's
    place.
We got Mr. Lamy to alter the Caswell house,

we've built on to it, done outbuildings. Now Mr.
    Lamy—
he didn't say so, perhaps he was too modest—
is designing for us a thing we call The Barn,
a beautiful building. It houses an auditorium.
I suppose I needn't explain, it's common
    knowledge,
that the purpose of this is to add to the village's
    pleasure
and possible profit, charity shows, and school plays,
that sort of thing. One doesn't take that sort of
    trouble,
make that investment to further a change of use
that turns the use to a rabble instead of a simple
and decent community. There's nothing unusual
about such work. We've all of us on Whales Head
and the zoned land north of the village, built and
    added:
the Manning Carpenters, Davises, Lamy himself,
my wife and I, Mrs. Gosford—all of us, all of us—
except Mrs. Ezra Browne.
                Mr. Lamy didn't,
perhaps out of kindness, suggest that perhaps Mrs.
    Browne
would like to plat out her land like the other if
    precedent
could only allow it. I even doubt, myself,
if anyone who could look upon such a change
so dispassionately would ever be hard enough
to plant the hedge he suggests.
                  I tell you, I
    would—
with big, strong trees, straight off, set close
    together,
so the hedge would solidly block from the very
    first.
I'd even contribute to his hedge, if he'd let me.
There'd be more and more of the same sort of
    thing, and soon.
And Lamy's right when he says that ultimately

the holdings would all go, the land would be
        platted,
and you'd multiply your population until you had
a town—a town of what? Of what sort of people?
They come and they make a settlement like a
        slum,
they bring the city habits into the countryside,
elbow to elbow, house against wretched house,
bungalow pushing bungalow—the bungaloid
        growth,
if you'll forgive the expression.
                                        Will you wax rich
out of such folk as these—when the other sort,
the present holders, have all been driven away?
I've always admired the kindness, the sensitive
        feelings
of Mr. Lamy—but I'll tell you here, I'll fight
till I'm beat to prevent this. And if that breeds
        dissension,
why—I don't know, really, if I should feel
        contentment
in a village full of the milk of human kindness
and none of its tartar sauce.
                                        I expect that's all
I can say on the matter—unless there are any
        questions?

RYAN: No, except this: I take it that you
            speak for your wife, sir? Perhaps
            for your mother-in-law, Mrs. Gosford?

MALLIN: For my wife, yes, Mr. Ryan. But no man speaks
            for his mother-in-law.

(*There is another ripple of laughter, easy, pleasant,
a few heads turn
to look at Mrs. Gosford.*
                        She sits
*smiling a little, erect, her chin raised, her hands
motionless in her lap.*)

(*Jacob thinking*)

85

Gone right back, now. Back to the beginning.
Lamy might have moved them, Sueton looking
　　　guilty,
Anna Hall remembering. Compromise the matter,
nobody hurt then. Now it's all where it started
and the old hurts ache:
all for just one voice.

RYAN:　　　　But perhaps she agrees with you?
MALLIN:　　　Perhaps she does—perhaps she does in this
　　　　　　　　　　instance.
MRS. GOSFORD: That's quite right, Rochester. I agree this time.

*(The laughter comes again, but not healing:
dividing now.)*

RYAN:　　　　Thanks, then, Mr. Mallin—and Mrs. Gosford.

*(Mallin sits down again, without looking
to the right or the left: he is still smiling, he pushes
the folded coat to a more comfortable
pillow.
　　　Serena turns to him, her lips moving,
no sound, but saying, 'How clever, Roche!' She too
smiles for him, then turning
her head smiles for her mother: the daily payment,
usual, habitual, for both; it would be hard
to say what the smile means beyond this.)*

RYAN:　　　　So.
Mr. Chairman, ladies and gentlemen, that's all.
I shall omit from the roll call others
who are willing to testify that to their personal
　　　　　　　　　　knowledge
there was never a store at Ben Sweet's house.
Mr. Manning Carpenter, Mr. and Mrs. Messler,
Mrs. August Davis, they are all here, they have all
expressed a willingness to testify to this fact.
If there is any question, I'll call on them.

86

(*He pauses. But there is no motion
made by Kellam or Mitchell Crane. The audience
sits quiet, expectant.*)

RYAN: You have before you, Mr. Chairman, a petition
against this change, a protest signed
by forty-three residents of the Chogs Cove area.
It speaks for itself. But what they would testify
would merely repeat what's been said tonight
            already,
and very clearly. We omit it. I think
that that is all now, for the moment.

(*He sits down at once in the chair
by the long brown table. His briefcase lies
still unopened before him.*)

JACOB: Well, thank you. I guess now it's your turn,
            Mitchell,
if you want to proceed?

CRANE: Yes, sir.

(*He rises slowly.*)

We don't have a petition, Mr. Chairman,
we have a permit to build, it was legally
issued by Orville Creston. It should have been
sufficient for such a matter. Nevertheless,
it will interest you to hear now from someone else,
another side of the matter.
                    If Mrs. Browne
will be good enough to speak?

(*The plump little woman sets
her handbag beside her, rises with a slight wriggle—
the accustomed adjustment
of a stiff corset—the anonymous red flower
nods on her hat. Her hand goes
up to the lavender spectacles, fingers lightly*)

touch the upslanted lenses, the hand drops,
clasps the other below
her soft, large breasts.)

CRANE: Mrs. Browne, you have lived in the village of
    Chogs Cove
    all your life?

MRS. BROWNE: Yes indeed. I was born here and raised here, I
    married here.

CRANE: But your husband's deceased?

MRS. BROWNE: I'm a widow, yes, sir. Ten years a widow.

CRANE: You knew Benjamin Sweet and his house?

MRS. BROWNE: Of course I did. I knew him and his daughter,
    Deborah.

CRANE: Would you agree with me that the house was a
    store?

MRS. BROWNE: Surely. It certainly was. I recollect my mother,
    Eloise Hall that was, she died in the year 1935,
    she'd say to me or my sister, "Go up to Sweet's
        store
    and fetch home some buckeys"—or whatever it was
        was wanted
    of the things he sold.

CRANE: But she didn't mean the fish store, the one on the
    Landing?

MRS. BROWNE: No, sir. She meant the house. The house that set
    on the site
    Mr. Kellam's trying to build his store on.

CRANE: It is said that you bought this land and then sold
    an interest
    to Mr. Kellam. Is that so, Mrs. Browne?

MRS. BROWNE: Why, yes. That's so. I don't suppose there's a law
    that says
    a body can't buy and sell.

CRANE: No, of course not. A sort of investment on your
    part?

MRS. BROWNE: That's right. I was happy to sell to Sueton, to let
    him
    have share in the property, liked the idea of a store
    again there

88

CRANE: where there'd been one previously.

CRANE: A good investment?

MRS. BROWNE: I haven't lost money on it. Not yet. But we are both satisfied,
or so I believe.

CRANE: So when you sold the interest to Mr. Kellam,
it was already with the idea of a store?

MRS. BROWNE: That's right. That was the idea.

CRANE: I thank you. That is all, Mrs. Browne. I'm grateful
to have such testimony from such an old resident
as yourself in this instance. Well, then, any
questions?

RYAN: If you please, one or two. Mrs. Browne,
it is true you refused, in the time
that you owned the land yourself, to sell
to the use of the school?

MRS. BROWNE: That is so.

RYAN: Didn't like the idea, perhaps, of the children—
so many children—as neighbors?

MRS. BROWNE: School land pays no taxes. The rest of us, all of us,
would make up the loss.

RYAN: I see. And the plat,
the one Mr. Gross made for you, that seemed
a better venture, more profit there?

MRS. BROWNE: Mr. Gross made it. It was his own idea, he done
it entirely
on his own. Mr. Westen was off on that. When he
got it all made,
he showed it to me.

RYAN: But you weren't shocked, Mrs. Browne?

MRS. BROWNE: No, I wasn't shocked any. The plat was the sort of
a plat
that was modelled on Hoxsies Cove. There's
nothing new there
for Chogs Cove neighborhood.

RYAN: You had no intention to plat it then?

MRS. BROWNE: There was lots of things to think about first, lots
of 'em.

RYAN: There must have been. Zoning laws?

89

MRS. BROWNE: All sorts of questions, mister. A widow has to look
                    out
                for herself. She has no lawyer to do it for her.
RYAN: A pity. And Mrs. Browne,
                you have stated that there was a store on the Ben
                    Sweet place,
                of your own knowledge. Yet you have heard now
                the testimony of others. And in particular that
                of Mr. Hoxsie, who lived
                across from the Sweet place, or anyway, close to it.
                Do you not grant Mr. Hoxsie
                is a competent witness, though he denies the
                    store?
MRS. BROWNE: I don't care to give an opinion on Mr. Hoxsie.
RYAN: Yet he knew Benjamin Sweet? And his daughter
                    too?
MRS. BROWNE: Yes, he knew Sweet. He certainly knew his
                    daughter,
                must have seen plenty of her in the days before
                    his cousin
                came to keep house for him. Or so it's said.

                (A soft, perceptible, uneasy, comfortless
                stir in the room. The sound
                is the sound that the dividing southwest wind
                contrives in the damp leaves of the oppressive
                cycle of August.
                            Rochester Mallin grins,
                whistles without a sound.
                            Quintus Lamy
                looks down at the floor.
                            Jerome Westen narrows
                his eyes, his mouth
                opens a little.
                            Mrs. John Gosford turns stiffly,
                body erect, and stares with a hard, disapproving
                look at Mrs. Browne.
                            Bad,
                thinks Jacob Ledbetter. Bad and bad,
                the old wounds.)

RYAN: I see.
                   But this knowledge, this intimate knowledge that
                   you imply: Mr. Hoxsie would know
                   the house very well? The rooms of the house?
                   The arrangement and use of them?

MRS. BROWNE: Some came to Ben Sweet's house to buy at his
                   store, some did.
                   Others came there for other reasons. The rooms
                   you knew
                   would depend on the purpose of the visit,
                   maybe the time of day, too.

RYAN: You mean, perhaps, that he didn't come there to
                   buy?

MRS. BROWNE: I don't know as I'd care to state. Or whether he
                   came to buy—
                   the things that were sold in the store. I mind
                   my own business mostly.

RYAN: I trust it may prosper. That is all, I thank you.

                   *(Mrs. Browne still stands; a slight
                   flush has risen now to her face, her clasped
                   hands move slightly on her stomach. Her pose
                   awaits an event whatever.)*

CRANE.   That's all, Mrs. Browne, and thank you.

                   *(She sits down slowly, picks up
                   her bag again.)*

CRANE: Miss Anna J. Hall. But please, Miss Hall, don't
                   stand
                   if it will fatigue you.

MISS HALL: I can manage, I guess. I've been standing up
                   and setting down for close on to eighty years,
                   so once more won't hurt me.

                   *(Deep voice, resonant, sprung
                   from the full chest, the tones come richly and
                   fully forth: the words
                   chiselled and cut with the clean edge*

91

of her accent. It is not
the voice of an old woman.
                    The bench creaks, the
            others
seated on it are shaken as her massive
body rises, ponderous, short-statured.
The wattles of skin, a-quiver, fall in fleshly
flutings from chin to body. The curved
hoods of her eyelids cover the outward
whites of her large open eyes: wide set, green and
            brilliant.
Her huge hands rest
on the back of the bench before her, the nails
square cut and flat.)

(This audience
must be attentive to this figure: here
is strength long grown.)

CRANE:	You knew Benjamin Sweet, Miss Hall?
MISS HALL:	I knew him.
CRANE:	You knew his house and his daughter's house?
MISS HALL:	I knew it.
CRANE:	Would you say that the house, or the ell that attached to it, was ever a store?
MISS HALL:	I knew it as such.
CRANE:	Can you tell us how you arrived at that opinion?
MISS HALL:	I can tell you.

(She pauses now, her lips move, pursing,
in and out as though
she were tasting the words before she would utter
them: the firm seeds
stripped of their soft husks.)

MISS HALL: God gave us eyes to see each in his own fashion.
I saw that house as I saw it. It was a store.
There was occasion arose in which to know it;
had to be studied. This happened

when I went over to Sweet's at the request of my
    father,
asking Ben Sweet to move the barn, the tall barn,
    still there,
that was attached to the ell as the ell to the main
    house.
Ben Sweet considered it. Yes. My father had
    offered
to pay for the move.

CRANE: Your father had offered to pay for moving a barn
that belonged to Benjamin Sweet?

MISS HALL: He offered to pay for it. He was a man was
    closeted
into the confines of one room. The big tall barn
stood in his moonlight, blocked the rise of it,
    shuttered
the shine on the water. My father, an old man
    crippled
into his bed, was choice of his moonlight,
    particular
cared for September, said it outdid the other
    months, nothing
akin to September moons, noble.

(The voice grew, word upon word, volume
adding to power, the deep tones
closing around the minds, compelling the ears,
fusing the spirits:
                minds
saw the tall march of the days make into the
    pattern
of eleven circled months that discarded
one by one the imperfect, the failed
moons of their own begetting until they were last
    delivered
of the twelfth perfect, the wholly desired
moon of their love, their justification.
                    The soft
    voice,
the clean, the accented

syllables of impassioned speech, diffused
like the sun in the haze of the warmth that follows
the cold winds that blow too clear.)

(Mitchell Crane looks down, fumbles to pick up
a sheet of paper, but
doesn't look at it. His voice when he speaks
is for the first time uncertain, hesitant: interest
has superseded intention.)

CRANE: Well . . . and the barn, Miss Hall—it was
moved?

MISS HALL: Never was moved, no, never was moved an inch.
Ah,
deals fall through at the end with a man like Ben
Sweet—
props his steps with the stones took dark from the
graveyard,
names carved on them. Memory hidden
under the footfalls.

CRANE: Oh, I see, I see. But during this time,
the negotiation, you had the chance to study
the use of the house, the ell?

MISS HALL: You back to the store? Why surely, Benjamin
Sweet
he kept what he made to sell on the shelves of the
ell,
laid out neat and orderly. And he sold them. He
sold
anything that he had. He'd have sold his daughter
too,
for a price and maybe he did. No use to blame
now,
he's dead and Deborah's dead, both of 'em's
buried,
nobody's took their stones.
The book's closed, the account's square.
                                   It was a

store,

94

	if that's the question.
CRANE:	Yes, that's the question. We're trying to say that change
	of use is but to return to a former use here.
MISS HALL:	Ah, change!
	Benjamin Sweet was the last of his line, or Deborah was:
	land was held on deed back to King Philip's time.
	Wasn't a zoning then to protect them, the Indians,
	hunters robbed for the farmers. My own grandfather
	saw that land when there wasn't a square inch wasn't harvested,
	planted to crops or grass. My father saw
	Abijah Sweet cut down the tall forest, tree by tree,
	that grew where the harrow rusted. A hard strong man
	was Abijah, he drowned himself in an inch of water.
	Change? Oh change is the accustomed. I said
	God gave us eyes to see each in his own fashion.
	My eyes seen plenty of change.

                                                  You want

any more from me?

CRANE:	No. No. I guess not, no. I thank you, Miss Hall.
MISS HALL:	You're welcome, I'm sure.
JACOB:	Mr. Ryan? Anything you got?
RYAN:	No. There's nothing.
MISS HALL:	I'll sit, then.

(*The massive body lowers itself slowly, steadily
onto the bench, with a creak and a squeak.*

                                                  It is

    over,
song's ended.)

(*Jacob Ledbetter stirs and shifts his chair,
he glances sidewise at Crane.*)

95

JACOB: Well now, Mitchell—it's getting late. I don't want
         to hurry things up unduly, but I reckon
         there's all of us will be happier when this is over.
         What's next?

PARRY: Yes. Me, too. I'd like to enquire, is there
         something new to be added to what's been said—
         or just some more of the same?

CROSS: That's it. I'd sort of like to know that too.
         Anything we can sort of condense?

CRANE: There's no new evidence, gentlemen. There's
                  simply
         the fact that I have here Mr. Clifford Peckham,
         and Mr. Asa Congdon, both to testify
         in the same vein.

JACOB: If you wish to let them speak, then by all means
                  do so.
         I'd suggest that you state what they wish to say.
         We'll just ask them if they agree—if that's
                  agreeable?

CRANE: That'll be right as long as the Board allows
         the same weight to their evidence as was granted
         to the other speakers?

JACOB: Yes, we'll do that.

CRANE: Both Mr. Peckham and Mr. Congdon state
         of their own knowledge that they had seen the
                  house
         of Benjamin Sweet often enough in the days
         when he still lived there, or his daughter did,
         to say that he ran a store and that they bought
         goods at that store. The goods were the sort of
                  thing
         I have outlined already. In talking to me,
         both men were quite positive in this opinion.
         I'll ask Mr. Peckham now if that is the case.
         Have I quoted you correctly on this, Mr.
                  Peckham?

PECKHAM: That's right, you have. I'd like to add on my own
         I'd be glad to see a store again on the site
         of the old Sweet place. Be good for the village.

RYAN: (speaking quickly, sharply)

96

That's your opinion. And does your wife concur
in this, Mr. Peckham? She's Mr. Dexter's
daughter?

PECKHAM: (a trace of anger)

RYAN: I guess we could leave her out of this. Too young.
              Too young perhaps to have gone to such a house?
              Her father, maybe, would not have permitted
                  that?
PECKHAM: Don't know what her father'd do or wouldn't do.
RYAN: I see. Go ahead, Mr. Crane.
CRANE: Thank you. And now, Mr. Congdon? You agree?
CONGDON: Yes. It was a store.
CRANE: You've nothing to add to what I stated for you?
CONGDON: Guess not.
CRANE: Is this satisfactory to you, Mr. Chairman—and Mr.
                  Ryan?
JACOB: All right for us.
RYAN: All right, all right—as long
              as Mr. Congdon doesn't add to his list
              of articles purchased those that were contained
              in glass?
CRANE: In glass?
RYAN: I spoke of that before—
              Sweet had a trade in things that were held in glass.
              Unlicensed. Well, Mr. Congdon?

              (He is a man of forty, well-built, still good-looking;
              grins as he answers.)

CONGDON: I bought some eelskins, for fishing. They was sold
              in a glass jar. Pickled.

              (There is a sibilance of laughter runs through the
                  room
              like the small waves on a beach in a still day.
              Walter Hoxsie, the old man,
              throws back his head and
              looks down the length of his nose at Congdon.)

97

HOXSIE:	Pickled in alcohol, Asa?

(*The laughter comes again, and again splits*
on the rocks of their cleavage.
                         Congdon flushes,
looks at Hoxsie, his mouth shuts
in a disagreeable line.)

JACOB: Well, sir, well now, Mitchell, I take it that's all?
CRANE: That's all we have to say. We are well content.
We're sure you gentlemen will decide the
                         precedent
establishes the reason for Mr. Kellam's
permit to be now valid. We hope you note
that there is more than a shading of self-interest,
of what at the outset I described as animus,
in the protest against the building. I trust the
                         Board
will decide the case on its merits.

JACOB: Mr. Ryan?
RYAN: No more, sir. I believe
the Board has sufficient knowledge of what
                         impends,
of what this exception leads to, to render
                         judgment
justly as usual.

JACOB: Then we'll say that that's all, folks. Hearing's
                         over.
We'll give our decision at the end of the week,
as customary. Thanks to you, and good night.

(*He rises firmly.*
                         Parry gets up too.
                                   Cross
gathers his papers together, rises slowly,
almost reluctantly.)

(*So the Hearing ends. One hears*
its finale in sound of rustle and creak and scrape,

of voices muted, restrained. The sound
is the reflection of no decision, the puzzlement
of a yes against a no;
man against man: the lie or the truth, or
the truth for one is the lie for the other, the seen
        thing,
the known, is contested, called unseen, unknown,
non-existent.
                The audience
files out now: they are returned
to their individual forms and ways. They move
one by one, two by two, no groups. No wish now
to accrete or congregate.
                In the avoidance
of this one's glance from that one, is the unspoken
clear testimony of their division, the saturation
of the desire to meet, to speak, to hear.
Who's wiser now?
                Was wisdom indeed
grown in such soil?
                To speak now, to this one,
would it not then commit, express?
How speak when the mind is troubled, bruised,
        uncertain?
How say it was a lie or you said I lied and
meet on the morrow?
                Silence
is the dense coat against the uncomfortable
cold rain of hurt:
bundle up.
                Here
are faces that say we are more convinced than
        ever,
all that was said against us but confirms us:
we will not listen to other.)

(But not Jacob Ledbetter.
                He moves in with the
        crowd,

speaking easily, pleasantly, the personal
query. How's Mabel? What do you hear from
      Harry?
You get your new car, Simon? His clear
Rhode Island voice carries, and carries goodness;
and the sound changes.
                          Listen:
the creak of the floorboards, the soft
shuffle and scrape of feet, the sudden increase
of a laugh added, the voices rising,
multiplying: they have discovered again
there are other matters, the easy
words will bridge and tide over, they will postpone,
the night and alone are for further thinking,
the soft lamp and the shut door: you can
say your anger then. Now,
how's Mabel, the boat was hauled up early,
it's hard to find steamer clams, the scallops
was really plentiful: hatred
is covered over, the volume
includes the external kindness, the convention
of the easy question. One word
breeds another. Out of such little
words is the truth?)

(The soft wind envelops, the cool
October night includes. The far
stars are immovable in their swift flight. Time
devolves in its revolution. The acrid
smell of mankind is lost in the sweet wind.
The cars start, the whirr
of the motor caught, vapor exploded, headlights
lance dark to death, make dark
deeper and richer.
                      The singles, the couples,
the occasional threes speak and divide and the
        sound
of feet on soft earth, the metalled road,
grows and diminishes, and the lights
flick off in the Town Hall; rest

will lie on the drab corridors, the empty
room of the Hearing, it will await
man's next harsh or good impulse, it will be
the same but changed tomorrow, harder for
      daylight, another
layer of confusion added, it will be richer.
                            There
    are still
the odd voices, good night, see you soon, be good,
remember me to Alice or to Virginia,
sleep well, sweet dreams.
Dreams are for those deserve them: the turn
of the mind is the rare and the wonderful,
the mysterious power not comprehended. Dreams
are for day as well
as the deepening, the devious night.)

(The soft wind
accepts the absence of all humanity, unthinking,
never caring, it blows
leaves or dreams, no matter, it touches
love or hate, no matter, it recaptures
night without rapture, the sweet
air of October, it lays
the high stars bare now over
deserted darkness, gentle, unhating, unloving,
in being only.)

ENTER within another shell.
Ah! how smooth, how polished it is!
And beneath the smoothness the ever hell.
Serena, Serena, whither your goings?
What do you do with all your days,
and the plots of the days' sowings?
Bracketed between age and youth,
subtle supporter, unsupported:
lie for the truth.

SAY GOOD NIGHT now nicely. It is expected of you,
it is habitually expected:
you have been well brought up.

Hearing the voice behind her now, Serena
turned her head.
       "Good night, Mr. Ledbetter.
The meeting beautifully run, I really mean it."
"Well, thank you," the man said, his voice so firm,
his face invisible in the solid shadow
of a wide brimmed hat. "About that baby tractor,
I reckon the cutter-bar wouldn't take your meadow.
Do you still want one?"
       "Oh. Roche?" Serena said.
"I'll see it tomorrow on my way up to town."
Rochester dropped his voice as he turned around.
"You could sit for a judge, the way you handle lawyers,
you had Mitchell Crane on toast."
       Serena peered
through the dim night in hope that she'd see more
of Jacob's response; but it was too dark.
       "I thank you."
The phrase repeated. "See you tomorrow, then."
The heavy vague form disappeared in the huddle
of moving figures.

Learn to absent yourself from the difficult
by moving firmly away. But men,
not women: the woman absents and stays.

"Come along, do, I'm chilly.
Ready, Mother?"
"I'm ready. Heavens, a muddled
situation. Come along, Rochester,
drive your women home." The clear, cool tones,
critical, uninvolved, content to be quite alone—
as long as she was above? Age set you above?
"All right, we're off," said Rochester.

She could feel
the satisfaction in him: a different man now, moved
by the sense of something done. What had he done?
The speaking . . .

Turn it off now, absent from it, staying. Later.
The drift of night, or better the clear
lonely excellence of the waking
dawn over water.
Accept, accept now,
reflect to prolong his mood in you. The wife,
woman: the mirror.

And Rochester's voice now, calling:
"Good night, Quintus, I hope I wasn't too bold,
but you're too kind-hearted."
"Yes. Well, maybe I am."
Q's voice is tired, Serena thought; his shoulders
sagged to fatigue.
"You planted it very well,
fine hedge, but you cut it down too soon entirely.
Hope that I planted again, green and thick."

Oh, the green, fine hedge! It belonged
to Rochester Mallin now.
What else would it serve to hide?

"How wily!"
Mrs. Gosford said. "You are far too clever, Roche."
"How goes the painting, Jennifer?" Rochester's voice
with a new sound now—or an old sound encroaching
out of the past?

103

"It's awful, Mr. Mallin."
"I don't believe you."
                    "You would if you saw the stuff."
"Bring it over, Jenny. I'd like to see it.
I know about that—quite truly. It's not enough
to judge your own work. Isn't that right, Quintus?"
"Right," said the tired voice.

The paintings shown in the lee of the new
hedge? Oh, it didn't matter.
How confident is happiness, even
the evanescent! How happy
is confidence!
                    But you: become now
the image that you return.

                              "Try to get in
tomorrow evening on your way home, Quintus.
I go to Providence, and I might have word
on the hospital project. Think you'll have the time?"
Suddenly now the tired voice is heard
informed with laughter.
                    "I guess I'd better make it.
I've got to eat."
                    "Good!" Rochester said. "Good night."
Now the dark air is full of the changing tones
of the partings spoken: the old voice, firmly, brightly
closing the moment; the tired one; the confident
male resonance; the young, uncertain,
appealing; her own—but one's own voice is curtained
by the veil of echoing bones: what tone here? Hers,
or the echo of confidence?
                    The car purrs
after the snarl of starting. Into the rear,
Mother in front, her bad knee. Pity so cold,
or stars and the pure night with top flung back, clear
wall of the rush of air, the air enfolding,
setting alone . . . and above?
                    Mrs. Gosford now:
"Rochester, dear boy, that was clever, able,
but hardly kind. Poor Quintus Lamy!"

104

"Maybe
the man's too soft."

"No, Rochester, no. Too good."
"Too good for his own good. Now I begin to wonder
whether in going to Providence, I should
speak for him for the hospital."

"Oh, you must!
Virginia's ill. He needs it. No one can help
people like him directly. It must be done
with that sort of help. It isn't just her health,
it's the whole drain of living. Your influence
is strong, dear boy."

"I wonder if it is strong.
But even so, there's one thing that you judge wrongly,
my dear Mrs. G. Serena can help directly—
and help at once."

"You mean, of course, with Virginia?"
"Oh, with Virginia, yes. But if I'm correct,
there's little for us to do there, any of us,
it's a job for a doctor, a good psychiatrist."
"You mean that she isn't ill?"

"Oh, she's ill enough,
in bursts. Or because she must now so much insist
on the illness she's had so long, a habit, a way?
Malade imaginaire, to a certain degree?"
"That's far too easy, I don't in the least agree.
And if it were so, then how does Serena fit?"
"Like this," he said, his voice full.

Going full-blast now; but a reaction
later, the old despondent
drop to his spirit. How
to prolong the upswing? Sit now:
be a subject.

"Isn't the man
worn out with do-gooding? Well, if that is it,
he needs it back again. Back again from a woman."
"Goodness, Rochester, you are quite beyond me,"

Mrs. Gosford said. "I don't understand at all."
"Must I spell it out? To you? Two women fondly
cherishing all your kin?"

"I'm stupid, Rochester."

Stupid like Machiavelli. Or better,
stupid like Talleyrand, never
for long on the outside.
But speak now, it's your turn.

"Darling, you see both like a male and a female,
all at the same time. We're just a couple of frail
women without a man's mind. Help us."

You could sit back now, quietly, let
the road flow by like the sound
of their voices. Dangerous.
More than is on the surface now. This
was foreshadowed earlier, dinner-time,
blank day, blank page

"Yes, do,"
Mrs. Gosford said. "We depend on you so much."
Rochester laughed aloud. The sound ran through
and over the pure sound of the motor, dissonance
perfectly pitched.
"You're a wonderful team," he said.
"I love to watch you together. Well, team, it's this way.
What does the man get? Can you be always ready
to give out, give out? You both know his nature,
he's full of screwball notions, One World, that rot.
At moments I think that the man is really potty,
but it comes from goodness. Well, when does he get it
back,
and where? From Virginia? Isn't he going to find
a source some day?"

"What do you mean, a source?"
Mrs. Gosford said, her voice sharp.

How cleverly designed

106

to needle him into speech!

                    "Ah, Roche, but me,
where then do I come in?"

                    "You be the source."

Source for the goose is also
source for the gander. Laugh
at your own plight.

"The man's mad," Mrs. Gosford said. "Or else
I don't understand."

               "Are you really trying to force me
to say it in so many words? All right. Serena here,
he knows her, loves her. She ought to woo poor Lamy,
make him feel wanted, cared for, warmed at her flame.
She's wonderful at it, practised on me for years.
He'd stop his fretting, he'd get on with his job,
Virginia'd profit, the do-good side that wears
him down on top of the rest, would all disappear.
D'you see what I'm getting at?"

                    "But my dear, good man,"
Mrs. Gosford said, "do you dare to ask your wife—
my daughter, too—to try to capture the fancy
of her cousin-in-law?"

                  "You misunderstand," he said.
"I know Serena. Perhaps I trust her more
than her mother does. Because you open a door,
must you then close and lock it? And have you thought,
is it better to turn his mind to affection now
than to have him discover, perhaps a—hotter source,
and handier by?"

Sudden the flash, sudden the light,
this is the sound of warning. Bells
clash in light. Vanish.

            "Rochester, Rochester, really!"
said Mrs. Gosford. "This is too much, it's not good.
The novelist's mind, you have been writing fiction,

and I don't like it."

"A little blind, or you would
see it clear."

"Perhaps you see too much.
But I shan't discuss it, certainly not discuss it.
Well, we're almost home."

"Aren't you being stuffy,
dear Mrs. G?" said Mallin.

"No," she said.
"Sensible, sensible only. No more now."

"Serena?"

Just his voice and the one word: light comes
bright again, too bright:
hedge and the man's charity diminished
into a weakness.

Wife of a need, unwanted;
the new spur. Pretty, oh pretty youth,
and the hedge owned outright to close
in two directions.

"Too clever for your own boots, dear. A bit of bed
is all I can think of now. So hot and airless
that awful Town Hall! Let it go now, darling,
we'll talk tomorrow. I never dismiss your thoughts,
you're too percipient."

Car draws up at the big green
door of the big house, Mother's house,
Gosfordville? In humor,
or in resentment?

Good night, good night. Over now, home now.
Bed and the bright light? Will it
illumine—or but hurt
the attentive eyes?

◻◻◻◻◻◻

TURN OF the mind is the rare, the wonderful thing,
this the mysterious power not comprehended.
Here is the loneliness as the lone thoughts take wing,
the love and the hate, the good and the evil blended.
Here are the bodies so near, one, two, and three,
only a phase of darkness is set between,
voices fetter but minds go wholly free—
never a chain or a wall that can intervene—
off to the soft-seen prairies of secret past,
past and present become but the intermingled
binding of vision that holds the future fast,
doubled or trebled it yet is forever singled.
What is the sight is seen by the inward eye,
what is the sound to the ear of the spirit's cry?

HERE ARE three people seated in one car in the half
        dark.
Listen: they will converse, the words they issue coming
over the rush of the still wind in the car's speed,
motionless moved now, the round tire twist.
Voices proclaim a common aim and a common purpose,
voices are cheats for the hidden mind behind them:
light on the surface bright in the stirred reflection,
light bent darkly beneath in the liquid deeps,
light lost, no voice heard
other than inner wish and the secret wanting:
wanting's like water, deep refracting,
depths of the memory's will.

Asa Congdon first: man of the flesh unsatisfied,
not to be satisfied, appetite greater than satisfaction,
male attraction wasted on two old women;
money's the thing now, think of money.
So he speaks, his voice comes loudly against the deafness
of old Miss Hall in the back seat. "What d'you think'll
        happen?
Sueton won't get to get his permit now,
seems so. I'd judge old Ledbetter is against us.
What d'you think, Miss Hall? Any chance?"
Ah, you know the answer inside you, Asa—

why do you ask, of two old women,
what you know already yourself?

Pause in the dark: Miss Hall had forgotten about it
       entirely,
she was off and away, lulled by the whispering motion,
by the bright shaft of the headlights closing the darkness
softly, completely, around their brilliance.
One word pierces: Ledbetter: he is a good man—nowadays;
stories they used to tell of Jacob when he was young once,
when I was young, the big fields, leaning, leaning,
rye in the south wind, silk, acre on acre,
over the silk to the blue of the bay.
Love ran past and away in the breathing rye,
Father's a hard man, crippled, a sad man.
Hetty Browne answers the question.

She is not off in the world of the inner: here, in the hard
       world.
"Mitchell Crane talked too much," she said. "I knew it,
knew he'd lay himself open to Cullen Ryan—
smart little man, he gets right down to it.
No, you're right, I'd say that Sucton was blocked off,
       neatly,
all that work and all that money for nothing.
Wait till I skin Ted Gross for talking to Jerry Westen,
blab-mouth fool. It's the last I'll deal with him,
he's out of this job. Now I wonder, I wonder . . .
should we go back now, I wonder, to Jerry Westen—
call off the scheme before it's decided,
settled against us, a precedent?"

Old Miss Hall just sat beside her, her head a-nodding,
wrapped in silence, fatigue, dark shawl of night around her.
Asa listened, startled, his mind assessing:
Jerry Westen, what could he do now?
"Guess I don't rightly follow what you are after," he said.
"Now he is on their side, he has spoken against you
       already."
Hetty stirred on the back seat, her voice came stronger:

110

"Get him on our side, he can influence people."
"Who can influence Mallin?" said Asa.
"Only his wife," she said, "or another woman.
Influence Lamy, hit for his soft side,
he is the key to the question."

Asa whistled and said, "Well, you might have something at
       that.
Influence Lamy—he might. He might if he had something
       on him."
"Don't need anything on him," said Hetty Browne,
"hit for the soft side, appeal to sympathy."
"Easier if you had something, but maybe you're right," said
       Asa.
"Compromise on the size of the lots," said Hetty.
"Get the permit for Kellam, break the zoning—
Kellam's in deep already, Lamy would see that,
he don't aim to ruin the man.
Oh, if we did have something, something against him,
that would help. He'd cherish his good name.
He's too good to be true."

Asa laughed and he whistled again, and he said, "That's
       smart.
But nobody in the world, no man, or I never met one,
is all that good. I guess Mr. Lamy's human.
Round a lot with Jennifer Messler."
"Asa Congdon," said Hetty, "you got a mind like a sewer."
Laugh again in the dark, the car goes faster,
road leaps at you, the car is the sense of power,
women, the pretty women, the young and the pretty,
held all warm in the mind of a man.
"No," said Hetty Browne, and her voice was harsh.
"Do it my way, hit for the soft side,
play up Sueton. Use Jerome."

So she turns her head and she lays her warm hand softly
over the folded soft hands set in the lap beside her,
speaks with a gentle voice, saying, "Anna Julia,
you been listening to what we're saying?"

111

Now the great eyes that were brilliant open, but they are
      clouded,
sisters to night and the veil of night.
Now the deep voice issues in resonant beauty,
beauty like thought is the rare and the wonderful thing,
current of power so generated.
"No," says the voice. "Why, no, I haven't been listening.
Guess I'm tired. I just been thinking
back to the once on a time."

Silence again except for the sound that the wind wove
stretched to sibilance by the dividing progress of metal.
Off and away the old mind: the rye is bending
under the breeze: memory's wind.
Why do we do the dangerous things that we do to each
      other,
witness a truth to achieve a hurt or an end of harming?
Love refused: so the setting of love is altered—
why was love denied in the rye a-bending,
grey-green rye and the far blue sea?
Benjamin Sweet, the big man, man with the fair face—
it was all dead, it was all gone:
grave of the cause of love's loss.

Images clearer and clearer, lit from within by the mind's
      light:
Benjamin standing, feet apart, strong pose, under the hot
      sun
saying, I want you, I guess you know you are mine,
come to me now, come, Anna Julia.
Flesh that turns to water with force of its own desire,
desire beyond the self or the pound of the flesh's pulsing,
all confusion fused to a single pattern,
crippled father, the widowed man, the alone man:
that forgotten, that was the small thing.
Wanting the whole of love in the completed pattern,
man and wife to each other, desire blessed,
not the single, the gross.

Ah, for the words Be mine with added word Forever:

sun on the face of love in the ripple of ripening grain,
flesh and spirit torn by the disparate needs:
out of the bottomless pit comes no.
Done and over, the rage and the hot sound of pleading
      voice,
passion distorting now, terror turns bowels to weakness of
      water,
big man turns and goes in the fury of anger—
and now, the fury of anger, long remembered,
breeds what purpose, the queer destruction?
Settle the little houses all over the fields of love,
change and destroy and bury, the stone
laid on the site of love's loss?

Turn of mind is the rare, wonderful thing: mind turns:
soul revolts at the very aim of its recent wanting;
save and preserve, what madness would now destroy
lean of the fields, contours of love?
Push the weariness off in the dark of the night's progress,
use defeat as a weapon to save the realm of memory,
speak to the worldly voices, diverting, changing:
"Well, now," she says, "it seems that it might be better
to cut the losses, try it elsewhere."
"Where?" cries out Hetty Browne, voice sharp, inquiring.
"Standeven's place," says Anna. "Naius River.
It's stood empty—a long time."

Asa Congdon, one hand on the wheel, the other fumbling
pocket for cigarettes, says, without conscious thinking,
"There's an idea, that's good, the Standeven place,
there's no zoning covers that land.
Big house there already, I guess it's in fair condition,
maybe could be a clubhouse. Yes, that's smart enough."
Hope arises again to displace disappointment:
houses, houses wanted: for houses hold people,
people are money, people are change.
Here it is all the same, the familiar persons—
something new, the young girls coming,
fun and the chance for profit.

113

Hetty Browne sits back, her eyes half-closed, absorbing
now the suggestion, weaving it to her pattern,
putting the thread of one idea with another,
happier now: a scheme is pending.
Draws her hand away from the warmth of Anna Julia's
        hand,
speaks with the distant voice of the one thinking:
"Nothing in one idea to deny the other,
neither need be abandoned, that's the beauty,
compromise on the scheme for the platting.
Sueton will get his store, the rest can wait.
Harlow Standeven's maybe at Lamy's—
everything seems to combine."

Silence while mind plots and the heart is silent (long time
        silent);
silent the others: if you could weave together
thoughts of the three minds, the clashing, disparate colors,
fused to a single cloth?
Hurt that returns to love in the vision of the rye bending,
face of love protected and the hard choice thinned with
        the years;
need and craving for something, the new, the novel,
damn the familiar wife, the too known faces,
too knowing friends about him;
passion to do, to rule, to equalize,
hate of the new intruders,
need for importance.

Pattern is once of age in confusion, kill to protect death,
twice of selfhood, the passion to move in power,
the blind, the instinctive appetite never sated:
notes in a strange, harsh tune.
Tune unheard, there is only the sound of the wind that's
        passing,
still and in motion as motion divides the stillness,
minds divided and minds coerced by darkness,
symphony in the end and the aim of thinking,
discord in all its reason.
Old head nods, tired now, finished;

114

man at the wheel attentive;
hardness alert.

Hetty again now: voice like a hand that fondles a treasured,
delicate object, turning it over and over.
"Yes, yes. Everything seems to combine together,
visit the place, see Jerome after."
Turn of the head now, eyes peer: the neighbor eyes fast
     shut, big lids.
"Could you drive us to the Standeven place tomorrow?
Would you be busy, Asa, the afternoon?"
"Busy all day on Saturday," Asa answers.
"How about Sunday, would that suit you?"
"Sunday be better, really. Call after dinner.
Anna Julia and me, that's the party,
we'll look it over together."

Tired old head that nods, Miss Hall is asleep, the deep
     folds
curve and shake below the chin and the heavy head;
Hetty's awake and happy, alert, the mind turning
over and over the new scheme, polishing.
Man at the wheel content: fun to be now included,
part of the plot, you never can tell before the event
how such stuff can be used or where it will lead:
maybe to tell, or maybe just to keep silent—
play for the moment, play for the near gain.
Silence now of the voices; the soft sound,
wind in the passage of night, the homeward wind,
night is for resting: all things grow that the night has
     planted.

DAY'S ended, though with hurrying night it's fused—
so the heart hopes now: just a space of time
before the flesh that spirit so abused,
to lonely sanctuary of its sleep may climb.
Consume familiar easiness of miles
in no attention but the accustomed hands'
guiding of progress down the nervous aisles
of that hypnotic light a touch commands.
But there's a voice here and a presence here,
an effluence beside you in the dark,
it is beyond you, it can interfere,
impose itself, light the reluctant spark.
The space of resting, it is soon denied—
this seeks you out no matter how you hide.

QUINTUS too said good night over and over,
he could hear his own voice saying it, see you tomorrow
(tomorrow and tomorrow, ironical echo!),
you did these things in spite of yourself.
                                        "Come on,"
he said to Jennifer. "Let's be off, I'm weary.
Will you drive, dear?"
                        "But I'll just make you nervous."
"Nothing could make me nervous now. You drive us."
They entered the car and the girl started the motor,
warmed it a little, the night was cool. The sound
of the running engine soothed; the car in motion
softened the needs and demands.
                                The needs, the
            demands:
weights to be lifted. Too tired to lift the weights.
Home and sleep. Sleep alone, single bed.
Forget it, sleep was the thing, the mornings came
better for night. Or the waking to feel alone,
the loneliness down in the hollow stomach's pit,
the unending alone? But this was weariness;
life was full: it was better it was too full
than to be void for self.

116

                              The familiar road,
even in darkness, spoke to him. Every tree,
that clump of bushes seen in the fleeting light,
this rocky ledge, that house with unspeaking windows,
each cried out to him, calling to memory:
full of his life, his love. They contained and held
all past happiness, they were saturate with it—
or were they now? Did places retain their joy,
or harbor and give it only as long as persons
harbored and gave? The half-seen things of the night,
deepening the known, took color from present being.
Was not the past, too, mutable? What was joy once,
could it not turn to agony in remembrance?
But this must stop. He seized hard hold on his mind,
turned it to something else.
                              The night went by
waving the great half-visible banner of time
that stars make indefinable.
                              Only children
know of the size of time, he thought; they see
time as the present piece of present being:
that has a measure. The punctual clock's a liar,
calendars all are cheats. A night, a year,
a month, an hour—they grow to a verity,
a truth by the spirit's growth, the body's resting,
the use of joy and pain. Tomorrow's nothing
but the transfigured now. We build tomorrow
by the heart's present clock.
                              Be quiet, Lamy:
your mind's the poor caged squirrel, his bushy tail
is his only pride. For God's sweet sake, be quiet.
Lock up the bolts and mortices of your mind:
it rattles open and lets the draughty thoughts
to idiot gambols now.
                              The night flowed by,
the long green river of the time-laden sky
that stars make current for.
                              He closed his eyes.
Jennifer's voice beside him: "Are you asleep, Q?"
"No," he said, eyes closed. "No, I'm not asleep."

I ought to say, be quiet and let me rest.
This I would say to Virginia, I used to say it—
then why not now?
                    "What did you think of the meeting?
Will the Board decide for us?" The cool young voice:
no trace of weariness here.
                              He opened his eyes.
"Yes, I think they will. But that's not the end, you see;
no matter who wins the case, we all of us lose,
there's the pity of it. And we can't stop
a woman like Hetty Browne. She'll find some way
of using this or of doing something different,
and then there'll be more unpleasantness, more of hate,
and fiercer feelings. God, it all makes me sick!"
"You did what you could. You were wonderful," Jennifer
          said.
"I was so proud, Q. You do speak so well,
they were so moved. But why did Mr. Mallin
speak as he did? As soon as he spoke, he spoiled
what you had said."
                    "He spoke as he saw it, Jenny."
"No," she said. "He spoke from a sort of malice—
I heard it, everyone heard it—why did he do that?"
"Oh, I don't know," he said. "I didn't notice it.
Funny you got that out of Rochester's speech."
"Funny you didn't," she said. "It was aimed at you."
"No!" he said. "You're silly. If he was bitter,
he probably had a bad day, work went badly—
that'd be all."
                    "I think you're too kind, Q."
"Oh, no," he said. "Hell, I'm not really kind.
I'm prejudiced as the devil."
                              He thought, it's years
since anyone praised me so, right to my face.
He felt life flow again, the river of sky
flowed as the night in his veins.
                              "You spoke one time—"
the cool, sweet voice again—"it wasn't long back,
of something to do to hold the village together,
to give them a common aim. Is that possible?"

"I don't know, Jenny," he said. "I've tried to believe it.
I'm going to keep on trying."
                              "How then?" she said.
"Your meeting on Thursday night?"
                                        "On Thursday night?
Oh, yes—I'd almost forgotten that. I must be slipping."
Or maybe the mind, he thought, rejects the memory
because it's afraid of it. I'm afraid of this—
I don't know what to say then. It's too important
that I should know what to say.
                              Maybe I do, though—
maybe I do, he thought with a sudden excitement,
the positive angle, the thing to be dreamed and cherished
and moved toward, upward, the everlasting motion
of man's slow progress onward . . .
                              "You must be tired,"
the young voice said in the dark.
                              "Hold it, my love—
be quiet, darling, I'm trying to fix an idea."
Only the sound of the car now.
                              My love and darling:
words got mixed, joined in confusion,
came between mind and the mind's purpose,
queer, impossible light shone in the eyes,
eyes that were used to dark, blinded—impulsive effort:
mind whipped savagely into obedience now:
love and the love of others, the only progress,
nothing but this was measurable, everything else—
illusory, fragile, melted away in the sun
of the daily day—washed out in the rain of tears,
burnt in man's fire of appetite.
                              It was so clear:
truth seen was always clear.
                              No words in the dark:
only the sound of the car now.
                              The night flowed by,
the sky was swept of time by the broom of trees
that stars made manifest.
                              "A pity," he said.
"There should be two things, each playing into the other,

making a whole. The school was the obvious one.
You'd think that people—essentially they're good people—
could sink their little spites for the sake of children.
But no, they can't. Or we try it another way,
the way that they failed. Feuds, hates, self-interest—
it's wrecked now. So we attempt to produce another.
I don't know if it'll work—we'll give it a whack.
Perhaps the idea of government for one world
is just so damn big and so inevitable
that it can capture their minds. If we form a chapter,
it'll be something new in the life of the village,
of the whole community."
                              He paused for a moment,
fumbled for cigarettes, found one and lit it,
drew in the grateful smoke.
                              "You ought to have seen—
you were too young, of course—the struggle there was
to get a library started. It failed three times—
as a community effort. It finally took
old man Carpenter's money—and Mrs. Gosford's—
to turn the tide."
                      "Q, will you speak at the meeting?
You, or somebody else? I hope it's you."
The cool voice warm at the same time: paradox
of the drifting night.
                          "I hope to get Harry Jeffers,
I haven't heard yet. A really wonderful speaker.
He's studied Federalism in all its history,
he knows the analogies and he's quick to answer.
And more, he's honest—and more again, got humor—
an awful help, that."
                          "Then you won't speak at all?"
"I'll introduce him and I'll wind up the meeting.
A movie first, his speech, then a question period,
and a few words from me."
                              "I wish it were you.
You move them, Q. I think they need to be moved,
if what you say is true."
                              "It's true enough, Jenny.
Couldn't you feel it about you? It lay in the air

120

like smoke at a cocktail party: the tensions, discords.
They had a sound, too."
                                    She said, "I felt them.
But maybe I got it by being so near to you."
Before he knew it, he said, "I was glad you were near."
But the words had an innocent sound.
                                        What's the
            matter with me?
he thought, and he sat straight up, in a sort of anger.
"Well, we're almost home," he said.
                                    Sweet curve of
            shore
deeply declining into the star-seen ocean,
fragrance of salt and seaweed, the endless whisper
of wavelets moved by the night wind to wanton
love of the cleaving stones.
                                    We are almost home:
the thought provoked a thought, it took shape in words,
deeply within him: what is a home? As soon
as the inner ear had heard it, the mind recoiled.
No, he thought, and no!
                                    And aloud he said,
"I hope your mother's asleep. We mustn't wake her.
We'll have to be quiet."
                                    "I will be," Jennifer said.
She turned the car now into the narrow driveway,
followed around to the back of the yellow house,
and stopped.
                    "A good night, clear one," Quintus said.
"Let's leave it out. The garage doors make a racket."
"Yes," said Jennifer.
                                    The engine's soft sound
died to the silence: and then silence filled
with far, delicate love of the water's wooing,
the wedding of salt and stone: the long, the perpetual
soft erosion of love.
                                    With an effort now,
Quintus got out of the car and closed the door
softly and slowly. Together they walked to the house,
rustle of foot on gravel, the distant waters,

riffle of wind in leaves reluctant to stir,
tick of the leather toe on the step's riser,
click of the latch of the back door, darkness, darkness,
finger's dry small rasp as it felt for the light switch,
and the light's silent flooding.
                              Here is the kitchen:
everything here is stood at attentive rest,
the clean, the ordered: needing the touch of use
to bring life through disorder, disorder's method.
And the white note on the grey of the lead-topped table.
Quintus, it cried in pencil.
                              It crackled open
in the strong, draughtsman's fingers.
                              "Darling," it said,
"feeling awful again. Do come and see me
before you go to sleep. So sorry, dearest,
I won't be asleep. Hope that the Hearing ran
smoothly for you. Love." It was signed Virginia,
it had a postscript: "Harlow has come from Harvard,
sleeps in Lanier's room, joins you both for breakfast—
kiss for Jennifer, I don't want to see her—
only you."
            Bad, bad! said Quintus's mind.
The fingers folded the note back to a neat shape
and pressed the folds flat.
                              "Your mother's not feeling
      well."
"Oh," said Jenny. "Oh, dear. But she seemed so well
when we all had tea."
                              "I know," he said, "I know."
I know too much at times, he thought to himself,
and never yet quite enough. "I'll go now and see her.
Get yourself some milk and go up to bed, dear.
Harlow's come, she says, he's asleep in Lanier's room,
you'd better be quiet. He'll join us both for breakfast,
that's good, anyway." He wasn't really thinking
of her or Harlow, his voice was simply speaking
out of itself by rote. The mind was upstairs,
dressing itself in the costume of its comforting,
the used, worn costume with the rips and the rents,

122

and the bullet-proof vest below.

Looking not looking,
he saw the girl go still, the smile that came
and left, a shadow passing, the pose of attention,
the self consulted stilly lest any motion
disturb the advance of thought. What thought, what
thinking?
Pleasure, or joy, or pride—or what? No matter,
put it aside now, it must keep till later—
or put it aside for good? Why touch it later?
Too many things to grasp.

"So Harlow's come!
Isn't that *nice!*" Her voice had an edge to it.
"Surprise! Surprise!"

He could see the color that came,
faint and warm, to the contours of her face.
She turned away from his gaze, went to the ice-box,
opened the curving whiteness of its big door.
"Let's plan our day together, Q, and without Harlow,
what we'd have done if he hadn't come down at all.
Maybe some day he'll stick to the plan he makes—
and let us know. Let's teach him a lesson, Q,
just you and me together. So Harlow drops in,
and we drop everything? No. Please, will you do it?"
She turned around, her hands held the bottle of milk,
her eyes were large and open, her gaze was pleading,
her lips were open. Before he could answer, she spoke.
Her voice was confident now. "I want to be with you,
I want to talk to you—about lots of things—
I don't want him." She smiled. "I know you'll do it.
Pretend it was planned ahead. I'd hate to be forced
to escape with Mr. Mallin."

"Listen," said Quintus.
"There's no use planning, my dear. Depends on Mummy."
"You know the answer to that one," Jennifer said.
"Morning is morning and night is always night,
and you were out. Dear Q, you were out with me,
her favorite unmarried daughter."

My God, he thought,
where do they learn so young?

123

                                        "Just skip it, Jenny.
I've got to go up now."
                                        "Do you have to go up?
Or do you go because you have always gone? Oh,
none of my business, darling, forgive me, Q,
you are so sweet—and good!" She set the bottle
down on the table and quickly came and kissed him,
lightly and sweetly, as quickly turned and left him,
finding a glass now in the ordered cupboards.
"Milk for you, too?"
                                        "No, I'll go up now. No.
Get me a drink of whiskey and water, will you?
Put it in my room, I'll have it before I sleep."
"You need it now."
                                        "No, not now."
                                                        You couldn't
        explain
the need to be all yourself, no matter how weary,
wholly yourself. Then he left her, going quickly,
not wanting to see youth further. He almost ran
up the wide, white stairs. But he couldn't escape
the speed of the mind by the body's speed; the mind
said, running away from, friend, not running toward.

Here is the shut white door,
wood that can lie between
spirits forevermore:
love is not evergreen.
Love's a deciduous thing,
leaves must wither and fall,
winter awaits its spring,
bare as the tree is tall.
Oh, will the rind of life
dry to a useless crust,
branches but fit for the knife,
growth that returns to dust?

Quintus opened the door to Virginia's room—
funny, Virginia's room, one phrased it so—

124

and entered and closed the door. The light was on.
His wife lay propped in the double bed, book on lap,
the table beside her bed had the small bottles:
he knew them well. There were the small, white, flat
cheaters of pain, the sleep compressed and heavy,
the hope of health or strength.

His wife looked at him.
The smile on her lovely face was a little wry,
but it was a smile. You could see the effort made:
no matter the cause.

"Oh, I'm so glad you're home,"
the husky voice said. "I was terribly lonely.
I'm better now, no need to worry at all,
I've taken the pills. It was just, the note I left,
that the effort of seeing Harlow, of you away,
Eddie asleep, and you couldn't wake him, could you?
It grew too much. I apologize, darling. Truly.
Did the Hearing go at all well for you?"

Quintus stood
with his feet a little apart, his hand on the dark
wood of the bedpost. "Yes," he said. "Not bad,
not bad in one sense. Simply a lot of tension,
the old feuds subtly renewed. I think the Board
will decide for us. And you, Virginia, dear,
are you sure you're quite all right now? You don't want me
to call the doctor?"

"No," she said. "Oh, no.
I'll be O.K. The pain came and it passed.
Now that you're home, it's all right. It was being
alone in the house—the night—I feel so useless,
and stupidly lonely, sometimes. Now I'll sleep.
Is Jennifer pleased that Harlow did come down?
He called me after you'd left. I said to come.
I hope she's pleased. The poor boy sounded lonely—
he is so sweet."

"I guess she's pleased," he said.
"It's hard to tell, that age. It's always a feather
to wear in your hat—your rather heartless hat.
But I guess it should be a little heartless at first—

125

how else do you know?"

"You don't," she said. "You
don't,
you have to find out. What will they do tomorrow?"
"Don't know," he said. He heard his own voice sounding
his long fatigue. "We'll see tomorrow. Depends
on how you are. Let's see tomorrow. Sleep now.
That is the thing for you."

"And you," she said.
"So kiss me, Q."

He knelt on the bed and kissed her—
lightly and swiftly: there was no more within him
than this to give. "Good night," he said. "You'll wake me
if the pain returns?"

"I'll wake you. Sleep well, darling."
"And you," he said. He rose and he left the room,
shutting the door behind him.

You shut the doors,
you locked them up, and all of the things behind them—
behind thick panels and the steel bolts and hinges—
pursued, unbarred.

Quintus went to the little
single room on the other side of the bathroom.
The light by the bed was on, the bed turned down,
pyjamas laid on the sheets. He closed his door,
swiftly and fumblingly took off his clothes,
put his pyjamas on, then his dressing gown,
and slipperless went to the bath. The cool grey tiles
of the bathroom floor felt pleasant against his feet.
When he had washed he put out the bracket light,
left everything tidy and clean, towel refolded—
the habits that stick so hard through all fatigue—
and returned to his dressing room. He looked for the
whiskey,
reckoned to drink in bed, smoke with the drink,
let mind relax and cease in the hope of deep,
the dreamless sleep. But the whiskey wasn't there.
IIe opened his door and looked down the straight hall—
the light was on, it was near, the hall grew dark
as it faded off to the soft obscurity

126

at the far end where the black of a window gave
on the perceptible night. There was no one there.
He turned toward the bed and walked to it. Then he heard
a door click open, and turned again, still standing
beside the bed. He could see Jenny coming.
She carried a glass in her hand, he could hear the tinkle
the moving ice-cubes made. She wore her nightgown,
her feet were slipperless too, her dark hair shone
as from a recent brushing. She came from the shade
into the light and passed it, it shone behind her,
it silhouetted her body in the thin garment,
body that moved with grace, soft and the strong grace,
firmness of curve and contour, beauty's delight.
Where was fatigue now?

                        There was no fatigue.
And anger mounted within him. He stood there, waiting,
feeling the thrust and surge of this new emotion:
old and new at once, the duality
of the whole of life.

                 Jenny came into the room.
"I'm sorry, Q, I forgot to put it here.
I carried it into my room. I hope it's right.
I made it a little strong."

                      "Thank you," he said.
He took the glass she held to him, set it down
on the table beside his bed. The light of the lamp
caught in the yellow clarity of the whiskey
and broke in the cubes of ice, made golden shadows
on the white of the table cover.

                   "Listen," he said—
his voice was rough and husky. He cleared his throat.
"Listen," he said again. "For God's sake, Jennifer!
You can't go wandering over the house like that,
the boy's here, damn it. My God, you're a woman now,
you're not a child any longer. Just look at you!
That damn nightgown, no wrapper."

                   Jennifer's face
showed her surprise and a little of shock, at first.
Then she looked down at herself, her hands fluttered,
touched the skirts of her gown, but didn't hold them,

127

fluttered the fingers, the fingers clasped together.
Then she looked up, still with the signs of shock,
the lips apart, eyes wide, and slowly, slowly,
the blood ran into her face and down her neck
and over the flesh below.
The hard white rays
of the hall light showed her body beneath her dress,
dark and lovely.
So they stood there, frozen,
seeing each other, new eyes.
They did not hear
the faint click of the door latch, nor see the fatal
crack of the opening door—so small, so thin—
in the far dark of the hall's end.
"God!" said Quintus.
Fatigue and anger gone now, only the terrible
force of the shape before him, the color of blood
under the young skin. He clenched his hands,
shoved them hard in the pockets of his dressing gown,
his hands were trembling, he felt his body tremble,
his legs were shaking, the knees had lost their power
to hold him straight except that the will made them
continue duties.
"Quintus," she said, in a whisper.
"Go," he said. "Go, Jenny."
"Yes," she said.
"Tomorrow, darling. Tomorrow. Just you and me?"
He could hardly hear her.
"Go," he said in a savage,
harsh, hard whisper of laboring breath.
The girl
turned and left him, she shut his door behind her.
The click of the latch as metal struck on metal
had a dividing sound. It said Tomorrow—
tomorrow and tomorrow, but now the ironical
echo was changed and transformed.

◻◻◻◻◻◻

THIS IS the knife:
it will thrust into your life,
it will turn,
and the wound will burn.
This the refined
test of the soul of mind:
when it is gone, is past,
it will yet last.

HARLOW lay on his bed on the border of sleep and waking,
    the mind
keeping the body awake lest it lose the
savor of consciousness, the queer
half-happy, half-sad feeling of being within, all enclosed by,
this house, her house, Jennifer's and her mother's, all mixed
into confused emotion.
                    Not here, presence here, surrounding:
breathe in the air: of love. So sleep
not intervening now carries you toward the awakening, the rising,
the sense of presence, the knowledge of seeing.
Would not this be marriage, the small daily
miracle of together wrought from the forward passage of sleep?
Home:
long wanted, long lacked, the place
you go from and return to, the core of living that gives life
meaning and substance, the happy substance.
                            Nearly
asleep now, but the mind turns and rends, the betraying, equivocal
demon of mind.
                    If she will not have you, refuses? Maybe another?
Stake your life on the one bet? Wager the whole of living—
is it the whole or how do you shape it to be part of the whole—
on the one great gamble, give all or nothing, and then, boy, then,
suppose you lose? Well?
Where do you go, what do you do, how do you manage the long
    devious
act of living? Emptied, what fills you?
Why did you come down here?

Did not Fatso tell you you were a fool to be coming,
did he not warn you, saying,
absence, absence, stick to the plan made, go to the Big Bounce,
let her miss you? Now, you had played
straight into the hands of your own weakness. Failure
bought of the impulse heeded?
                                    But this—this was always
the calculated, the expedient thing, the clever, designed, the
          mental approach,
foreseeing and reckoning, splitting the bet: what greatness came
ever of the expedient? Damn the worldly! Was not
the stake too large, too fine?
                          Or perhaps too important now
to warrant the whole on one play?

God! he thought, I must control this, turn it off, can it, this
is the doubling of weakness, you play it or you don't play it, but
do one or the other, boy. Now stop. Here
is the house of love, take happiness, stop the fretful searching
          for every final disaster:
disaster comes or it doesn't come, life
is but war in little. But war had a clear pattern, lost now.

He thought of Fatso, making
his thoughts turn to his friend. The image
rose in his mind of Fatso standing under a huge shower
with the tittering twins entwined. It made him smile, his body
relaxed and lay flat, the mind came softly into a quiet of near
          sleep,
the drowsiness rose and swept him, fatigue easing now into the
          good
measure of rest against it. Lightly, lightly,
drowsiness closed the urge of the mind as a book is softly
closed and laid by.
                    Then Harlow woke up hearing
the opening door and the sound of the closing door and the
          lock's
clean latching.
              Jennifer?
                        No sleep now, the mind

stretched to attention, only the body, its cords and tendons, its
        long
muscles, rests still, but not relaxed now.
                                        Lie still?
Jump up and open the door, cry out the name, the syllables of
all wanting that concentrate
a whole in your mind: say something?
                                    Say what, and hope what?
Hope for the look of pleasure, the greeting that
says I am glad you came? Or risk now—or postpone the risk—
of the greeting, the look of pleasure absent? Where
will sleep go then for its darkness? Will not the hard, the
        brilliant, the piercing, the blinding
lights of your grief crash into the closed futility of the lids,
pierce to the nerves of the eyes, penetrate into
the pain of the mind? Or, not knowing,
where will you find sleep? Is not the terror
of light within as without?
                            Harlow got up then slowly, not
        knowing
why he was rising. He went to the open window, raised the screen
        softly
(yet half hoping there'd be a noise heard, the evidence of his
        presence),
leaned out. He heard the water
smoothing the stones of the shore with infinite patience, the
        sound
of love anonymous as a priest's dusky whispering penance.
Pleiades rising high in the eastern sky, Orion
dominant now, the familiar
stars one steered by, the course laid, the mathematical certitude,
        the mystery
drawn from a seeming knowledge, the clear, charted   ·
way of the balanced compass.
                            How
do you steer now, Harlow, in this new war of loving?
Not by the stars now, but by the heart, or by
the pull of the stars on the heart, the majestic
conjunction of time beyond time, space filled by the beating
of the heart's star-time.

Now again the sound of the door that clicks open.

Look but don't look?
                        He went to the door softly, stealing,
bare feet noiseless, the hand on the knob turns slowly, deftly,
with infinite caution,
the door latch is released, the silent opening granted
in a thin crack of seeing.
                        The heart contracts
in the peril of sight.
                        Seeing too much, seeing too little,
hearing too much but yet not enough,
movement of grace and the revelation, body and movement,
pose and speech, but the pose of another, words,
pantomime that speaks to the cruel, the cutting sight.
Now coming toward you, movement of grace, as once
it came toward you, long past, the coming that
gave to you, was received, was given to, the delirium—
once possessed, once had, lost now, the bitter sense
of the had that is lost, gone.
                        Close now, too much seen,
blush seen, body seen
(that was once seen, once yours, how did it
slip away, slip away, cease to be?),
door once more and once more close it softly, hold latch
to lie open, no sound (no love); close
when the other clicking is heard, for heart beats echo louder
than any doors: this is the latch to the heart.

And now, Harlow? What shall you do?

I do not know. I am contained in sorrow and anger, and a vast
confusion.

What did you do when death threatened you?

Ah, that was easy!
There was just fear then and the calm of fear, and the crystal
seeing of all things, and the needs

132

of others assumed for strength.
                                        You stood in the glaring
brilliance of equatorial sun and you watched danger
coming at you, it came
beyond your will and yet by your will: the little man
hurls himself and his charged machine to death to bring death;
the huge towers
of the spray spout upward in green and intolerable white to
        declare
the menace and failure of death. But all is seen, around you
are the eyes of others.

And the eyes of others—in Italy?

They were the lovers, only:
they did not see me, I was alone. Therefore
there was a fear then. But these others,
the eyes around you seeing, these
are a strength to you.

Were you not then afraid?

Afraid and not afraid: there was no time for fear
to become possessive, the noise
drowned out fear's impulse, the deaths demanded
more of the living because of death. There was
a singular clarity. You were supported by
all the needed, the urgent acts, the motions
long drilled to the mind and hand.
                                        But these things,
they were the wanted, the long awaited, the justifiers. For the rest
there was just repetition and heat and the long boredom
and the homeward craving and the body's
poor satisfactions and dull rest.

And now?

Now it is night and the dark and alone, and there is nothing

drilled to the mind. And love—unlike earlier fear—
has become possessive with fear.

Nothing for others now?

Nothing for others but the confused hate and the
distorted love. There are now
no orders given or to be given, no sound
but the water's far-off, familiar,
utterly changed music: dissonant distance
in blackness.
                    There is only
terror and pain, and the absence
of all order and security, the soft, sticky
mass of the marshy thoughts.

Was there not order once in the far
days before war, then?

There was order then, in those days.

Has it gone? Does anything perish, once
you possessed it?

I do not know. I can remember.
I can remember the faint, distant ordering of love
from my mother, but it is too far off, and death
came too soon for a clear recollection, there is only
the shadow of it.
                    I can remember
the hands and the words of nurses, the protecting
arm or the comfortable
lap and bosom, the presence at night, near, breathing,
keeping the night within the order of comfort.
I can remember the long walks of the garden, the neat
borders and rows of flowers, the clipped box, the sweet
scent of the flowers' variety, the things
to be touched or not touched, the places to go
or not to go, the times for the going or staying,
all within order.

I can remember the hours
laid out in neat rows like the little wood blocks for the building,
the red
and the purple threads of the stitched pattern on cardboard;
the minutes
were set into a stitched pattern of yes and no,
ordered, absolute.
I can remember the presence
of power about me forever, the figure
of my father, real and distant, near and far off,
the absolute and the unquestioned, the reason
for do and for don't and for the pattern
of the yes and the no. Even the flowers, the curved
walks of the framing trees, the seeing or the enclosing
in green or the colors of autumn, the movement
of water to silence or to the dropped music, these
moved to his will and made order, and the days
grew long in the pattern of the threaded hours.
Oh, yes, there was order, then, and peace, and the will
had nothing to fear but the exercise of the will,
unneeded, hardly wanted.
These things
I can remember.

They are gone now?

They are gone in the tumult of growing, and death
has removed them, though they are clear—
clear as a distant light on a night of storm,
the storm of living, the being, the uncharted, the self-wrought
hours of doing, the explosions
of the war of being, the mad, unwanted,
crazy, is it not crazy? Am I not
mad in the instant, is there
purpose to sanity when the sane mind sees only
the terror of all futures, the loss
of the pattern of all wanted things, the God who died,
the cynical cursed things, the mean and the sordid,
the unusable minutes tangled into a web of the painful,
knots upon hard knots, the sharp

135

needle-pricks in the fingers of mind and spirit?
Crazy, am I not crazy, who
would be sane?

There was sanity once: will you not
go back to your sanity?

It is lost, it is lost!

Is anything lost that you once knew?

Is it not lost? Poor Harlow, alone,
will he seek it now, find
old peace in the garden, the ordered
rooms of the once-on-a-time, poor Harlow,
crazy now?

Seek it, and find it!

So he turns from the door and walks softly to the window, his
        body
shakes with his quietness.
                        Stand here now till the little, bright
rectangle of yellow light on the grass and the bushes below flicks
into the dark that is harmony with the darkness?
Stand still, long still: this is the night watch, the bridge for
the seeing of stars, the sound of the water dividing, but now
their motion is not yours, your trembling vibrations
from within not without. Soft air moves to your face—cool,
terrible fingers of night—by its own act and will, you
are the motionless, static, the waiting.
Darkness unpierced now, but with the erasure of light,
no harmony, only unison.
                        But stand still, the watch
is not over. Count to a hundred. Again. And another hundred:
this prevents
mind's use, and will's use, and the seeping
of thought into consciousness. Stand still, the eyes
pierce into nothing till they see order in nothing, the ears
hear order in unwilled sound, the exterior, the impersonal,

136

the beyond you, the touch
of the long past.
                    Now.
                              Move now, softly. Dress,
but in silence, silence. Open
the door in silence, creep in the unlit, the leading
corridor now beset with its images in its blackness:
love and hate.
Down now, step by step, the shaking hand
touching the smooth wood of the banister rail, the newel
warns of an ending—ending! Ah, that's funny! But silent,
creep, creep, no squeak, no false
movement of sounding betrayal, the door and the big door, the
          stars
let into the house, close them in, let yourself be closed
without in their echo, so
softly, softly, there are long miles to go, foot by foot, step by step,
          no car,
no noise, seeking
the order, the dream of order to make into a reality,
in the late of the night for the perception
of the enclosing, the safe, the engrossing
fixity of the rule of the old day, the threads
stitched to peace again?
                    No word left?
                              No word.
I am Harlow, alone, I shall seek
the garden of being and the ordered, the old
peace of the former, crazy. But who
will be sane now in these days? The road
leads on mile on mile to the edges
of the wanted and the desired, the enclosure
of thought in the once-had, the shutting of the big, hard, loud
          door
against all others now.

So Harlow left in the night, walking, in darkness,
in his self-pivoted madness.

ROCHESTER lay in bed with the light turned on,
his diary on his lap and the pen poised,
when he heard Serena knock. They had said good night:
it was unexpected.
                    "Come in," he said. "Come in."
He closed the diary, laid it down beside him.
The door swung open and Serena entered.
She wore her hair down, and a deep-rose wrapper,
high waisted, a flaring skirt with a flowered pattern
of palest pink.
                    "Do you want to talk a moment?"
Rochester stirred in his bed; he said, "Well, yes,
if you've something troubles you?"
                                        "Oh, troubles?" she
            said.
"No, nothing troubles exactly. I'm just confused
by what went on."
                    "By what I said in the car?"
"Yes, that," Serena said. "Or would you rather
let it go till tomorrow?"
                    "No," Rochester said.
"It's really not complicated at all, my dear.
It's perfectly simple."
                    "Explain it to me, will you?
If I understand, I'll sleep. If I don't, my mind
will have trouble shaking it off."
                                        "I know," he said.
"Let's begin with Jennifer Messler. She's the key—
or one of the keys. The other's Lamy himself."
"May I perch on the bed?"
                    "Yes, surely, do," he said,
and he moved his body over to give her room,
and she sat on the edge of the bed and the light fell
on the deep-rose color of folds that covered her knees.
"Go on," said Serena. "You have such a good, clear mind,
and mine gets muddled with people."
                                        "A pose," he said.
"But let that pass. Point is, the girl's a woman—
it happened last year, you can see it in all she does,
the way she stands, the look of her eyes, her face,

the set of her mouth. That mouth! It's made for kisses,
and kisses are what she wants."

"Do you think she does?"
Serena sounded surprised.

"Of course," he said.
"There's only one thing a man can tell of a woman
and that one thing is, is she in heat or not?
Sorry to put it so crudely, but that's the fact.
He can't tell who she wants, and only rarely
if it's himself—but the fact that she is wanting
is always evident, plainly. Jennifer's wanting.
The point is, who does she want?"

"I suppose it's Harlow,"
Serena said. "I know he's in love with her."
"He may be in love with her, but not her with him.
I doubt if she'd take him—take him in any fashion.
I think she likes to string him along, a beau,
he is a flower for her hair, that's all."
"You may be right," she said, and she paused a moment.
"What do you mean," she said, "when you say of her,
'Take him in any fashion'?"

"Come on, Serena,
you know what I mean. You know. You don't think, surely,
the girl is a virgin, do you?"

"Why shouldn't I?"
"You know too much and you see too much," he said.
"You're a woman. Look at her face."

"I see," she said.
"It might be good for her then to marry Harlow."
"No," said Rochester. "First, she'll never do it,
that's my bet. And second, it would be bad.
She's sensitive, full of a big creative impulse,
she's not very steady, she's not the steady type.
She wants to be free. She'll have to find her freedom
in her own way—find it before she marries—
if ever she marries. What sort of a man is he?
He's sensitive too, and what's more, he's unbalanced—
maybe the war, more likely inheritance.
Nervous, high-strung, lost, without any pattern,
no ambition directed, no course to follow.

Intelligent, very—but what will his sort want,
with a father like his? Do you remember John?"
"Yes," said Serena, "I remember him."
"Clever, ruthless, strong, a dominant man.
He ran his life and he ran his plant and business
with a steel touch. Cruel. Everything went
his way, or not at all. They say his wife
died of that dreadful spinal meningitis—
but for myself, I think that John Standeven
killed her over the years."

"Do you really think so?"
"I really do. What other sort of a woman
than that soft, sensitive southern creature,
Marianna-Mae Hugeen, from North Carolina,
would have put up with John?"

"Perhaps she loved him."
"Perhaps she did. Perhaps she was just too frightened,
too thoroughly ruled by him to dare to leave him.
Look at the other boy, the one who was killed—
Johnny, the older brother—he ran off.
He had the guts to go, he couldn't take it,
couldn't take Poppa, his rules and regulations,
the absolute rules. But Harlow didn't run.
He's like his mother. And like his mother, too,
he's over-soft and much too intelligent."

She stirred on the bed and said, "How can that be—
too intelligent?"

"Nothing to use it for.
No direction. Not enough money to give
support for that sort of life. You've seen the boy—
what will he do? What can he ever do?
Go in business, like John? It makes me laugh
even to think of it. No particular talent,
introspective, moody, soft—we hear so much
of our lost generation. That's what *he* belongs to.
Too delicate for the world he has to live in.
Marry him off to Jennifer and it'd last
about three months. I'll bet you that young woman
sees that already. Clearly. *She's* directed,

she knows what she wants and she is going to have it,
and I believe she'll get it no matter how
and no matter what it costs."

"You make her sound
awfully selfish," Serena said.

"Not selfish.
She can be generous—but only on her own terms.
Never against herself."

"A fine distinction."
"A true one, Serena."

"Perhaps. What does she want?"
"She wants to work at her art, wants to create,
she wants a man—and the sort of man she wants
has got to be the creative type himself—oh,
it's not what she ought to have—I know that, too.
She needs in a man what Harlow needs in a woman.
She ought to have someone solid and good and steady,
immersed in something practical, maybe lacking
in that particular kind of imagination
that's hurt by the artist's moods, that shrugs, that says,
'Oh, well, it's only Jennifer.' "

"Clever, Rochester!
Awfully clever. You see too much."

"I see
the things that are under my nose. But what she *wants*
is—to use that awful phrase—a kindred spirit,
if he's attractive to her. And someone, too,
she can get in competition—to prove her power,
to find her power."

Serena turned her head
and looked full at him, and then she looked away,
back at the pattern of the rug, and said,
"And who is this, this man?"

"Who do you think?
Who's handy by, who is a good creator,
who is directed and who is most attractive,
who is good-looking, and who can also be
taken in competition?"

She sat unmoving,
her hands lay still in her lap. She said, "Virginia?"

141

"Up and down," he said. "Ill—or neurotic?
Loving—or just possessive?"

"You're hard," she said.

"Or hard about her."

"Not hard, just realistic."

"You really believe this?"

"Did you see her, then?
Did you watch Jennifer tonight at the meeting?"
"I watched her. What did you see?"

"I saw what you saw."

"No," she said. "You always see more than I see—
of things like that."

"A compliment—or a crack?"

"A compliment, dear."

"I wonder. It's not important."
He shrugged his shoulders, settled against the pillows.
"Look at it another way, from a different angle.
Can you spread yourself so thin, if you're a man—
live under a constant strain, give all your hours
to the discipline of work and of being part
of every effort that promises—never mind
how fatuously—to be a help to all others,
and not crack somewhere?

Isn't the life we live
a sort of transparent envelope partly made
by our own heredity and our environment,
and partly by ourselves? A social fabric,
transparent, whole, within which we must live?
But doesn't the envelope break when the pressure grows
too strong at some point? Will not the inner man
generate pressures—maybe animal pressures—
too great for its fragile strength? And if it bursts,
what will become of such a man?"

"Too fast,"
Serena said. "Your mind, it goes too fast,
I can't keep up with you. But it's clever, clever—
when did you think of this?"

He smiled with pleasure.
"I wrote it last week. It's been a long time brewing."
"I'll think of it," she said. "I'll think of it later.

It'll take time to see."

"And when you see it,"
Rochester said, still smiling, "apply the knowledge.
Doesn't the case demand a counter-irritant?
Or, keep to the image: can't one relieve the pressure
without bursting the envelope?"

"You mean me?" she said.
"Better than Jennifer, isn't it?"

"How?" she said.
"Ah, come!" he said. "You keep on saying, 'clever.'
Clever yourself, Serena—God damned clever.
Don't ask questions like that."

"I see," she said.
"Or I don't see. I don't know. I don't see good
to come of calculation. There's lots and lots
that I don't see. And that I won't ask you, either.
And what I want? Or what I feel?"

"That's you.
That's you," he said. "No one can say that for you."
"And if I say it myself?" she said.

"Then say it."
She clasped her fingers together, the clasp so hard
that flesh turned white at the contacts. Then she opened
her mouth to speak, but closed it, no word uttered,
and rose from the bed.

"Good night," she said to him.
"Sleep well." She walked to the door to the other room.
With her back to him she said, "Interesting, very.
I'll think of what you've said." She took a step,
opened the door, but stood there. "It would be
nice not to sleep alone tonight," she said.
He turned his head now, lazily, looking at her,
and he said, "I'd snore."

"I shouldn't mind—the snoring."
"I'm weary," Rochester said. "A long, long day."
"Well, then, good night." She went through the opened
      door
and closed it softly behind her.

"Damn!" he said.
"Selfish—or self-preservation? Mustn't you keep

143

some part of yourself to yourself for the things to do
that only yourself can do?"
He put the diary
down on the little table beside his bed,
switched off the light, arranged the pair of pillows,
turned on his side. Within his mind he saw
the flush of Jennifer's face as she looked at Lamy
while Lamy spoke.
"In heat," he thought. "In heat."
Sleep could come now. One waited upon tomorrow.

□□□□□□

HERE is the giving that is not pure giving,
here is receiving that is but a gift:
this the encumbrance of a dual living,
heavy the weight that is so good to lift,
heavy the tide on which you choose to drift,
drifting directed by its own direction,
only the movement and the languid shift
currently forward from your heart's dilection
now in the warming spread of its convection,
drift and receiving fuse into a force,
giving is but the obverse of reception,
opposites each the other must endorse,
sudden the flame and sudden now the joining:
love is new minted in its oldest coining.

"EVERYONE up on his ear. Or almost everyone. Jacob kept
    calm
as a pan of milk. What a man!"
Voice in the dark, the warm,
half awake listening, eager to hear the story or
eager to hear the voice? Be part of. Whisper:
"What a man!"
Voice again, soft, enclosing, supporting, the touch—
elbow to hip, lie still, not yet, the wanted and
the not wanted. Voice:

144

"Wish you'd been there, Millie. You should have heard old
Hetty Browne, she was in rare form. She stuck
her knife into Walter Hoxsie and she damn well got into
poor old departed Deborah, too. If ever Deborah
had any reputation, it's gone now in the village of Chogs Cove.
      Well, Hetty,
she got a sort of a rough ride too from Cullen Ryan, he
was going good tonight. He ran her
over the bumps about the school site and about the platting by
Ted Gross of that land. I'd have really laughed, I swear I would,
if it hadn't been sort of sad."

Now the hand touches: accident, intention?
Nothing now, warmth, say:
                          "Sad? Why sad?"
"Because," he says. Pauses. "Too tired, Millie?
Tell you tomorrow?"
                    "No, not tired, Jerry. Tell me."
Moves his body, stretching, the hands
up and back of the head, elbow gone now, only
the warmth of nearness, the dark warm of near. How tell, how
      say
the warmth was made, of what, years, the able
to lie near but apart, freedom shared,
guarded by nearness, the long journey within the brightness
of the alone lit
by another's light, the brightness of
own discovered. Listen now with the dual
ear of self and of love; voice:

"Lamy," the voice says, the current of voice.
"He can see it, Millie, and he can say it, clearly, he
moved them—almost had it back to something, it's hard
to say what it was back to, something good and decent. Jacob
saw it, I saw his face. All the divisions—
what do they get us? Nothing. Nobody profits. Nobody
gets anything but what they think is their own way, but they find
it's nothing. That's what he said but I can't say it. He has
a sort of a gift to move them, he isn't afraid of it, he says
what is in his mind, for them. A curious guy. And then—

145

it blew. It blew in a breath. The great man,
Who's Who Mallin got up and he blew it higher than any kite,
by God, it was cleverly done! When he was finished,
Lamy appeared a sort of an idealistic
fool with a soft nature. The man's not soft, he sees
what the whole is, could do. Not Rochester Mallin. He sees
what Rochester Mallin can do for Rochester Mallin. I sound
bitter. I'm not. Too used to it, Millie. Then Hetty Browne
stuck in her knife. But, Millie, listen . . ."

Body turns, leg moves, the calf of it
touches warm, lie still, let
touch be sweet now, silent and still, later, the
wanting is for the giving . . .
                    "They put
old Anna Hall up. She, like Hetty, and Asa, like dopey
Clifford, claimed Ben Sweet had a store. A store in that house!
But then—God, but I wish you'd heard it—
she let her mind go and she spoke of the old times, and
you'd have heard a pin drop. Mitchell Crane,
he didn't know what to say or how to take it, it sounded
like someone reading poetry, you had to listen
and couldn't quite understand, and be moved, and yet
all of these things at once. I just watched Jacob, he sat
with his eyes half closed, but listening, listening. Millie, you
could see how it touched him. How? I couldn't say now—how.
Too difficult. And soon,
everyone had his say and it was all over and the whole mean
background was there to see, the store as a wedge to open
the way for the platting. I'm not sure about Parry but Jacob
and Willoughby Cross, they saw it, Millie, they won't
let it happen. And now, not happening, there'll be
more of the old feuds. Damn! It's good
to be home again."

The arms come down again now,
hands run over the long length of his body, the elbows touch
briefly, depart, the hand
moves over, touching, not yet, the moment

146

is not yet, say:
>"What did you say, Jerry?"

"Nothing, Millie. I gave them the facts, the cold facts,
my part and Ted Gross, and the sale to Hetty, and Sueton's
buying in, and the rest. The hell with it, I'm sick of it,
I can cope in the morning, not now."

Hand lays
flat on thigh now, moves, gentle and firm, demanding, not yet,
the wanted is not yet for giving, the need
dual and single and for the one for both, the confusion
of night and alone and darkness and the double
warmth of the hand.
>"You'd better sleep now."
Soft laugh, movement of shoulders, the body turning, the
other hand, not fumbling, clear demanding, the wires
telegraph to the body, the mind? The not yet
becomes the now, the counterpart, parting joined, the flow
of the other and the other and one and both, the time
is now and now, and soon
freedom and the within and the light brightens, self
and self's counterpart in the wholeness, and then,
rest now, the giving
received and was given, the darkness is
dual and sleep turns, night turns, the voice
is stilled till the sound comes, and the morning
is but another, day
divides and closens, night
joins in the liberation.

BOOK TWO

◨◨◨◨◨◨

Dissonance and

Counterpoint

Part One

HARLOW STANDEVEN

🔲🔲🔲🔲🔲🔲

ERE you shall see the madness of the sane
and sanity grown weary of its bound:
the unconscious' storm, the ego's hurricane,
the roots of youth torn upward from the ground,
the shattered branch pruned with the cutting knife,
spring leaf divorced in fall's blown agony,
and from this earliest death another life—
the fruitful graft upon the wounded tree.
Oh, not for this that you were born and made,
to reach an ending that you might begin,
to enter passionate darkness, hurtful shade,
that thus you see at last the light within?
Devour your madness till you can digest
its matter into wisdom, into rest.

POOR HARLOW! Poor boy, orphan,
no father, no mother, where
is poor Harlow going?

Maybe I'm going crazy, you
want to come? Joke. No joke. I'll follow
the dark road home.

Poor Harlow! Poor boy, orphan,
no father, no mother, no love: where
is home then?

Ah, home! Home is where Mother is, she
is where Father is: thus the surrounding
of all security. I am going
toward home, to my home, I go
the dark road to my house of youth.

So the two voices:
                    one is madness and that which sees it so.
The other is that which creates it, both
the thing and the thing seen.
                              In darkness, under the stars,
to the distorted sounds of the enveloping night, to soft pat
of leather on tarred road, to the far
bark of the uneasy dog,
Harlow followed the road northwest toward Dark Corner, a
          journey
divided and split: and always the voices spoke, one
against the other, question and answer equally
reflecting schism.
                    Soft silhouette of unpunctuated buildings: barn,
dwelling and corn-crib, the Hoxsie place, to the north
of the road; cut across fields now toward the bridge
over Seldom Brook; steer west
by the old ordering of the heavens, the eye lifted, seeing
Perseus bright overhead, Andromeda bound high in the western
velvet of blackness, the long, liquid, soft-seen
shape of Aquarius dips down near the horizon, pulling
feet to refreshment, home. No
schism here, the stars
are competent in their unity, diverse to
a common purpose, unknown, the comfort of long
motion towards. Cygnus, the complex, the radiating
bird of the spokes of light says northwest, northwest, the sky
is all for your knowing and home
is northwest, northwest, Naius River, the narrow

flow of the known: home.
There was a path once, there
were the open fields; not now. Briars
tear at the clothes, cut hands, the trace of path is but
a faint thing, residue of itself and the once pound
of so many feet. Turn back? Eastward the Gemini, these
are backward, these
toward pain and the east is pain and westward is
forward and home again. Crash through, the tearing, the
rip-sound,
good and forward, the pain of the piercing spines
not felt, or felt, welcomed. The thin
residue of a way leads down, down, gently now
to the white shadow of concrete standing square
over the story-told water, the story-telling of
water at night, the frightening
sound of the blackness of running liquid whispering
deep, deep, the heart is
less at the small time of the sinking of Cygnus.

Cassiopeia crowns the height of the western
heavens: did not her boast of beauty
join Perseus to Andromeda, but where
the devouring monster? East, by the sea? Or within?

Now the sound of the feet on the metal of road, the ghostly
mass of the houses, the sharp
bark of a dog, the stars seen, Aldebaran and the Hyades
upside down in the mirror of Indigo Pond southerly, and
the fork of the road, northwest, northwest, toward
Cygnus, toward home again, home again,
home is
where youth lay in a mold of the sure and the ordered.

Home is nurses and the long, neat
paths of the gardens, home is toys and the enormous
chairs that contain and harbor, the punctual
rhythm of meal-time, play-time, bed-time, home is
father.

153

Will not your father be
angry at night wanderings now?

He will be angry, but perhaps
I can steal in: the small door leading
into the flower room, or the window letting the cool
air of night into the room of the shears and vases, careful
of touching, breaking, foreseen it can
all be accomplished, softly, carefully.
Hurry now, time
slips past like a ghost, like the sound
of wind in the tired leaves, hurry home, the door
is waiting, or
the window lies open for you, the bed is alone in the small
room of the sleep of youngness, the neighboring
sounds of sleep to comfort two ways.

Trees and trees now, right and left, the branches of great and
     little
tangle the stars to a webbing of black and brilliance, the road
rises, rises, rough now, rutted, the scrape
of dirt and the stumble
of the small stones, the outcropping
worn-smooth ledge of the sharp rise, no
houses here, no dog's
reassurance of the quick frightening bark, only
the soft lone
hoot of the owl in the trees, trees, to the right and left, low
menace of the small time of the darkest time.

Something is wrong here, Harlow.

What is wrong, then?

Why are the ruts deep and the road
rough and the stone
of the ledge bare? Is not this
the road of your father's going and coming?

154

It is the road. It leads
to and from home again home again.

Is it not scraped and filled and worked on,
twice every year, to make smooth, to let
the big car glide softly over it, the long
car and the blue seats, the big
blue robe and the fur side folding on bare skin
of the young legs, the enfolding, the comfort
of ordering?

It will be fixed and scraped, made smooth.
It is a temporary thing, perhaps
the dark exaggerates. The car
will glide over soon. Now
feet must accomplish, toward home,
home again, now alone. Dark yields
soon to light, see now the high stars and the low
pale in the first cold
foretelling of day.

Are you not tired?

I am neither tired nor am I rested. Now
I am, only.

So on the soft and the cumbrous, the ambitioned
wing of words we fly now over the mortal progress
of Harlow Standeven: youth marching in the first
decline of night, seeing, detached; the ant that crawls down
the infinite space of its world. These pinions, many-syllabled,
beat between us and him: we fly always
alone, the singular, the everlastingly
separate life: to look down, to see, but not being,
except ourselves: the inviolate, the inviolable
aloneness of living. What's he to us?
Are we not safe here, the untouchables, viewing
in high detachment the incredible other

155

progress of other? The unshared, the not to be
shared fate, the movement that springs now madly
from not our causations?
                    But the heart?
Oh, not that restless, that needed and most necessary
muscle of the impermanent existence, the beating, fluttering
pump of the red blood—but the symbol
of dread compassion, the magical and the betraying
cause of admixture, which traps us, one by one, into
identification without, the spirit caught at long last
in the toils of another: grief become ours that sprang
from no grief of ours to involve our sorrow, the joy
shared into treble strength, the potent
wine of the doubled drinking, the confusing, drunken
awareness of truth beyond us that is
not our truth, but all truth.
                    Not safe this, not
safe now: the flight above,
this is the safety, the ant in his agony
is not us—stay above? Or descend the heart
to the slow, painful progress of young love torn
into its long travel—or travail—it matters nothing, the near pun
is but a sum of living.

It is a long road Harlow travels, it is four miles
seven hundred and sixty yards, two feet and four inches:
it can be measured with a chain and a scale and
a theodolite will betray the least rise and fall
of the long way, or the short way, or
the infinite passage. He goes
between there and there, and it is beyond
mensuration: one may not measure the passage
of heart to belief.
                    There is faint light now.
This is the chilly, the unwelcoming first
grey of the day's parturition. Dawn
is the red after-birth: it is not yet, and who
shall be proud to suckle the new day?
All trees are black now, even the gold
of the elm and the crimson of maples or the blood-red

156

of the oak and the tupelo or the pastel orange
of the dark walnut, these
are forbidden to burn, they wait
for the candles lit on the birthday cake of the cycle
of the oldest renewal.
Stay aloft: we shall view this now
from above, intact, one part of the verity, the
objective thing, half true. We shall descend
later, later, to complete, to make whole.

Here are the two square granite posts of the gates
and the gates themselves, grey now that once
were the brown of creosote, sagging a little, closed,
chain locked into padlock locked
into rust past key's wisdom or cunning.
Here the driveway: overarched with the long
branches of maples, the once-smooth surface
fissured in miniature canyons by constancy
of water's impulse, gravel heaped now here and there
into unwilled tiny dams. It is a long drive,
it curves first to the right and then to the left, skilfully,
well-thought, the double curve lovely, conveyed
by the boles of the punctual trees. Branches
dead and broken, the bark curled off and rotten, white with
          fungus,
strew the driveway: traps
for the unwary foot in the dusk of the time of day's
morning to chilly grey.
                    Now is the house:
big and balanced and painted grey and the trim once
white with formality, the exclamations of the
blanched pilasters, the horn curve
of the Ionic capitals, saying established, we
are gentility and prosperity, as always, conforming.
Closed, all closed and shuttered: but round about,
here we can see, here's trace of design too, the box hedges
still define in the tangle of dropping land, lovely
patterns and shapes and forms—a garden? Once
it was a garden, it blew
fragrance and color carefully, cared-for, over

157

the air of spring and of summer and early fall till
frost made the box hedges into the perfection of all
things that endure and suffice in the time
of the resting of earth. Here's yew and hemlock, once
clipped that is now ragged, the masses
still betray the shape and the pruning of other days. Lilacs,
budleia, japanese quince and mock orange,
dogwood with passionate leaf and forsythia
uncut and dangling, the altheas, and the shining
greens of the rhododendrons, and multiple berries of
cotoneaster, all the choked, nameless
shrubs of the love of the gardener. See,
beech trees posed in a grove here, a grove there, open a way,
insist that the eye go down the slope of the once-garden to
the far glint of the water, the river: the view made
remains: but the way is choked. The thin, the loamy,
poor sandy soil, and the gravel and clay beneath, the
needing-of-care earth, it holds within it the passion
of jungle growth: the blackberries and the catbriar, the arching
sprays of the stag-horn sumac, the quick black
birch of the white stem, delicate and remorseless,
passion of poison ivy and the young spiny locust,
clusters of meadow-sweet heavy with dead blooms, the thick
clumping of the frosted joe-pye weed, the air-loved
white of the fluff of milk-weed, these, all these
have captured and made their own, they have laughed
at the former hand of man, at the glove and the spade and the
        knife
and the sharp clippers and the rhythm of whirling mower:
all long and soon defeated by the impoverished jungle. Here
is but the suggestion of what has been, the imprint, always
        indelible,
of man's order, but become now
the graveyard of things remembered, the cemetery
of times past, the place where no one
paid for perpetual care.
                    And the house?
Pierce through the walls—we may pierce as we fly, in fantasy,
into emptiness. This
is the home of the mouse and the spider, they have acquired

freehold on vacancy. Bare, bare, bare: there remains
the rusted stove in the huge kitchen of many steps to and from,
there remains one mattress to breed mice in a small room;
else nothing. The support of the chairs for the word spoken
in comfort, the length
of beds for the sleep or the passion eluding or captured,
the pictures to mark space, give time to
walls and areas, the concession of clocks to the
sun's will, moon's orbit, sequence of zodiac,
the chest and the cupboard, the supporting table of
game or drink or book, the nightly and needed
comfort of lamps, the multiple colors of the hard
welcome of china, the gleam or the blackness
of pan and broiler and griddle, the easing
rug and carpet—all gone, all sold or divided or
stored under the thick brown
paper of keeping in close packed
little tight rooms of no use but the far promise
of some other day, some time, somewhere. The sound
of the wings of our word-flight will echo from dust,
from cobwebs, from the dull
unpolish of floors, there is not even
the ragged remainder of curtains to soften the harshness
of things done now to a sounding of life.

Come away now: we are not to remain, seeing: we fly
out to the tangle, to hear
the lone, harsh cry of the dawn: the little blue herons
down by the wide river, unchanged.
                                        Now
is the time to descend, to share, to become, to see
the other part of the truth.

Why is the gate closed, Harlow?
Why is it locked?

It is not closed, it is open. Or, being closed,
it was shut by the gardener, whose name is MacKinnon or
by the gardener's boy, his name is Theobald, I

159

am not allowed to play with him. Open or closed,
it makes no difference, does not one
climb it often?

Climb now. Thus you may see.

What shall I see?

Here you shall see the madness of the sane.

This is the long driveway: endless: beautiful.
It is the enchanted curve that leads one always
home again. The wind of the fading night
must have blown fiercely, perhaps the remote edge
of a huge storm: I do not remember the wind, but here
it has blown, the branches have fallen on ever-neatness, there
will be much for MacKinnon to do. How much
may the unremembered storm destroy and loosen!
I must tell Fatso this—but now, Fatso . . . what
is now . . . there is here a confusion, the maples march
curving to homeward, I said that, to revisit, to be
at one again. Oh, the confused and the simple, the driveway
is the long and the simple path winding, winding, all else
is of unreality now. There are other
names to be not remembered: beyond the veil
of the curve and recurve of the repeated ranks of the maples,
house and home and the way to steal
into the ordered, the sane.

And sanity grown weary of its bound?

I am weary of not knowing, of doubt and hesitation,
of the lack of direction, of no path, of
the hurt of alone and the undecided, betrayed, the bleeding
of day on day into nothing but vapor.
                                    Now
the good road, the sound of feet on the gravel, familiar sound,
follow and follow, ah,
there's home, home again! Sweet grey, soft white,
sweet light of the pallor of early day, form, the arranged,

balanced and perfect! Not to be questioned.
House all shuttered. The storm? But
not to be questioned. Quietly, quietly, no sound, follow
around the house, the great front door will be locked, around
to the little room of the flowers.

                                  Shuttered here too. Oh,
I know the trick to open! You pry the knife blade under
and the catch swings loose, and again the blade and again
the casement opens, the old trick, the knowledge of how
things are at home, all known, all known. Quietly,
over the sill and within, be careful, the multiple vases,
china and glass and pottery, row on row, the bright, clean
shine of the big steel scissors catching the first white
light of the day, the glinting
of day on the nickel of spigots and valves, the glitter
of metal sink, flower smell, pot-pourri, the gathered
scent of the day on day of the always flowers, the rooms
beflowered and ordered. Oh, sweet and good, quiet now
in the scent of the known. The bench, be careful, it
has a wicker seat, the foot must
rest on the wood of the edge lest the yellow caning
crunch into damage, betray.

                          Be careful!
Close the shutters?

                  Yes, and the window too, who knows
who will be first in the morning? Darker now, thin
lattices of the grey light only, but there's no need
for light for the old familiar, for the known.

                          Open the door softly:
the hallway. Audubon prints, color almost entirely extinguished in
dusk of the dark of the time of the day's arising: big birds,
little birds, eagle, the mallard ducks, wild-winged osprey,
hall of the birds: remembered. Feet go
softly on the soft carpet of green like autumn grass, like
moss in the shadow of trees of the woods of the damp cool.

Now to your bed: is not the time of rising, the stirring,
sounds of the opening windows, the doors opening, are they not
      soon?
Or look first, room on room? Why look? The mind

  161

splits into its dichotomy: the need to go softly and
soon to bed unnoticed, uncaught, the no-need to see
the familiar; the need to see if the familiar is still
unaltered, the exploration suddenly, illogically demanding.
Open the door: dining room door: squeak of the hinges, a sound
betraying and frightening. Why squeak? Are they
not always oiled to the noiseless? Silver and the oval
Hepplewhite table, the ladderback chairs, the grey-blue of the
whiteness of china, old, Compagnie des Indes, the
graceful Waterford chandelier absorbing light, returning it
in the primary rainbows. Close the door.
Open the door: library, book on book, the paper and leather and cloth
bindings, the manifold colors, the thousands
of books on the bare and dusty shelves—paradox:
why are the books on the bare shelves? Let mind
flow to another room, body go
noiseless again to the double door, open, squeak and whine again:
living room now: the familiar, the desk and the tables, the flowers
in cloisonné vases, the crystal vases of flowers, armchairs,
the lamps unfunctioning now, light resting, the first light
of the new day supplanting their need, the multiple
objects and ornaments, all here, all in the dust, except . . .
no sofa.
     No sofa.
          The huge, the embracing, the soft one—gone?
The place of the resting, the refuge, the everything of the small
and the young imagining: ship under sail, the huge and rushing
locomotive, the car and the breathless plane, the delight
of the books' devouring, knees curled
up to the chest in the vicarious danger, the earliest
hint of the love of the body, the heroine seen now, all seen—
no sofa?
     Gone: it will be explained. There is
always a reason. Later, later.
          Hungry now. Kitchen
alone at the hour: soft careful progress, the place
of the many foods, milk and cream and butter and sugar and
jam and marmalade and the box of the rich cakes, the
round sliding tin of the cover to greed's joy—but now,

no food and the multiplicity of the furnishings, metal
and white and copper and black of the burnt iron, set
in the dust of nothing: paradox.
                              Why eat?
Split of the mind, the two things seen as a double image:
did not Christ fast? Forty days, forty nights of emptiness filled
to repletion. Did not the Buddha arrive at purification of
thought by the long fasting, the going without? Contemplation
of emptiness soon filled to the overflowing. Purify and devour
the food of the mind, the spirit, cast out
the devils of all else, let
spirit grow on the imagined, be nourished
on purity, seeing and not seeing.
                              Did not
the body go easily on nothing, not wanting, when
war flew colors over the long Pacific? But what
was war then . . . what war . . . Time
folds backward, hides future under, do not
disturb the folding.
                     No logic here: time: books set
row on row in the emptiness of the bare shelves, kitchen
full of its emptiness in a panoply
of its old usage, its used things, the used-to . . . no sofa?
What is logic but the turn of the mind's illogicality, is not
the great lie known to be seeing is believing? Do not
science and the deep coils of the psychology, the probing
of man's entrail-spirit, foot on coiled foot, declare
sight the deception, knowledge the point of ignorance, the
decision the reflex of the unknown? Belief:
this the reality; the illogicality, this
is the logic of man. Hunger
is but the source of the appetite, fed
at the spring of the soul. Be wary now, wary, be
now believing, let mind see
unity here—go softly, softly, unquestioning, unnoticed,
uncaught, unheard to your bed. Up!
Stairs up! Tip-toe, child step, up and up, so soft, the
hardly hearable sound on the softness
of moss green lying over
the dust of the bareness, seen, not seen, seeing

163

is not believing. Paradox.

Bed now.

Will you sleep, Harlow?

I do not know: it is not sleep or waking.
There is the sound of a high wind:
remembered.

The unconscious' storm, the ego's hurricane?

There was a storm but
I did not hear it. I heard only the winds
that blew within. The outer, it tore
branches from trees, they must be gathered, the fractured
stumps on the trees will need the cold
cutting and pruning of Mr. MacKinnon's knife.
I am confused now by the storm and the not storm, by
the calm and the wind, I hear
the first instinctual flutes of the hungers
of birds awakening in the stillness. No storm:
or where now?

Sleep now, Harlow.
Are you not tired?

I am neither tired nor am I rested. Now
I am, only.

My bed
is the brass bed with shining globes of brass
or a battered mattress, or I climb
within the ever cool, ever freshness of
sheets drawn tight, unwrinkled. Paradox: dust and
the thousand books.

Sleep now.

So Harlow Standeven slept, the young man, going
to the world of dreams; but which was dream now,

164

the sleeping or the waking? He lies sprawled, arms flung
back and away, on the riddled mattress that is the endless
source of the nests of mice or in the small brass
bed with the polished globes of brass and the cool sheets—
who knows truth when he sees it, meets it?
                                    The spirit
lives in the body, the body harbors the spirit, and both
yield sovereignty to the other or there is war
between one and other. Out of the needs, the lusts
of the body comes the twist of the spirit, and which
owns precedence? Which is the dream? Will spirit
prosper for body's inclination or for the discipline
of the flesh; or the body grow to a firm casing for the brightness
of safe held, well-grown spirit by spirit's doing? So now
sleep is the dream and the dream is also waking and flesh
is confused with the over-reaching
of the thing within.

Then, in the course of time, Harlow awoke.

(Awoke: let wakening be then the act of rising, the simple absence
of the posture of sleep; and time: let time
be its own verity, for it is collapsed now into the everlasting
truthfulness of the timeless—the petty measure
of man's relation to light and dark, to sun and to sun's departure,
the confident and the frightened, the
high tide and the low of the arrangement of hours: these
denied and forgotten.)

This was Saturday: but not for Harlow.
                                    Light came
barred through the closed shutters. Rising, he opened these.
Shadow said only late afternoon, said sunlight, the blue
of the deep sky southward said clear day. Seen
now through the lightness of hunger, the emptiness, beauty
lay over the garden: flowers
in long, even, the well-kept rows: flowers of autumn, always
the same, year after year. Far off and below,
the gleam and polish of metal of Naius River framed
in the groves of beech trees, yellowing now. Yellow said only

165

autumn and the blue of the gleam and the polish
more intense: fall blue. Everything
seen through the soft haze: the haze of autumn?

People,

misty and undefined, they moved in the far
parts of the garden: gardeners.

Hungry: the time
for eating. But not eating, the well-determined
fast, the Christ and the Buddha, the purging, now no
paradox here. Sounds came
from the far side of the closed and closeting door: servants,
brother perhaps, and Nurse, and not yet
Father till dark and the big car. The ears hear
sounds within or without, a ringing, musical, soft sound,
tick of a distant clock, the footfall, punctual, oh!
the perfection of light on the ordering of the garden and the clear
treble of water contrived to its dropping, its willed
coda of silver notes!

Thirsty: down now, to drink
at the marble bowl of the music, as always, the sweet
soft coolness of spring water: the accustomed.

There is a dizziness in the descent of the stairs: the hand needs
the run of the dark mahogany handrail. People
below and half-seen. It is not wise
to speak to them yet: one is here and not here, joy
needs silence a while yet: home and home again. Feet seek
soft covered risers and treads, the moss green, down and down.
Door closed, door bolted. It is drawing toward evening, the day
is chill, and Father is absent. Unbolted, the big door
swings to admit the time of decline of day, the smell
of the moist autumn earth, the pungent
scent of calendula and of marigold, of the fallen
red and the yellow leaf.

There were people: but now
none: gone: day's over, nearly, time to cease work. Within
will be the sounds of the tea things, the ringing is
this in the ears. But silence, cut by the endless
music of the contrived and the guided water-drop, waterfall, this
is the silence of evening coming, the known

166

and lovely peace.
                    Here's water. Leaves in the marble, the taste
of mold in the sweet water. Someone
will catch it because the leaves are there, when Father
comes in the big car, day's end: the marker
of time returned in another round, unalterable.

Thirst quenched—time quenched—he walks the paths,
the between of the high box, the fresh and the goodness
of the smell of the hemlock, the yew-smell, the
flower-surrounding air. Rose bed. But not
to pick roses, never, the red and the pink and the white,
the yellow and golden, the white blushed over in warmth, these
are not for you: Father. Once Mother: ah, long, long
back in the half forgotten, a softness
beyond the comfort of ordering: gone now. The grasses,
the high weed and the briar, the red darts
of the invading and capturing sumac's leaf, these too
gone now: the mind and the spirit
remove and refuse.

Now to walk down to the river, of course, the usual
curiosity: will there be ducks there? Sometimes
black ducks and the solitary, the red-crowned merganser, or
maybe a pair of the teal, and to watch
 the ripple of fish-rise, the skim and the skitter and false
wind-flaw of shiners that leap to safety
of air from the skipjacks, and blue crabs, long clawed,
and once and again
swans, the wild and the rare, the makers of
sad music, or hearing
the passage of geese now, the upside-down of
the opposite trees in the still and steel
water of evening.
                    All this, or the osprey, the noble
bird of the swift stoop, perched on the long, grey
dead of the chestnut long dead, or the unequal
passage of crows aloud to the far woods,
or the white immobility, unreal and too posed, poised,
of the white herons on shallow of sand seen

167

brown and yellow through the still and the stee¹.
All this: to see: long accepted
periphery of home again. Walk now?

Walk as you walked in the night, to surpass
the strands of the briar, the tangle of trip vines where
path was green and grass mowed to the safety
of sandals, bare feet, bare legs? No matter:
mind walks.
Fish hawk, the long-down diving
merganser, the riffle of bluefish, preying . . .

and from this earliest death another life? Echo:
but only echo . . .

None sees circles of endless
ripples of perch rise, lancing and light-struck
thinness of wake of water rat, muskrat:
mind seen.
No matter; mind walks. Must one
see to believe? Man lives not
by feet alone. Clay: in another language
it is the word for key, the opener of the secret of
fission of mind and body: so unity from
the divisible.

Harlow walked to the marble bowl of the fountain
below the miniature waterfall, music-fall; drank there
greedily, taste of the leaf-mold; walked back
to the unlit house with lights bright in the mind.

Thinking:
water guggles within your emptiness,
the good guggle, the
gut-guggle: giggle, it's Fatso.
      Who
is Fatso? Not now. Not here. Night now:
deny, deny before cock-crow.

Do not deny your Christ nor the Gautama!
168

Do I not fast?

Why do you fast, poor Harlow, poor boy,
orphan Harlow, alone now, lonely not lonely, surrounded but
chill with the hotness that overlays
the cold of the body?

I fast to seek: seek home: seek love.

What love then do you seek?

I have forgotten, it was
long ago, long ago, it lies
in the pain without, the within is
home again.

Now without passage Harlow is in the living room,
lights a fire: the old and the dried logs, crumpling
newspaper eight years old—but the date's unseen, for time
has become the timeless, the verity
of the child's existence.
                              Child-part, believing, fainting,
stretches out on the welcoming rug by fire, hears
all the familiar sounds of the surroundings of
comfort ordered, the footfalls, the authority
of older voices; sees
softness of lamp-light, all, all about him the wanted and
the remembered: except the absent sofa.
                              Where is the sofa?
It will be all explained, it is like the fire
that was not lit, the cat's
away and the mice will play, the unlaid
fire of Father's absence, perhaps New York, or maybe
Currituck for the ducks, or the many
mills of the far south, the unexplained and the reasonable
trips and the being away. Home soon, home soon again, sofa
and fire explained and the now is
but the exhaustion of the sweet passage of
no time counted. No search: not now: here
love is, is not needed for searching or

169

must be, the accepted: the unquestioned, or love?
or the ordered? or home again, fire-light,
fire or lamp-light, the mind
needs but belief and to rest: heart
needs but to rest, all pain, all confusion,
this is not yet arrived, the clock ticks
loud to its chimed reversal.

Now it is Sunday and day dawns in a brightness
of the clear colors of rose and of red, another
October day, unflawed.
                    It is not
Sunday for Harlow.
                    Light came thinly
through lattices of the closed shutters. Rising, he opened them.
Shadow proclaimed but morning, announced sunlight on
brilliance of the red maples, the blue
of the pale sky southward said clear day. Seen
now through the purity of hunger, the purged, the marvel
lay over the garden: flowers
in the dense, the kept ordering, aisles of color, of autumn,
always the same, year on recurrent and ordered year. Far off,
remote as voice in a dream, the sound
of the drop of water, the metal-drip, marble harp
of the gone days come again.
                    Sweet sound
of the chimes of the many clocks (or the remote-soft
church bells tolling?) uncounted strokes, long, long,
tolling and telling the time to the pound of the heart-sound
in the gold and the yellow of day.
                    The haze of day: remember:
the still passion of April in Italy, when
the pure aspirants of distant campanili then
decanted bells in the bronze afternoon.
                    Why now
remembering, time displaced, the clocks
chimed forward? Not now—banish: the
figure vanishes. The day
is the gold and the blood-red of youth: no Italy but now

hours new blown of glass
of such fantastic, of such Venetian shapes and twinings,
even their memory's fragile.

Italy was escape?

Italy was . . . is not yet . . .
this is Rhode Island. I am but now, I . . .
the confusion! Water now, I am thirsty. The burning . . .

Burn, then, Harlow. Burn to an ash.

Ashes of hardwood taken out to the garden but
not on the irises, Father said. No iris now, autumn.
Iris is June, the goddess, the many colored
iris, Osiris the sunlight, all-color, all-good, ah!
how educated you are!
> For your age.
>> What age?
Ashes, for God's sake! Get your ashes hauled out,
and act your age.
> What age?
It is to be forgotten now. Thirsty:
the burning.

So he goes again to the marble bowl of the contrived music,
drinks of the leaf-taste: drink and drink again,
plunge the face in the cool, quench
burning, thirst gone, fast long forgotten, mind
turned but one way now.
> Rising, straightening: let
water run down, drip down, the cold drops—
let them fall to the clothes, what matter?
Garden is full of people, not many, but full of them, busy,
here and there so busy, and watching—watching?
Don't let water drip to your good clothes, Harlow,
or I shall have to make you change again, all
by yourself to change.
> So many people!
People to guide and to guard you, people to watch over,

watch you. And now returning,
people within the house—oh, people and not people, maids
and not maids, here and there, usual, morning's
the busy time, maid-time, gardeners, the weeding.
Not near and not far, not speaking and
not silent, or not exactly silent, the undefined
presence of people, people. They are the known, the familiar,
and I do not know them. Queer.

                   They are watching.

They are watching you, Harlow?

Yes, they are watching me.

Are they not watching over you, then?
Was not this ordered?

Yes, it was ordered so, always.

Was it not for the ordered, the ordering,
that you are here? The secure
comfort of long fixed?

But there is nothing to do. I may not
play with Theobald, it is said
Mrs. MacKinnon wouldn't like it, feel comfortable,
break my toys; but no toys, now
in the light of morning run outside, there must be
something to do for a great big boy like you, but
don't touch, don't touch, don't break,
don't and don't. But do.
Mother had beautiful little scissors, she let you
cut the paper to curls and to squiggly shapes but
Nurse has taken away. Sharp. Don't. The order.
But it is all here, only not my mother, long gone, long gone,
all here—expect the sofa, except
Father is not here. But still don't,
they're watching you, they
watch and watch over.

172

Is it fragile, Harlow?

It is fragile, it was the Venetian chalice, old,
the blue pattern of the serpents springing
from the long, light-filled stem, the fluted,
gold-specked chalice of cup-form: broken: you see,
you must not touch: and the anger coldly
in the big man's voice, the smell of cigar smoke cold-grown
in the grey of the tweeds, the red
of the hard lips and the grey moustache, the
source of the ordered: anger
is also terror, so don't, so don't, so don't!
Now run out
into the garden, the after-breakfast garden, there is
the patch for you, the weeds grow, is it not
shameful to leave the weeds and to choke the lovely
generous flowers, the thing was given, to you, but
don't pick the roses. How
did you get your shoes so scratched? New shoes:
shoes cost money, dear boy, your father,
your father. Take your dirty
scratched shoes off the sofa, Harlow, and run
out like a big boy now.

I am not on the sofa, there is
no sofa.

Don't argue. Run out. The sun
is where you should be, morning, it is routine,
don't argue.

The ordered.

So out again from the eyes in the busy house to
the eyes in the garden: the beautiful rich-full garden,
the close-cropped grass and the rows of even flowers,
the colors sorted and patterned into beauty, the
clipped and lovely box, and the flowing shapes
of the yew cut to its forms, and the briars and brambles,

173

the sumacs and the invading birch and time's
now out of joint to me—there'll be a joint
for dinner if Father's home. If Father's
home again.
                    Sunlight,
bright and clear and warm, and incandescent, showing
the figures moving and working, working and watching,
everything is so clear. No hiding—
no hiding place down here.
                        There used to be hiding:
now you're too big to hide, a big boy now, and
the sun's so brilliant, all light, iris-osiris,
all revealing.

Now it is afternoon. How did it get so?
Time has collapsed into a verity, let us borrow
the verity, it can be paid back later. Faster now,
truth may not be wasted into a dawdling. Lazy-bones,
lying in the sun, how do you expect to get
your day's work done?

But there are people in the house now. There are two
old women. They are the maids, or the cook and a friend, maybe,
but they are oddly dressed. The cook
didn't wear, usually, a hat in the house. But
Father's away, the cook will play, it doesn't
matter: what matters now, of a sudden, is
not to be seen. Are they not watching you, set to
watch you? The fun
is to be unwatched. Voices: they say,
"It hadn't ought to be open, doors left open."
It is afternoon: of course they are open. Silly. What time?
Watch stopped, unwound? But watch itself
is anachronic, Anachronos, Chronos.
Who is Chronos, what is he, that
all our swains commend him? No, not Chronos: Sylvia.
My mother had a maid called Sylvia; she was in love,
and he she loved proved mad. Oh, no. Not Sylvia—
Barbara. Barbara was my cousin and we tried
to make love in the beech grove, it was fun, exciting, but

174

we were too little, we couldn't do it. Why
was it fun? Oh, it was wrong, and we were not caught, we
escaped to the grove and no one knew.
Escape now. Do not be caught. Keep
a corner between you and the two maids, cooks, someone
in hats. Know them but have no names, the
nameless people and not people, everywhere. Out now,
escape to the garden, back of the hemlock hedge, and
none can see you. Perhaps.
                              There is a man
out in the garden. Of course, why not? But
I know him and should not know. You
must not know him! Keep down, keep down, below
the line of the hedge, watch him who's there to watch you, while
he weeds and cuts—or he ought to be weeding, pruning, but
the cat's away? There are so many people
it is hard to escape, and there's no Barbara now—
no Barbara, you have lost her, it is a pain
beyond enduring, but now not Barbara, no,
say I'm growing old, but add—
Sylvia kissed me? Who is Sylvia?
                              Here
is the warm place, the high yews, the sun trapped
into a green chamber, the gold all spilled
over the brown of the earth. Roses.
                         There are no roses. There
        are
briars and sumac and a young honey-locust, but
these are the unreality.
                    There is a rose. A rose
by any other name would smell as sweet. Romeo.
Romeo wasn't built in a day, that's very funny, tell it
to Father, he'd like that—or maybe would, but Father
is not here—or perhaps is not?
                              A rose:
dark red and full and sweetly smelling, so dark; I
know it, Gloire de Dijon. A single rose-bloom
red in the green and the trapped gold.
                              For Father:
rose is for him. Don't pick it. Barbara

    175

by any other name was once a maid.

Pick the rose, Harlow.

I must not pick it.

*Pick the rose, Harlow, there is
no one looking.*

There is the man on the other
side of the yew hedge.

He cannot see you.

He cannot see me—or perhaps he cannot.
But why should I pick it?
Why should I want to pick it?

It is not a want, but a need.

Why is it a need, then?

*Because you may not: therefore
you must.*

Standing still in the warm shafts of the sunlight, his mind
moves with a curious clarity, the emptied body releasing
thoughts and the power of thoughts.
                         You may not: therefore
you must. That which you came to seek, the controlled, the
     ordered,
the secure because of the ordered, cannot exist
until you have proved it by the one, simple act of destruction.
Everything's into a pattern now: the light and the day,
the people, the garden, the flowers grown in the mind,
the sumacs that the mind and the spirit rejected, the
one rose seven years blooming in its survival among
the rankness unseen (rankness protecting); it is
of Father everywhere, everywhere. All that is yours is his
for the one, light-struck moment: security

176

lies like a tangible cloak to cover your body
against the ills of the world.

What ills of the world?
Ah, there is no need now to answer the rushing questions, the
whole
is a whole, unanswerable but needing no answer.
The moment exists and is. Harlow has borrowed now
the verity of belief in the reality
of the unreal imagined.

So Harlow bends and he plucks the dark red rose, his fingers
avoid the thorns and the overarching long
strands of the briars. For a moment, unmeasured,
he holds the rose in peace. The purged
senses give to his fingers the full softness, the dove-feel
of the long petals, the scent
rises in utter purity to surround him, the eye
sees form and color doubled in excellence, the deep
chalice—this unbroken now in the gentleness of the
sensitive fingers—of the symbol of wholeness made
in the delicacy of the curves of the parts to the whole.
The moment is peace: the fulfilled.

Peace is now shattered. A man's voice
cries out, distantly, distantly, clearly, crying,
"Harlow!"

Ah! they are after you!
How did They know: the rose? Oh, but Authority
knows all, sees all things. Soon
They will gather for the pursuit. They know now: He—
no need to define the he—will send Them
to find you out, there is
no hiding place down there!

Again the cry is heard, in the soft distance
of the still afternoon: the man's voice: *Harlow!* and then
a woman's voice is added, clear and so lovely, it pierces

into the mind, its beauty
should not be fear: and *Harlow!* sings in the air,
the mote-filled golden haze-wrapped
air of October.
                    So They gather: so many!
They will be legion shortly. They will find you,
no hiding.
                    Ah, but there is: They cannot
trap you now, the time's different, time has grown now,
this is an old and used thing: escape.
They, the many, with Him behind Them, directing,
They will expect the usual flight to the beech grove, the
often and accustomed: Barbara: where the buckdrops
shot their purple and yellow, their sterile flowers
under the tree shade—but that was the passion of summer and
the overmastering heat. Long gone now. None now.
Start so, They will expect it, They will believe
first the beeches and then the meandering patch cut
out of the dense of laurels down to the yellow-grey
sand of the river's edge. Easy to fool Them:
cut from the grove to the swamp, the swamp to the pines,
the tall and the malformed white pines, the huge candelabras
burning their flames of the dark green.
                    So one escapes:
but never hurry, and do not run, the motion
of speed betrays.

Slowly (careful!) Harlow props the red rose dark
in the prongs of the bronze leaves. It rests there
in indolence and repose. There is no use
to be caught with it on you.
                    Now look, but slowly,
over the yew hedge: no one. That man has vanished.
Terror: that he's not there, for where now? Slowly!
Cool and slowly! The man was summoned
by the clear calls, the bass and the alto
piercing of peace; sound that said
the place you had to come to's the one you must leave.
Escape now.

Go to the west from the close of the yew surrounding
the roses that were and that are not, passing
softly the gap in the hedge—ragged, incredible, passionate
growth of the trumpet vine covering
darkness of flat green needles of yew—but under it,
it is protection. Sidle
back of the tool shed, the door hangs crookedly open,
hinge gone, but shed still
solid against the searching eyes.
                      The terrible thing
is to be seen now. Later it will not matter, for later
you'll be a man, and none can say to you
why or when. It will be soon, in time which now
is but a being, child-time. Fear
(terrible and engrossing until the later time of
the growth—oh, when?) makes the heart pound so,
and hearing the cries and the counter-cries, the people
calling and looking; or is it within?
                        Remember:
the battering sound of the big guns and mortars and then the long
      following
days, the months of the ear ringing, the bell-sound,
the tick of the pulse-watch, or within or without, you
could not discriminate. Now
the sounds are the sounds, acceptable, echo or memory,
you must escape them, bending
the body to the unseeable, the feet following down
the choked and familiar path, down, down, and down to
the place where the land rises and the great
nobility of the beeches spreads in the air's glory
its gold and its brown. Stamp sound, hoof sound, the fluttered
breath of a horse through vibrated nostrils. Imagined? No,
the horse is there, tethered, reins thrown
over the broken beech bough. Man there,
still and regarding: not you: other view. They
were quicker and cleverer than you had foreseen. No use for
beech grove now. The man's known and you know him, but
let him be nameless: to name him is to forsake
the hope of escaping: something: Them and Father, the broken

179

stem of the ordered rose. Turn eastward,
the swamp is safety: across the swamp the tall pines
burn for your freedom, green in the golden light, the
enchanted October lighting of fear.

                          Crawl now: you have crawled
for safety before this. Ahead is the tall thickness,
the interlaced black of the alder branches, beyond them
the little low huckleberries, seen in the mind, their leaves
will be the color of blood.

                He did not see you,
the nameless man with the bay horse: not Father: He
is everywhere, everywhere. The voices
called to his word to call.

                Lie on the wet ground now,
among the closeting alders, till breath comes
even and gentle: listen, be quiet: a whistling—down
in a slanted dropping of brown wings, legs braced,
the woodcock settles before you. Huge eyes
wide in the head stare at you as you stare at him, both
motionless frozen. They put him up, he flew
to safety also. Be still, unwinking: he stands there,
long beak, wings folded, the delicate
tan of breast against tan of the fallen leaf. Time goes
in the tick of the eardrum, endless and nothing, breath
held to a softness. Soon now
all forgotten but this: the still bird.
Then, but without transition, unfrightened, the woodcock
walks in odd little steps off, off and away, not hurried,
back of a branch, more branches, gone now. The bird
never saw you. You were not there. Remember:
Indian lore in the red book, the brave
pursued in the open, lying, only the shelter of
sparse growth, dwarf sage, motionless, thinking,
I am not here: believing: unseen, uncaptured.
I was not there.

             Ah, for the bird, yes: but beyond now
lies the open of swamp, and the many, many
of Them in the search, and fear, and now in the open
to be not there? Yet

one must be there to be beyond it, to come
to the flame of the pines.

Why must you reach the pines then, Harlow?

Beyond the pines and the sweet
carpet of brown redolence lies
the stone wall; beyond the wall
is the reach of the road.

Why to the road?

I must go to the road, it is
the place of safety: final.

Why is it safety?

It is not to explain, it is something
known and sure: the road now.

It is not your father's?

No. But later, later!

He has crept out of the thicket of the black alders, the crossed
and the interlaced, the scarlet of long-strung berries
embracing the bosom of sky, and is out
in the small growth, thick matting, sharp thorns
of the blood and the rose-colored swamp.
                              Lie still there, lie
till the way is safe. Lie and then look. Raise dark head
slowly to peer above the olive of the sheep-laurel,
the eye to perceive and note.
                    The great white
oak on the island knoll to the northeast, not far,
spreads its silver grey branches, clings to its red leaf,
secret and cloistering shade, the multiple
birches grow below in a pale burning of yellow
held on the white ash of the stems, the black ash

of the new members. Hidden place, sheltering,
gently containing, sturdy place, dry ground with
the grey and the silver of brittle moss turning to green of jade
in the sadness of rain.
                          Love's there: sun-touched:
clung together enclosed in the sun and the crimson
and the yellow flaming, kiss-held, arms moveless
gesturing love, lips now
soundless speaking.
                          I know them: first pain:
then laughter. But keep laughter
soundless as kisses.

Why do you laugh, Harlow?

If my father catches them! There they stand,
paid on his time to do his will—and kissing.
What would he do to them? What will he do?
Do they think they can fool him? Crazy.
Or someone's crazy.

And you know them?

I know them. But in the birth
of the thought, mind divides again, a triple division:
I know them, but now they are nameless, I cannot
speak the names: speaking, there would be pain again; unspoken
they are but They.
I know them, they are the voices which called out
in the gold and the silver tones, to call me, they
are that which I flee from, they are of them
surrounding now and pursuing.
I know them, I have seen them, they stood
on the rise of bare ground in the high
hills south of Piacenza, the pair of lovers embracing
who did not see me: my fear
reached not to them in their love or passion or
the twist of a moment on the body in spring lust.
Three ways I know them.
                          Piacenza, that

was the fear and the candles and the sound
of the bell and the high
beauty of voices. Italy. Remember.

Italy was escape?

It was escape, yes.
It was after so many things.
There was the transfer from the Pacific and the time home
and the time in England, and the Savoy Hotel and
the women and leave and the cold fog and the blackout and after
      that,
the destroyer sunk at Salerno and the many
dead and the wounded and rapid sequence of
the three prison camps till you got to the camp
that was once a monastery and cold and beautiful and
Christ! how infinite was the boredom and the incessant,
the daily and nightly and weekly and monthly passion to be free,
      to
see the world move!
                All this was before. It was
the old, the repeated story. You lived suspended, you
      contemplated
your navel till you were sick of the damned umbilical thing,
and sick of the guards and sick of the small corruptions,
and sick of the better food of the blacker market and
exercise and the endless plans to make an escape, and of
all the prisoners and of yourself too. You were sick:
there is no health in prison.
               But the thing began
because the wops had dropped out of the fight and the krauts took
      over—
and there was no love lost there. When the spring came,
the April of '44, we could not stand it longer, the grapevine
said you will all be sent to Germany soon now, the Germans
can't trust anyone here. There would be so little
hope of escape then, so the long-laid plans, the plans
that the wops aided—oh, not for love, for hate—the plans
were put into action, and we fled, six of us,
separately and alone. The plans worked,

    183

at least they did for me.
                    Oh, I remember
the things between: the man in the little village—you had to
finally turn to someone, take chances, you had to eat—
who turned out crazily as the brother of Alfred,
the waiter at the Savoy in London, the old pal,
and sent you on to his sister; the sister sent you
further again to the priest who was no damn use and looked
as if he would turn you in; the man in the car,
the fat Italian, smoking his fine cigar, in the big, expensive
limousine with the suitcase full of money, who
dished out lire, thousands and thousands of them, and gave you
the name of the partisan in the hills, the safe man,
who wore two pistols, a knife, and a short sword
and ought to have been in a comic moving picture
as a stage bandit: his name was Giuliano but
he liked to be called Il Lupo.
                    It runs together now,
image on image, sharp here, blurred there, the recollection
of the pasty-faced man who supplied the beautiful
forged identity cards and the working papers, and
his pretty young wife who had to be slept with, always,
when pasty-face was away. The endless pasta,
the taste of olive oil, you were made of oil, you
stank of it, and the garlic. And the warm weather,
the passion of the Italian spring, the Apennine flowers,
the woman-hunger, the sharp red wine, the liquid
beauty of speech in people who felt its beauty
no matter what had to be said or how or when;
the bells and the bronze tones
and the penetrant, bodily sunlight pouring
over and through your bones. The wanderer, heading
always a little north and a little north toward
the heaven of Switzerland.
                    Switzerland grew
to a concept bigger than you could hold, a longing
like life and the hope of life and the hunger for living
free in the free air. Its mountains
rose to the height of dreams and the dreams held you,
waking or sleeping, and in all times

of still contemplation.
                    And then, at the end,
the way was open at last, and you took your courage, and walked
down from the hills to the town of Piacenza—a lone man,
you looked all right, you looked an Italian workman,
your speech was good enough if a German questioned, but
the fear was always that there would be an Italian,
a Fascist ear to hear you. Down then, shunning the little road,
from Ferriere to Beffola, Ponte d'Olio.
                              It was then, on a hill path,
I saw the people: two people: they did not see me—
I stopped and I stood dead still. They could not see me,
though I was exposed to see. They were two lovers,
locked in the spring, in the heat of the metal sun,
there was no world other for them than the world they held
close to each other and in each other. I left them:
oh, if they saw me they did not want to see me, I
was outside their world, more alien in the being
than in myself an alien. So to the city: the heart
beat less madly after a while.
                        The tall dark
man with the green felt hat, who held, as I had been
told, the onions in his left hand, came by me, strolling,
and I said to him, "Lupo mi ha mandato, vuole
inviare il vino," and he slipped me the ticket
like one of those men who slip you the dirty postcards
in the streets of Paris, conspirator-dramatist; whispered:
an hour and twenty minutes exactly, here by the station,
the man—the other man—would be at the station, he would
brush past me: follow: and do not walk on the streets,
there would be a spot-check soon, that was the rumor,
keep off the streets, look natural, and in an hour and twenty
minutes exactly, exactly, without fail, at the station,
and he was gone, he merged
with the Sunday crowds.
                    And the fear rose
like a nausea: from Piacenza to Switzerland
as the crow flies, as the plane goes, it was only
fifty statute miles. It was twenty thousand
enemies distant. But you had to get off the streets,

the man had said, and someone would see the fear
that clothed you notably. Followed the street a little way,
the via Alberoni, past San Savino, but
too many people, so left here, via Legnano,
and there's the Duomo. I don't know what it looks like
on the outside, I didn't dare to look at it, had to
pretend it was too familiar, and entered. Stood by the font,
and a woman there, with her husband and three children,
dipped her fingers into the holy water and touched
the fingers of children and of her husband, and then, smiling,
touched mine. They crossed themselves. Because they were
      looking,
I crossed myself too, and it seemed both blasphemous
and good and comforting all at the one moment, and
having done that, I followed it out to the end,
and genuflected as they did to the high altar,
and knelt to pray. It was a place for praying, beautiful,
it was full of God then. And when I had prayed—for safety,
for Switzerland and freedom—I looked about me, covertly,
and thought how many people had thought that God
was presently here, and all of those thoughts, accreted over
the long and the many years, had left a residue
to touch the Rhode Island Yankee, the Baptist boy
who had crossed himself in spite of himself, from fear.

The mass was sung. It was fine, the colors
of the robes of the priests were beautiful, the ballet
moved with precision, in symbol after symbol—
ununderstood but yet it was comprehended in essence—
and the clear, trained and treble voices of the young boys
rose and fell and rose and the darker tones
of the men's voices pounded against the silver
of the alto singing, and the impressive
deep and husky voice of the priest would come and go
like a thread of blood-red running athwart the weaving
of the whole tapestry of symbols.
          And all around
were people moving, the couples walking,
the children crying or quiet—hundreds of differing people
fused in the sound and the small brilliance of many candle-flames

186

pointing the darkness, and the bell-sound ringing,
and the color of robes, the flash of golden threads
as the shoulders moved and turned and the ballet ran its
course in a dense light of illumined sounds.
And I looked at my watch then and I had ten minutes
to get to the station.
                    Where had fear gone? Vanished.
I left the Duomo and I followed the street,
via Legnano to via Alberoni, past the church
of San Savino again: no fear: one looked
at the old, old buildings, the color of stone and brick,
and the sad faces and the multiple black
of Sunday and of mourning, the black of widows
wedded to black by war, and the cries of children
in immemorial shrillness of their games, the running
of young feet. No fear.
                    The big man
in the hideous brown suit with the sharp lapels
brushed past, and was to be followed and was followed,
and there was the train and the carriage was full save one
seat that another man rose and left from and you took it
and later—freedom and Switzerland. All that's after,
and there was fear again, but never the nausea
of the fear of the many eyes.

And now, Harlow: in this escape,
what fear from the many eyes?

It begins again with the vision of the two lovers, but
this has been overcome.
I go now, slowly, escaping:
from the pursuers.
I am not here.

But you go where?

I go to the road: to freedom.

Why is the road free? Will they
not pursue you there?

187

They cannot pursue me there, it is
not my father's. It is a road: a road
somewhere, ahead. There will be a man
to guide me, and I shall follow, and then be free—
free of pursuit and of the broken rose, the
plucked bloom. Free from the pain of the lovers standing
within my sight, my pain: the bloom stolen. I am beyond this!
I have found the way. You live
with the immediate, minute by minute—so
the way comes clear, to the self. It is all about me.
Look!
The red leaves of the earth-bound running swamp blackberry,
the pink and yellow of cranberries. Ah, and here's
the place of the pitcher-plants, you can see the water
in the red and the green vases. All these
seen and discovered by the seeing eye, are music
and the bright candles and the robes of the mass
in the presence of God.
    And the ground rises, it is
like life itself, and here is the pearly everlasting,
and the bright partridge berries lie over the ground—
there is so much, so much! The scent
of the pine needles is rich in comfort. Here
when the spring has come and gone there will be again
the delicate veins of the pink lady's slipper,
and the white, waxen blooms of the striped pipsissewa here.
There will be spring again, it will all happen, it comes
in the cycle on cycle, free.
    And I am free.
They cannot catch me. The voices
are but the menace of mind, the spirit
lies beyond them. You live
if you wish to live. The October air says
go and free and do.
    Now here's the graveyard,
forgotten for half a hundred years, the names forgotten,
the nameless stones of the slaves at every angle,
the place of memory where jack-in-the-pulpit
preaches for everlasting over the dust grown
into the dust, and the pine roots

make bones their own.
　　　　　　　　　　Sun here, and the grey
of lichen on tumbled stone wall, bright sun
on the light brown and grey of the sandy road and
tumble down to the road, to the sweet
freedom.
　　　　　　　The man will come. Lie still: the body
need strive no more, the mind, the spirit,
purged, can be rested, rest. Lie still: you'll follow
the man to the new day: it was all commanded
in the ordering of the stars: and Gemini
can lead you now back to the east when night reveals
the pattern of things again, no fear, no pain, just
free to be you, alone . . . or part of the whole . . .
or the whole in part . . . tomorrow . . . the rose was plucked,
it is yours . . . and Father is dead, oh, dead and gone and . . .
the leaves are soft, their
rustle's a lullaby . . . and sleep's an end
and sleep's beginning . . . you . . . to reach an ending that
you might begin . . .
　　　　　　　So sleep.

□□□□□□

Part Two

SERENA MALLIN

□□□□□□

Sense of waking, sense of the first light.
Ears to hear: the harsh, the dissonant cry,
herring gulls over the water and on the pale
passionless tide.
                              I am suspended
between a sleep and a waking, touch
of a dream still, clouded. There were the stones
heaped up one by one, the long labor,
turned in a glare of light all too intense
into the ice; the glare and the hot sun
melting the ice-stones. Not my sun.
Weary, the labor melted. Stone on stone
melted in brilliance, light too intense. Dream.
The gulls cry, grey light, sun will be
soon: my sun? Day, other day,
another day. Soft, soft, the distant
wavelets say *sh! sh!* The waking,
this is my body.
                              So the eyes open:
open to close, they have seen the door
closed and near too. Who shall open?
Let it be closed now. Let the mind
lie in the mist of sense, the half-sense
building the truth in images. Warm bed
holds and enfolds the senses. Sensual.
Sensual is body, body's the poor house
spirit dwells in. Bed is the poor house
body dwells in now, house within
house, all builded stone upon stone,

190

and the stones to ice and the ice melted,
dream and image. Images.
                    Jennifer.
Oh! the key image and perhaps the sun
melting the stones of ice? Why not?
Young sun, hot sun. What did stones enclose
not to be melted?
                    Stretch the body now:
toes to ankles, leg to the knee and thigh,
stretch and stretch, the small of the back,
spine to the chest and the uplifted breasts—
still so firm, unchanged. And what then,
what would change them? Here brown nipples,
high now, nerved and demanding, never
suckled except . . . except . . . but no child
suckled at these. Ah, but no child!
Stone on stone into what, the house,
home or habitation or but the simple
marking of boundary, the formal
garden of being? No child suckled—
passion and love and both in a building
into a life? For whom, for what?
Terror lies under the thought, the concept
emptied of meaning, purpose.
                    Who am I?
Who is Serena, pretty and middle-aged,
sensual in her bed, in the warm
touch of linen, the body warmed so
gently to feeling—who is Serena,
what is she? The wife—no mother—
toward what purpose if now the given
comfort's rejected?
                    I am awake now.
Sun is risen, the day is golden,
shaft of sunlight, levelly piercing,
distant gulls on the loving, wanted
breasts of the water, suckled on water,
shaft of the sun to touch the crimson
flowers of autumn, pretty, home-flowers:
day's ahead. And life is forever

191

still ahead.
                 Jennifer's life.
Jennifer's living and she is pain too,
she is passion and hurt, and the act of
being: another stone, added and placed.
Stone into ice and ice is melted.
Stone's not melted, pattern is stone
never to ice, the pattern of love,
habit of loving, the simple, recurring
flowers in vases, prettiness for a pattern
to make the trivial sweet for importance,
pattern surrounding, pattern to leave,
freedom, the unpossessive, the gentle
room of the many doors, all made
at a touch to open.
                   I am awake now.
I am aware now, and I know.
Day is for being and setting free again,
keeping the pattern, the trivial pattern,
door to enter, toward the comfort,
place to return, the base to leap from:
let him go free!
                 I am aware now.
Who is Serena? Simple! a woman:
she is alive. To comfort, to aid,
to be—toward death and dying? Time
runs faster—runs out? Time is being.
Death's but a semi-colon: another clause
still's to be added. Passion's a comma,
phrase from phrase. Possession's a full stop:
there is the death. Be me, me only,
I am the pattern and the pattern's law,
law is to change, to amend, to break:
law is being. There is no time
in the infinite space of love.
                   Arise!
Day is up, is cool, the bed is
too warm, too close; be free, let free,
let be!

Part Three

ROCHESTER MALLIN

🁢🁢🁢🁢🁢🁢

THIS WAS the need. But it was self-created,
the spirit whirled around a single pole:
the pole was you, the field was generated
by magnetism of one need, one soul.
This was the road. And it was fair but strait,
it ran its length as such a narrow way
there was no turning to anticipate
till at its sudden end you went astray
and found divergence of the tripled lane
and the confusing signposts pointing other
than your one destination, hence to pain,
and thence to love, and this way for a brother.
Oh, take the road to pain until your wire
burns to more current than your own desire.

THE MAID knocked on the door, said "Eight o'clock."
He woke at once and wholly, called out, "Thank you,"
rolled to his back and lay quite still. His day
came full to mind. Up, dress, and breakfast,
talk to Serena, off for Providence,
drive the convertible, fine clear day, one stop
to speak to Jacob Ledbetter, little tractor
and last night's meeting. Lunch with Harold Peckett,
discuss the hospital, speak for Quintus Lamy?
Yes, speak for Quintus: that must have been determined
in the deciding sleep.
                        The mind branched off:
so easy to do, it wished to fly around
Serena, what to say to Quintus Lamy,

and what to do tomorrow—to Jennifer.
No place for Jennifer in the day's plan—
everyone else tucked in so very neatly:
the God damned orderly day!

                Let mind not wander!
To wander was to dream but not to think;
to think was discipline.

                Oh, discipline?
To think of these things, and to put aside
the stalled work, the inertia that must turn
into momentum to produce a book?
Well, this was Saturday, Saturday's for rest,
or if not rest, for other things than art;
the act of living.

           So: Serena first.
No problem there today. Breakfast and plans,
the day's trip and the talk to Quintus Lamy,
the dinner mortgaged to the Messlers, bridge,
the couple there to meet him. Could be fun,
or could be dull; improbably contain
excitement. Sunday was the vexing day.
Morning was garden, garden was Serena.
How trapped you were in all the ancient pleasures
now become obligations! But after lunch?
Was young Standeven down? If so, if so—
no use competing there. So, Sunday out.
To ride perhaps, the mare needs exercise.
At least alone, legitimately alone.
Oh, how legitimate you are, my boy:
from habit or from fear?

             But Mondays come,
if you'll but wait. And Monday afternoon,
and pictures brought, the studio, we two . . .
and see what happens. Good. And so the morning
fruitful for what it futured? Good enough,
flexible. It could all be played at sight,
and better so.

          I must get up, he thought.
The comfort of the bed, the golden morning,
the plan of doing (perhaps the plan of having?)

194

stirred up his body, his desire.
                                  Serena.
Selfish last night? I'm rested now, he said,
his lips almost in motion; but then so tired,
so flagged out with the day. Nothing to give.
Why should one try to give when one is empty?
A mockery of living. The rested body
restored the spirit and the mind. Or mind,
rested and moving now, or looking forward,
restored the body?
                        I am neatly hung
between youth and old age, I want too much
for what I see and know. Perhaps in age
balance achieved, body to lie at peace,
mind to predominate and give surcease
to the tiresome flesh? But not yet tiresome!
Not yet!
              Outside the future-frame of window
there was a flash of brown and white, a yellow
like metal, and his mind said simply, "Flicker,
always the flickers in October. Up."

Rochester rose then and he washed and dressed,
unthinking, the habitual; and descended
toward breakfast with his wife.
                                  As he went down
he saw in his mind's eye what he would see:
Serena sitting placid and receptive,
now undemanding, last night wholly buried
except the public parts, the communal.
Quite suddenly he thought, how does she do it?
She is in essence the aggressive one,
a man shaped into the soft form of woman,
who's learned—and maybe by the battering years,
by force of all around her—the old trade
of being a woman, cherishing, receptive,
gentle and subtle—all against her nature.
A man trapped wrongly in a woman's body—
and it was once exciting—passionate,
wanting to do, to lead, to initiate,

195

and having now to get her purpose always
in the obliquity of action hidden
behind the female's way: the way assigned
as proper to her sex.
                          I am the woman,
woman by nature. I have learned the trade
of manhood, made it mine. But it is not
my perfect nature. Are not all my books
excellent in their women, with false men
that will not take that final full dimension
which can convince? The women live. They live!
I plant the hair upon the manly chest,
write the aggressive, the demanding words—
conventional emptiness. So perhaps my own?
But having learned the curious trade of being
man as he's so conceived and so expected,
must I not practise it? I would be asked—
if I could have my way—and never ask;
possessed and not possess. I do not know,
now, at my age, true hunger of pursuit,
who longs to be pursued. I am a man?
I am a man or a man fashioned: so
condemned to be it.
                          This the morning vision,
the truth seen at the start of early day
in the transition space upon a stairs.
Remember and record. But act the man:
pursue: not anyone—not Jennifer—
will now pursue you till you have pursued
in the conventional, the imposed, the false
pattern of being because your fate decreed
man's organs to your loins.
                          Or was it more
that having man and woman in one body,
monoecious, self-contained, one could but find
climax in self-love, could but fertilize
oneself by intercourse with self and bear
fruit in the own womb of own penetration?
What monstrous being or what perfect thing
could then be born of one's own pregnancy

by passion of oneself, self joined to self,
forever drawing, from no outer source,
but nourishment for this?
                              Serena then
(oh! in the earliest days!), now Jennifer
(the incessant future), they were but the dew,
the rain, the humus, the phosphate or the dung
spaded to feed my roots until they grew
or grow to procreate myself?
                              No child begotten.
Was this the reason? First by our intention—
but ours? or mine? And later, past our wills,
a simple failure. Children: the strong lie
to bind your freedom, complicate all life,
put art in second place—or give it meaning?
What meaning could man see who saw the whole
in its mad quantities, the greater part
cloaked and enwrapped in dark, unguessable
deeps of subconscious? How tiny was the surface
that could be seen and known—a treacherous scum
over the boiling or the stagnant ooze
that was life's sum, opaque and fathomless.
The wisdom lay in knowing that one knew
and could know nothing: the illogical
accepted as the course, the core of meaning.
Children: one had them or one did not have them;
the folly was to say it was the will
that so dictated: what gave orders then
to the scum of will?
                              As suddenly again
his mind revolted and he said, "Oh, rubbish!
I'm getting sentimental and confused,
a mystic rubberneck."
                              Opening the door
he saw Serena just as he'd imagined.
What prescience! he thought, and smiled. The smile
could serve two purposes.

PASSING the Lamys' house he slowed his car
and brought it to a stop. The girl was standing
alone on the front lawn, a pair of clippers
glinted in silvery metal in her hand,
a garden basket on her other arm.
Lucky, thought Mallin. He called out to her,
saying, "Good morning, Jennifer."

She waved
and walked across the lawn and to the road,
to the car's side: grace moving, sweep of youth,
sweep of desire, desire personified.
The clear young voice said, "Hello, Mr. Mallin,
you have got going early."

"To the city,
the big, bad city. Wish I didn't have to,
on such a day. Ah, well, God will reward me,
I'm going to speak for Quintus to old Peckett."
"The hospital?" she said.

"The hospital.
He's the key man. You'd better wish me luck."
"I do," she said. "How long before you know?"
"I just might know when I get back," he said.
"I'm to see Quintus then."

"Yes, I remember."
"Will you be there?" he said.

"Oh, can I come?"
"Of course you can. How is your mother, Jenny?"
Jennifer shrugged her shoulders and she said,
"She had a bad night. She's O.K. this morning,
or so it seems. Better, at any rate."
"Tell her to come too, if she's up to it,"
Rochester said. "Let's say at half-past five,
tea or a drink. All three of you." He paused.
"Did young Standeven come?"

"He came," she said;
her voice was dry. "He came down late last night,
while we were at the Hearing."

"Bring him too,
if he'd be interested."

"Thank you," she said.

198

"I'll ask him if I see him."
                         "Won't you see him?"
Jennifer laughed. "I really couldn't tell you.
He's left, he'd gone out, sometime before breakfast,
and left no word."
                    Rochester smiled at her.
"Isn't that rather odd?" he said.
                                  "Oh, no.
He comes and goes, he comes and goes. His plans
are rather sudden."
                    "Where do you think he went?"
"Haven't the least idea," she said.
                                    He noticed
complete detachment, almost a total lack
of any interest in the young girl's voice.
It gave him pleasure.
                      "Look," he said to her.
"How about showing me the work tomorrow?
Sunday's a good day."
                      "Oh," she said. "I'd love to,
but Harlow may be here, he hasn't said,
and I've a sort of date with Quintus, too,
to dig pipsissewas and pitcher-plants
for the rock garden. We'd have gone today,
or so I'd understood, but Q has left.
Tomorrow's complicated."
                         "He has left?"
"Left early after breakfast. Gone to his office.
He won't be back till late."
                             "On Saturday?"
"He says he's so behind on all his work—
I wish he'd take it easier."
                             "He should,"
Rochester said.
                "Mother felt ill," she said.
"Upset him. When he gets upset he drives
back at his work. I never even saw him,
he'd eaten so early. He just left a note."
"I see," said Rochester. "Now I really wish
I didn't have to go to Providence.

199

Would have been fun to stay, to see your work."
He paused and smiled. "Have had a date with you."
"Yes, it's too bad," she said. "I'm awfully sorry
about tomorrow, too."

"Well, Monday, then—
come Monday after lunch. How would that suit?"
"Oh, fine," she said. "I'd love that. No class Monday,
Mensinger is in Boston."

"Good," he said.
"Come about half-past two."

A voice inside him
said, 'Strike while the iron is hot.'

"Jenny," he said,
"why not come up to Providence with me now.
Haven't you got some shopping? I'm alone.
I'd love some company."

The girl looked down,
then up at him and smiled. The smile was charming;
the look, he saw at once to his amusement,
was wholly calculating.

"I'd adore to, really,"
Jennifer said, "and I need company too.
But I can't do it, Mummy's still in bed,
Q is away, I've got to chauffeur Eddie
and do the flowers, and I don't dare leave
Mummy alone. Q asked me not to leave her.
Oh, dear, I'd so have loved to go with you!
Ask me next time you're going up there, will you?
I would have loved to, Mr. Mallin, truly."
"Too bad," he said. "We'll try another time.
So dull alone. Jenny, would it annoy you
to call me Rochester? I feel so old,
this Mr. Mallin business. Now you have grown up,
you are a woman now."

"Why, no, I'd like to."
Again the smile, the look—but now the look
more confident, less calculating.

"Good."
Rochester said. "That pleases me. Good-bye,

see you this afternoon, then, Jenny."

"Right,
this afternoon."

"We'll drink to it," he said.
"I'll need it," Jenny said. She took her hand
from the car door and backed a step away.
"So long then, Rochester."

"Au revoir," he said.

All the way up to Cottrellton he drove
carefully, slowly, but with his conscious mind
turned now to Jennifer.

Not bad, he thought,
a good beginning. What have I begun?
Where could it lead? Must everything then lead
to something else, or could a thing exist
but in itself? Existing in itself,
divorced from all else, there was here a surge
of living felt, warm, urgent, stimulating.
What harm, to whom? Serena? Did you take
something away where there was nothing now?
Harlow Standeven? There is nothing there,
or I am wide of the mark. No, I am right,
nothing there either: thus, nothing is destroyed.
Quintus? Take what? Or was this all imagined
by my own need, my hunger, emptiness?
No, not imagined, wholly. Surely not.
Did I not see and feel: the electric thing
woven already between him and her?
Will it not grow and act and be? And so,
that will cause harm?

But yet in honesty
I cannot say I'm moving now from any
fine Christian motive. It is but to know
that my own good is no one else's harm:
if it does good—perhaps as a by-product—
so much the better.

Well, I shall pursue it.
The word pursue tripped him: his mind went back

to the morning's thoughts.
                              Will you indeed pursue?
You, the male-female? Or expect it all
to happen as it happens, or be pursued—
by someone like this woman?
                              But I did it:
I did begin pursuit, not badly done,
the personal note, the date, the almost got
ride up to Providence, and Rochester
for Mr. Mallin.
                    But in the studio,
alone, the pictures seen, the happily
genuine interest turned toward Jenny's work,
the possible simple thing: the older artist
helping the younger not to help himself,
but to pay back his debt to his own start
when others aided? Would it merely be
this sort of thing, by his own feminine
cowardice of the lack of the aggressive,
fear of rebuff, the passionate, fatal need
to be required, wanted? Was not this
what bound him to Serena? Could there be
escape to life, the passionate act of life,
the vital sense of living, while the spirit
cringed from refusal? Could not act, but waited
passive for other's act.
                          Now suddenly
the thought of Jennifer held warmly close,
the intimate small touches, the desired
kiss, the release of energy, as love
released in passion, swept his mind and spirit
and he was flooded with a great well-being
and spoke, aloud, saying, "By God, I'll do it,
I'll find the pluck, I'll find the way, it's there,
it needs but some small touchstone to succeed.
I'll find that too."
                    Without the least transition
his mind began to plot the book he wrote;
the hard and deadly problem that had blocked
his work to blankness yesterday, was soon

202

forgotten in solution, easy, clear,
logical and—again the sense of living—
moving in essence.

               Is this not a reason?
His mind spoke now. Is it not this I've lacked,
this key to art is but the key to being,
and only I can count where I'm involved:
the I is work, production: I is art,
why should I then not honor this?

                            The blue
waters of the South Harbor told his mind
that this was Cottrellton. He found himself
happy to do his day, to be his day,
that would conclude with Jennifer: one more step
of fruitful progress, one more move to live,
to be, to do.

                 To hell with everyone!
Rochester thought. For are they, any of them,
more needful than myself or for a better
or yet more cogent reason?

                     Now he drove
slowly and consciously down between the pretty
houses of Water Street and stopped his car
in front of Jacob Ledbetter's.

□□□□□□

FEELING successful,
Rochester went in the store. There were several people
already there. The two clerks both were busy
and so was Jacob. One of the clerks came by him
and said, "Good morning, Mr. Mallin. Be free
in just a minute."

               Rochester said, "Good morning,
I want to speak to your boss. I'm in no hurry.
I'll wait."

            Ledbetter heard him and looked up
from what he was doing, nodded, and went right back
to the work in hand.

            Rochester half sat down

on the hard counter's edge to wait: you couldn't
hurry a man like Jacob, no matter the reason—
not even a fire. Waiting, he listened idly
to the clear, determined, the unrevealing voices.
They spoke of passionless needs.
                                When Jacob came,
he brought a catalogue, open, its brightly colored
pages showed red machinery and improbable
cloudless blue skies and the acidulous green
of printer's trees and the harsh yellow fields
of a grain that never was. The fields were flat
and endless, they said Nebraska or possibly Kansas:
but there could be no small and walled New England
in such wide pages.
                    "It's pretty small," said Jacob
without preamble. His finger pointed then
to the picture of a tractor. "But you can get it
within the month, with the snow-plow attachment,
and all of such winter gear. The cutter-bar
is ready too to deliver. The whole thing's small.
The one you really need—" he turned the pages—
"is this here tractor. But I can't get it for you
till January or could be February,
the orders have piled up so. And it costs more money,
the prices are all in the back. Two hundred twenty,
the difference is. It carries a larger cutter.
It's jest a question, then, do you want to pay
the extra money and be more satisfied—
in the long run, of course—and have to delay,
or take the small one now?"
                            Rochester said,
"I see. But are there no other makes to choose from?"
"Plenty," said Jacob. "But always the same story.
The ones is good, is rugged, won't fall apart
and eat you up with repairs, you got to wait
four to six months for. Why, I got ten orders
here at this moment, and I jest can't fill 'em.
So many goes, they say, out to foreign countries,
and so many farmers at home want new machines,
wore out the old in war time. That's the story.

You take the catalogue with you, you want to study,
I got another."
                    "Thank you, I will," said Mallin.
"I'm off to Providence, lunching with Harold Peckett,
the hospital business. It just might be he'd know
the people who run this factory and could say
a word to them. Perhaps we could cut a corner,
could get the bigger one early. And, if I can,
of course it'll come through you."
                    "Now you jest get it,"
Ledbetter said. "It makes no difference,
thing is to get it. Don't worry none about me.
This is the best make, seems so, for this country."
"Right," said Rochester. "Anyway, I'll try it.
Let you know Monday how I fared."
                    "You do that,"
Ledbetter said. "There anything else you wanted?"
"No, no thanks," said Rochester. "Quite a meeting
we had last night. A tough thing to decide.
Some said it was white, and then the other said,
no, it was black. Oh, yes, it was a store,
or Oh, no, it wasn't. Who is to be believed?"
Jacob folded the catalogue slowly shut
and he handed it to Mallin, and he said,
"Puts me in mind of a time, a long time back,
I sat on a jury. Sort of a civil action.
Man was suing to dispossess a farmer
for unpaid rent on a farm. Two months of rent.
Showed his bank books, covering all the thirty
months that he'd leased the farm. There was deposits
for every month, the exact amount of the rent,
except for them two months. I can recollect
they was April and June and was pretty well toward the
            end
of the time accounted. Tenant, he claimed he'd paid
all of the thirty months. He showed receipts
for twenty-eight of 'em, all save the ones was missing
for April and June. He said he'd paid them months,
and had never got one receipt and had wrote for it,
and had lost the other. He didn't have no copy

of the letter, a farmer, jest how it usually is.
They got no love for paper work, never have,
and more of it than they need today, I reckon.
Funny sort of a case."
                              "Did you decide it?"
"Yes," said Jacob. "We found for the tenant farmer."
"You did?" said Rochester and he showed surprise
clear in his voice. "But as you tell the story,
the evidence pointed to prove the landlord's story."
"Well, I tell you," said Jacob slowly, flatly,
"there was more to it. The farmer, he was a young man,
he'd sort of dallied around with the landlord's wife,
and the landlord got to know it. The same time, too,
or a little before the time of the two missing
months of the rent. Made us believe the farmer."
"Gives more reason, to my mind, to the landlord
for dispossessing."
                              "Guess that'd be for divorce,
not for a dispossess," said Jacob. "All a man
can do in a case like that is set and listen
and judge which one of the two who says, like you say,
the thing is black or the thing is white, has most
reason to lie about it. Or so we thought."
"I see," said Rochester. "Now you've got to decide
the same thing here? Who did in fact have most
reason to lie, you judge?"
                              "It's that," said Jacob,
"we got to decide. If you'll excuse me now,
I got some folks is waiting."
                              "O.K.," said Mallin.
"Thanks for the catalogue. Give you a ring on Monday,
if I can't get in here."
                              "That'll be fine," said Jacob.
"The little tractor's sturdy, it's jest I reckon
it's kinder light for you." He turned at once
and walked to a waiting woman.
                              Rochester left.
There was nothing more he could say, and he felt annoyed.
God, he thought, you just can't make these people
commit themselves to any sort of opinion.

206

Outside, his annoyance left him: the perfect day,
the thought (half-had) of Jennifer, made him feel
happy again and he found himself, of a sudden,
laughing to think of the farmer who had dallied
with his landlord's wife. Who else today would call it
dally except for Jacob?

THE HOUSE looked well when he got home. The flowers
were beautifully done, the vases held
the happy mix of dahlias and of asters,
yellow of sassafras leaf, and there was even
a bowl of roses. Lucky for October;
there'd been no killing frost.

It was near six
and lamps in the living room were lit. The dusk
was blue through windows and the diffusing veil
of yellow light.

Serena sat on the sofa
behind a coffee table which held the tray
of usual glasses, bottles, silver urn-bowl
of the bright cubes of ice. She looked contented.
Serene Serena, Rochester thought.

Beside her
sat Quintus Lamy. He saw the man's expression
was drawn and tired, and his face seemed grey
under his dark tan. He wore the flannel
trousers, the homespun coat he usually
wore to his work. Serena also wore
clothes of the garden's day.

On a wooden chair
Jennifer sat. He noticed first her color
enhancing beauty and proclaiming youth,
and then her dress. It was obvious she'd changed—
for the occasion? He felt a spasm of pleasure
until he thought, for Quintus, or for me?
No matter. Time would tell.

"Good!" said Rochester.
"How nice you're all here. Good to see you, Quintus,

and welcome, Jennifer. The flowers, Serena,
are excellent as always."
                        So there followed
the usual moves: the risings and the hand-clasps,
the simple greetings, the sitting down again,
the what will you drink and passing of the nuts,
the cocktail crackers. It was so normal
that Mallin was surprised he felt a tension
lying over the room: slight, without visible
evidence, but perceptible. They'd been silent
as he came in the room. Why not? How could they
have failed to hear his coming?
                        They were all
seated again, with drinks. Rochester turned
to Jennifer.
            "Jenny," he said, "you didn't
bring Harlow with you."
            "No," she said. "I didn't,
he hadn't come home when I left."
                        "No word?"
"No word. Isn't it funny, Mr. Mallin,
he didn't come back for lunch."
                        "It is," he said.
"But Mr. Mallin, Jenny?" He turned to Quintus.
"I begged your child—no, not a child, a woman—
your daughter here to call me Rochester.
The mister ages me beyond my wish."
"God knows you still look young enough," said Quintus.
"She first-names me."
                        Jennifer said, "I'm sorry.
Let me get used to it, that's all."
                        Serena
smiled at the girl and said, "Of course, dear Jenny,
it always takes a moment. But now, you see,
you'll have to call me by my first name too.
I can't be Mrs. Mallin to his Rochester,
and anyway, I'd love it. Is that too hard?"
Well done, thought Mallin.
                        "Oh, no, I'd love to, really.
Truly I would," said Jenny.
    208

"Good," said Serena.
"A pleasant change. Now, Rochester, come on,
don't keep us dangling. What's the word from Peckett?"
Rochester drank first and then said, "All good.
It's practically certain, Quintus. It's all yours.
I found him tractable. They'll get in touch
with you directly now. The job will run
bigger than we anticipated. I think
you'll have to scale the fee down. But all that
comes later. I am very pleased."
                           "And I.
That's really good news. Thank you very much,
it makes a difference," Quintus said. He spoke
so softly it was difficult to hear him.
But not Serena. She cried out, "Oh, splendid!
Oh, I'm so glad! So glad for you, dear Quintus,
and for Virginia too." She touched his arm,
briefly, affectionately, and she smiled and said,
still looking at Quintus, "Any trouble, Roche,
or were they ready for him?"
                           "They were ready.
The groundwork had been laid. I showed the plans
for our Barn too, they liked them. Peckett had
two other men to lunch, both were trustees.
They were impressed."
                           "Oh, my!" Serena said.
"This makes me happy! So, let's drink to it.
The hospital job, for Quintus, may it add
to fame and fortune!" She raised up her glass,
and Rochester and Jenny followed suit.
"Here's luck to it—no contretemps at all—
smooth sailing and no rows," Rochester said.
"To you, dear Q," said Jenny.
                           The three drank.
"Speech!" said Serena. "Speech now!"
                           Lamy turned
and smiled with wonderful sweetness at her then
and said, "I can't. I'm speechless. It's too good.
I hadn't dared to hope, it meant too much."
"Virginia'll be so pleased," Serena said.
209

"Yes," Lamy answered.

"What an awful pity
Virginia isn't here," said Rochester.
"How is she, Quintus?"

Lamy stirred a little,
heaved his wide shoulders, sat a little straighter
on the deep sofa.

"Better, thanks," he said.
"Or seems to be. I haven't seen her yet,
I came straight here. Jenny can tell you better
than I can, I'm afraid."

The girl looked at him,
a faintly quizzical smile lighting her face,
and said, "She's better. She came down for lunch.
She was a little upset at Harlow's absence,
she seemed to worry. But she stayed downstairs
till about four. There's been no pain today."
"Thank God for that," said Quintus. "Where was
        Harlow?"
"Haven't the least idea," said Jenny. Indifference
was clear in her young voice. "I said already
he left no word. He didn't take his car.
He's just walked off."

Serena said, "That's odd.
Considering he came down to see you."

"Did he?"
Jennifer said. "I wonder. He told Mummy
he came to study for his Hour Exams.
But when I made his bed up after breakfast,
his note books and his books were still stacked high
on Lanier's desk."

"Perhaps he had some others,"
Serena said.

"Perhaps he had," said Jenny.
"If so, he brought along half of the contents
of Harvard's libraries." She laughed, and drank
from her tall glass.

All good, thought Rochester,
all awfully good.

"Well, never mind," said Quintus.

"He'll turn up for his supper. A perfect day,
hard to stay cooped up studying."
                              "But alone?"
Rochester spoke it softly. "But alone?"
(Strike while the iron is hot.)
                         Serena said,
"Well, let it go. Who'll have another drink?
I will for one, dear." She held out her glass.
"Never a finer, lovelier excuse
to have another drink."
                         Rochester took
her glass, said, "Quintus? Jennifer? Some more?"
"No more, but thanks," said Quintus. "I must go,
I haven't been home yet. I must tell Virginia."
"Of course you must," Serena said. "Of course."
Mallin filled up his own glass and his wife's.
He could feel disappointment running through him,
Jennifer now would have to go. The moment—
bought at day's cost of effort—threatened now
to disappear too soon. Something was lacking,
some climax. As he gave the filled and bright
glass to Serena, suddenly his mind
saw the new opening.
                         "One more thing," he said.
"This hospital is going to take some nursing—
you know that, Quintus, dealing with a board,
a group of men. I've taken on that job—
took it when I decided to join them."
                              "Good of you,"
said Lamy.
          "No," said Mallin. "Amuses me,
Providence always does. The point I'm making
is simply it takes time. My book's behind,
but now it's moving, finally, thank God—
I'm past the hump. But I must stick at it,
or all momentum's lost."
                         Quintus, his face
almost expressionless, nodded his head
and said, "I know."
                    "All right," said Rochester.

"Then what will help me is if, for the time,
you'll simply leave me out about the Barn,
deal with Serena. It has really now
come to the point where all the major problems
have been decided. The rest are minor things.
We have seen eye to eye, Serena knows
precisely how I feel. If she is bothered,
well, she can ask me, certainly—but at times
when I am free. So I would like to give
my vote to her now. I'm quite confident,
and always have been, in her taste and knowledge—
indeed, the thing, in embryo, was more hers
than mine, at that. Is that all right with you,
and you, Serena?"
                    "Sure," said Lamy. "Sure.
If that suits both of you then it suits me."
"Dear Quintus!" said Serena. "Will you take
my odd vagaries, my female yes and no,
and not go mad, poor man?"
                    "Don't listen to her,"
Rochester said. "She knows her mind, that woman."
"She does," said Quintus. "Good."
                    "Then that's agreed?"
"Agreed," said Quintus.
                    "Lovely," said Serena.
"One more excuse to see my favorite cousin—
but cousin by marriage, luckily." She looked
straight at him then, and put her pretty hand
softly, almost possessively over his,
squeezed once and then, with the same hand again,
took up her glass and drank. "So, to the Barn,
and our collaboration."
                    Rochester turned
from watching her just in good time to see
the curious shadow show on Jenny's face:
hard to define, but still a shadow there,
some feeling stirred . . . deliberately perhaps,
wilfully by Serena?
                    Clever, he thought,
she's always clever. But it worked, it worked.

212

Now when he watched Quintus pull up his body
heavily from the sofa, while they all stood,
while all the usual good-byes were said,
he sensed completion: they could go, the future
already promised—something. There was not
the awful blankness now. Now he could watch
the grace of Jennifer, youth's grace, liquid the movement,
fluid desire, woman concentrated
into the shape of only woman: all
with patience in delight.
                          Or in pursuit?

□□□□□□

THE EVENING at the Messlers was successful,
good food, good wine. Loretta Messler cooked
the dinner in the modern combination
of kitchen-living room. The hours passed easily
without a sense of pressure. Rochester
liked the two guests, the man intelligent,
the woman giving him a close attention
most flattering. Serena, at her best,
led up to him in talk about his work.
It had been easy and wonderfully relieving
to hold forth on it, to be questioned onward
at each pause to new areas of intention,
of past and present, even future schemes.
There'd been no cards: the talk had flourished so
in ambient hours.
                    The ringing telephone
cut hard across their mood. While Jimmy Messler
answered it in another room, the five
made desultory talk. Mallin looked down:
his watch said past eleven. It was late
for calls in such a quiet neighborhood,
particularly October.
                       While they waited—
pretending not to wait—Rochester tasted
his day in secret pleasure: the hospital,
Jennifer in the morning and the evening,

213

the Barn, the evening, the flooding, lovely sense
of work to do that one knew how to do,
of days ahead.

Messler came back to them.
Rather abruptly, in a flatter statement
than was his usual, he stood to say,
"Well, that was Lamy."

"Quintus?" said Serena.
"Something about Virginia. Is she ill?"
The man turned his head slowly and he looked
down at Serena.

"She's upset," he said,
his voice still flat. He drew his breath in full
and thrust his hands in his pockets. "It would seem
this time she has a reason." Then he grinned
and said, "Sorry, Serena. No, he called up—
says he's called everyone hereabouts—to ask
if by some wild chance I had seen or heard
of the Standeven boy."

"He hasn't come back?"
Serena cried.

"Oh, you have heard?" said Messler.
"No. Hasn't come back, there's been no word. I gather
he didn't take his car. Virginia's worried,
and I'd say Lamy had begun to feel
something was odd." He turned then to his guests,
the other couple, and he said, "The boy's
Harlow Standeven, he came down last night
to spend the week-end, Quintus Lamy says,
but left before breakfast, didn't take his car,
no note or anything. Wasn't home for lunch
or even dinner, and is still away,
and no one's seen him. Must say it does seem
peculiar business."

Serena said, "No wonder
Virginia's troubled. And Quintus is worn out—
he's worked too hard." She turned to Rochester
and said, "What can we do?"

Rochester felt

a sense of power, of confidence. He said,
at once, "It's late now, near eleven-thirty.
Not much to do, and probably there's some simple
answer to all of it. But even so,
we'll pop along now, Jimmy, and stop in
at Lamy's as we go. It does you good
to talk things over. Myself, I shouldn't worry—
Harlow's a man grown, must be twenty-four,
fought in the Navy, both in the Pacific
and at the Italian landings. He can take
care of himself here in South County, surely.
No danger here."
                    "Yes, let's stop by their house,"
Serena said. "You're so right, Rochester.
Probably too, there is no need to worry,
it's just these young men, ones who went to war . . .
and then that long time in the Italian
prisons, too . . . you don't know. So—so abnormal,
the early years." She rose then. "Such a lovely
evening, Loretta."
                    The good-byes were said,
the kind, the pretty, and the meaningless
small leaving phrases, and the Mallins left
into the cold, clear night.
                    "The Pleiades
are bright and high," said Rochester.
                              "Yes," she said.
"October night. I wish I hadn't taken
quite so much wine, and then the brandy after.
We'll need our wits."
                    "I never saw you lose them,"
Rochester said. The cool air touched his skin
with sensuous pleasure. Would Jennifer be up?
That would be pleasant. Then inside himself
he said, I'll fix them up, I guess it's just
that sort of day—a day to fix things up.

Jenny was up. She wore the selfsame dress
of golden yellow wool. She looked as fresh

215

as though she'd just got up from sleep. The others
seemed old and tired by contrast.
                              Virginia sat
in her uncomfortable, arthritic pose
on the big sofa, Serena sat beside her.
Looking at both, Rochester saw the power,
the commonly hidden vitality of his wife;
but he saw the lines, too, graven in her face:
sympathy now, and somewhat of concern,
and something too of age. Lamy looked grey,
his hair untidy and unbrushed.
                              And I?
Rochester thought. How do I look? Against
them and against young beauty?
                              ". . . and really nothing,"
Quintus was saying. "Harlow's old enough
to look out for himself. We can't go calling
the State Police because he didn't come
home to his dinner."
                              "He didn't take his car,"
Virginia said. Her deep-pitched, husky voice
was curiously beautiful and contained
always emotion, no matter what she said.
"Where could he go, on foot?"
                              "God knows," said
     Quintus.
"I think I've called up everyone he knew
and some he didn't—tried to be casual,
though in this place they'll put it all together
and make some odd thing of it. Well, it's odd.
But no one saw him, no one, all day long.
Where can you go round here and not be seen
by someone—unless you hide yourself in woods
or something equally unlikely?"
                              "Yes,"
Virginia said. "That's it. Where would you go?
What was he doing?"
                              Serena put her hand
over Virginia's and she said, "You saw him?"
Quintus said, "She's the only one who did.
216

He was in bed when we got home."

Rochester
saw Jenny turn her head and look at Quintus,
and, troubled by his own incomprehension,
saw the faint, almost imperceptible
blush that arose upon her face, and watched
as she turned away, looked down.

Virginia spoke.
"He called from Cambridge, said he had to study,
had Hour Exams. He said he wished to come
to be away from Harvard, in South County.
He'd drive, he would be late. I was awake
when he came in, I heard him and I called.
He came and talked a moment. He was tired,
he looked it, too. But he was sweet as always,
seemed happy to be here. I asked him then
if there was anything he wanted done,
people or things. He thanked me and said no,
but just to be ignored, he'd come to study.
But if he found time, too, to see the autumn,
to see the countryside."

"That was all he said?"
Serena asked.

"That's all," Virginia answered.
"Except he said, so sweetly, warmingly,
it did him good to be here, it was like
being at home. It touched me. Then he said
good night and went to bed. I haven't seen him
since then at all. I didn't hear him go,
though I was wide awake by half-past six.
I don't know even that, what time he left."
"But he did sleep here?"

"Yes, so Jenny says."
"He'd been to bed," said Jennifer. "I know.
I had to make it up." Her voice was cool
and seemed to Mallin remarkably detached.
"It was so rumpled that it really looked
as though he'd had a love affair." She laughed.
"Jennifer!" said her mother.

"Well, it did.

Anyway, what's it all about? Why worry?
Harlow's a big boy now. Surely he must
be old enough to go round at night without
everyone worrying?"
          "Oh," Virginia said,
"but I am worrying. Look, Serena, dear,
I called his room-mate up, Paul Levering,
the one that he calls Fatso. Harlow brought him
here in the spring, such a nice, clever boy.
I asked him if he knew of anything
Harlow had had in mind. He said that Harlow
claimed he must study, but he didn't have to,
he knew the course already, inside out.
Levering said he thought he'd come for two
specific reasons. The first was to see Jenny."
"He goes about it oddly," Jenny said.
"Wait," said her mother. "The first was Jennifer,
he'd given up a huge big dance, a ball
last night in Boston, someone's coming out,
some twins as I remember."
          "The Leftwell twins,"
Jennifer said. "He told me, wrote about it.
That's why he said he wasn't coming down
on just this week-end. A terrific party,
he was so sorry."
          Mallin, with unease,
heard for the first time just the faintest tinge
of bitterness in her voice.
          "But still he came."
Jennifer made a gesture in the air
with her right hand. "What else did Fatso say?
What was the other reason?"
          "Levering said
he thought that Harlow was, well, not himself,
disturbed, troubled by something. He couldn't tell me
exactly what it was—the telephone
is such a poor thing for such talk. He said
that Harlow wanted just to be here, looking
for something in himself, perhaps some answer
to what was troubling him. That's all he said,

218

he wasn't more specific. It is this
that makes me worry."
                    There was silence
till Quintus broke it, saying very softly,
"He's insecure."
                    But then Rochester knew
what he should say to them. "Look here," he said.
"It's long past midnight. The whole thing has grown
to disproportionate size. You're busy making
mountains of molehills. Forgive me if I say
it's all ridiculous. You will see it so
in the good light of morning. Here's a man—
man, I repeat—he's fought in the Pacific,
he fought in Italy, he was captured there,
escaped from prison camp, lived out alone
among Italian partisans, made his way
through Italy, through the Fascists and the Germans,
to Switzerland. Returns when war is over
and goes, belatedly, maturer though,
to finish Harvard. What's the shooting for?
He took a long walk. Ten to one he met
some pal, or else some fellow veterans.
They had a drink. It was a perfect day.
Maybe the pal, or pals, were driving somewhere—
Providence, or New London, even New York—
who knows, or cares? Harlow is probably
happily plastered in some good warm bar
and loving it. Studies? The hell with studies!
There is Sunday still. I wouldn't be surprised
if he got back here late tomorrow, maybe
after his lunch, a little bit hung-over,
his tail a little bit between his legs,
and still quite happy. Let it go, my friends,
it's not worth troubling over."
                    Quintus smiled.
"You may be right," he said. "We're tired,
it's night. We let it grow, exaggerate.
Thanks for the common sense."
                    "No," said Virginia.
"No, no. You're wrong. The boy's not been the same

since he came home. It was those prison camps,
or something in that time. He's sensitive,
so like his mother. There is something wrong—
I don't know what it is, but I just feel it,
deep in my bones."

        "If there was something wrong,"
Rochester said, "it's probably been purged
now by some whiskey." He got up to go.
"Come on, Serena. It's getting awfully late.
Let's sleep on this. Sunday's another day.
Harlow'll be back—hung-over. Want to bet?
I'll give you two to one."

        "Not me," said Quintus.
"Thanks, Roche. I guess you're right, sleep is the thing,"
and he rose too.

        Jennifer rose and laughed.
"Fatso will think it funny when he hears.
Methods of study. He might as well have stayed.
I'll bet there was champagne and lots of it,
at the big Leftwell party." She stretched and said,
"Tomorrow to fresh woods and pastures new.
Stop worrying, Mummy."

        But when the Mallins left,
Virginia was still seated on the sofa,
and showed her worry.

        Or was it, Mallin thought,
a trace of disappointment? Like the rest,
it could attend tomorrow.

□□□□□□

ROCHESTER woke before the maid had knocked
that Sunday morning.

        Opening his eyes,
he saw the day was perfect as before,
crystalline, blue, suffused with early sun,
and polished bright by faintest, coolest trace
of northwest breeze.

        A perfect day to ride,

his mind said to him.

      Then he thought of Harlow.
Curious! Now the common sense of night,
absence belittled into just a lark,
seemed unconvincing. Was Virginia right?
The sensitive and troubled. The alone.
The orphan-veteran: veteran of a prison—
the drunk with pals, not right?

        It was not right.
Where would he go then? Oh, I wish I knew,
I'd like to find him, like to get the story
clear in my mind. The young rejected lover?
But could you be rejected till the time
after you'd been accepted? At his age?
Had Jennifer accepted once? Accepted
what and how far?

      Ah, no, the author's greedy
mind that must gobble up, exaggerate!
There was no past there, it was just a present
without a future. So, think back again:
where would he go? And why?

        The insecure.
Was that his key? Life, love: no future,
or not yet to be seen, a drifting then,
disordered and unordered.

      Yes, unordered:
who had been ordered? Was not war an order
beyond comparison? Where do they seek
for order, these young men who have returned,
in the chaotic, diverse complexity
of civil ways?

    Myself, he thought, I'd fly
back to my parents—and be discontented
as soon as I was there, the ordering
too long outgrown. But Harlow had no parents.
Back to their memory?

      How did you go
back to a memory, all the day and night,
alone? By being alone, that could be it.

221

Alone at night, all night? The nights were cold,
it was October, there'd be shelter needed.
Well, build a fire.
                    Hell, Rochester said,
I'm growing fanciful. Harlow's probably
asleep in bed at Lamy's. But curious
that I should wake to fancy who advised
sleep from the fanciful.
                    There was the knock,
the maid's voice saying, "Eight o'clock, sir."
                                        Yes.
Eight by the clock, I'll ride then after lunch,
I'll be alone myself. How many years
since last Serena rode?
                    Does Jenny ride?
Pity she isn't free.

⊡⊡⊡⊡⊡⊡

NOW HE was riding.
The bay mare walked her nervous, jerky walk,
the air felt cold and clean. He was alone,
yet with companionship, the whole tiresome
morning behind him.
                    Breakfast with Serena,
and she'd looked drawn and tired, she had said
that she'd slept badly, fretted; that she'd called
and Harlow hadn't come, and still no word.
"Well," he had said, "that's still as I predicted.
He'll probably turn up in the afternoon
looking a little guilty."
                    "I hope," she'd said.
"I hope you're right. But not to call them up—
he's always had nice manners, Roche, he's thoughtful,
it isn't like him."
                    "Oh, my God," he'd said,
"we live such neat and ordered lives, there is
no room for venture, for the unexpected,
the happy, the delicious sudden thing
that's right outside the pattern. Give him room!

You can't tie youth down to an ordering
so hard and fast."
                              "I know," Serena'd said.
"I know, Roche. But it seems to me he's had
more than his share of sudden accidents,
the unexpected and the unforeseen—
he'd crave the orderly."
                              "Perhaps he would.
Let's leave it, anyway."
                              The morning then
followed its routine course: the gardening,
the plans for spring, the many small white tags
tied to the dahlias that anonymous
brown tubers might take order in the summer
in color's hierarchy. Pleasant enough.
The sun was warm, the ground smelled moist and sweet,
the flowers still bloomed in masses richly ranked
against the rise of green grass slope. But all,
all were the same, the repetitious acts
for a repeated purpose, year on year.
Oh, it was good to ride, to be alone,
to have not even plans of where to go
but start unthinking, see the things that came
because they came and not to search them out
in planful curiosity.
                              The soft air
was full of scent of the deciduous leaves
triumphantly to die in all the gold
and scarlet of their coronation-death
before the regency of bare winter's sleep.

So without thought or plan Rochester rode—
westerly always, across the pasture lands
now brightly green, through woods on ancient roads,
past Indigo Mill and finally along
the dirt road leading westward to Cross Bridge
at Naius River. All he thought was color:
yellow of birch and sassafras and walnut,
of the long leaves of the doomed chestnut sprouts,
the many reds of oaks still intermixed

223

with darker greens, the crimson and the orange
of all the maples, the pastel display
of poison ivy's many-colored leaves,
the blood of sumacs, and of tupelos
already partly bare. He rode suspended
in sense of color against clear autumn sky
that needs no thought, but is.
                                        Then suddenly
he saw the car parked, and his mind returned
to life around him. A familiar car:
the local taxi-limousine. It belonged
to Asa Congdon.
                          Reining in his mare,
he saw the car was empty, that it stood
a little off the road before the chained
and sagging gates of the Standeven place.
He was aware of the pervasive silence
of all the woods: it had the comfortless
still depth of people present but unseen
who yet may peer at you.
                                      But what took Asa
to the Standeven place and on Sunday, too?
The shooting season was not open yet,
and if it had been, he would not have come
here in the taxi. Curious sort of thing.
He turned his horse and rode her back along
the road he'd come: there was a little rise
of land there, in the old days one could see
the house from there, a vista carefully
cut through the trees. Now it was overgrown,
but still the house loomed faintly through the wealth
of many-colored leaves, and Rochester
could see the great stone chimney.
                                                    Was that smoke,
that thin and vaporous spiralling that rose
pearl grey from rosy grey? Asa had got in
and lit a fire? Why? The day was warm—
and anyway, what business took him there
to enter and light fires?
                                    It would be

interesting to discover why. And then
his mind leaped suddenly and he thought, has this
to do with Harlow? Had the boy come here?
This he must find out, now.
                              Not good to tether
the nervous mare by the roadside and with only
a rein to hold her. And the gate was closed
and padlocked shut. Slowly he rode along,
looked for a gap. The stones of the old wall
were still in place. Then he remembered
the barway to the pasture further on,
down nearer Cross Bridge, and he turned again
and trotted on until he came to it.
Still there, still standing up. So he dismounted,
slid out the bars, walked the mare through and mounted.
The pasture land was dotted now with cedars,
with clumps of bayberry, and catbriar grew
rankly around them. How soon the wilderness
swallowed man's work here!
                              Slowly, at a walk,
Rochester followed westward and then south,
a course dictated by the open spaces
between the tangles. Soon he saw the house
must lie now to the east, but all the woods
had grown so dense that it was fully hidden.
So he continued as the ancient pasture
allowed him, always southerly, till he saw
the grove of beeches and beyond the grove,
the flash of Naius River. Carefully,
ducking the branches of young maples now,
he made his way to the beech grove. It would be
a good place to dismount and tether to;
none would disturb here.
                              Once again dismounted,
he felt the silence of the sun-infused
dry afternoon surround him. In the distance
crows cawed; nearer there was the rattle
of a kingfisher by the river's bank. They made
the silence deeper. Such a lonely silence
seemed now unnatural, tense.

He tied the mare
to the first beech tree at the southern edge,
and climbed the steep small rise on which they spread
their wide and pallid branches, till he reached
their northern end. Now he could see the bog
stretched out before him, he could see the high
grey walls of house, formal with flaking white
of prim pilasters, window trim, the dark
green of yew hedges around the former garden,
the brilliant music of the sumac leaves
where flowers once answered, the maples giving way
to the inviting softness of white pines
as land rose to the westward and beyond
the richness of the flat bog, and the high
knoll to the northwest crowned with its great oak,
huge spread of branches over yellow sparks
on the whips of small birch.
                              Standing very still
he listened: nothing. Letting his eyes move
slowly and carefully he looked: still nothing.
Or nothing human, only the great brown
wings of a marsh hawk planing in the sun
above the shadowed bog. Even as he watched,
the hawk went out of sight, the shadow grew
longer perceptibly. He did not know
how long he stood so, silent, motionless,
awaiting something, not as yet aware
he was awaiting, could not move to search,
but must stand rooted.
                              But then he heard the calls,
the male voice crying "Harlow!" and a pause,
and again "Harlow!" and the swift following
of the female voice, the same word, cast in silver
against the gold of afternoon.
                              Where were they?
Who were they? But he could not see at first,
stood an interminable time to peer
first here, then there.
                              He did not see or hear
the young man who, wholly impervious

226

to the actual world, but higher strung to sense
all movement and all presence, once approached
the edge of the beech grove, heard the soft and ruffled
breath of the horse and turned and disappeared
in the bog's tangle, crawling inch by inch
toward self-made safety.
                          But now Rochester
saw a man move in the relic of the garden
and knew him: Asa Congdon. Asa moved
down toward the yew hedge, stopped, looked all around
and lit a cigarette. The smoke was seen.
Rochester watched him, but the man just stood,
looked first here, then there, as himself had looked.
But from the house now others came: two women—
distant and hard to recognize—no, wait,
the big and heavy woman, Anna Hall;
the smaller—Hetty Browne? It must be they.
What were they doing here?
                          Minute by minute
the whole became more queer, and he could feel
his earlier sense of tension, of some thing
heavily imminent, grow.
                          His ear detected
the sharp clear whistle of a woodcock's wings,
and then he saw it—it flew erratically
toward him from northeast and the bird then took
a quick turn, fluttered, settled in the dense
bushes of the near bog. It did not rise;
so, nothing there: but someone started it,
out of the high ground over there? He looked
back whence the bird had come.
                          And then his eye
was caught by movement—there, northeasterly,
under the huge white oak, a man and woman—
had they been there before? So motionless
he had not seen them? Seen the brown and grey
of soft and autumn clothes? And then his heart
constricted in a spasm, hurtfully,
because he knew them.
                          Knew them? Ah, one knows

227

the outer shell, the surface's appearance,
the common tag and label of a name,
the timbre of voice, the accent and the diction,
some hint of occupation, of a skill—
what else?   You say, I saw him standing there,
his name is Quintus Lamy, and beside him
I saw her standing, her name is Jennifer,
she's his step-daughter, she wants to be a painter,
he is an architect, he's known to many
as a good man, a kind one, who is patient
in love and care of a neurotic wife
whose body's ill. Yes, it is Quintus Lamy,
Jennifer Messler, twenty years of age
lying between them, and they turn and kiss
and the whole passion of it, the intense
pose of the world forgotten in that act,
the selves for this one instant wholly fused
into the mutual, the oblivious,
the craving for a unity of flesh—
what do you know of this? You, Rochester,
who would be in his place? With thirty years
to stand between you?   Do you know yourself,
is even the name you give yourself a cheat
in ignorant illusion?   So he stood
frozen in his attention, all time forgotten,
watching the lovers motionless to play
their distant, perfect pantomime clear lit
by the westering sun.   And then the kiss was over,
the lovers stood apart—as lovers now?—
and moved and turned and in a moment more
the birches swallowed them and their intention,
and there was void and the yellow dotted leaves
and the oak's grandeur, but unpeopled now,
its branches widely spread to cover over
what had so briefly been.   But there were people.

228

Released, his head turned now, he saw their group:
Asa and the old women, they were posed
as though in eager or earnest conversation—
what had they seen? Did they not face the knoll
the oak made his? From where they stood together,
could they have seen, or did the yew, the thick
young growth of sumac cover up the play
of passion in the slanted yellowing light
of October afternoon?
                              He did not know,
he could not tell. He only knew he wished
urgently and unreasoning to be gone,
to ride away, unheard and all unseen,
to be away from here, to have the time
to think untrammelled, unconfused by force
of their near presence.
                              So he left, retracing
his path of entry, rode the long way home
by Cross Bridge lest he have to pass the car
and meet them there, too soon, before the time
of this digested. As he rode, he felt
his tension leave, the humor of the whole
possessed him, and he laughed and took the mare
into an easy canter, felt the cool
air of the evening delicious to his face,
felt strength flow into him, and thought, at last,
is not such knowledge power?
                              Life seemed full
to Rochester riding narrow roads toward home—
toward future doing. Harlow was forgotten.

□□□□□□

AS HE AWOKE on Monday, Rochester
recalled the incident of last night. It would
be good to know the sequel.
                              As they'd sat,
he and Serena, reading after dinner,
the telephone had rung, and she had gone
to the other room to answer. All he'd heard

was her excitement, could not piece together
the sense of it from her words. She had come back,
stood in the doorway.

"Harlow's found," she said.
"Found?" said Rochester. "What do you mean, he's
found?"
"Just that," she said. "But that is all I know.
That was Virginia, she was incoherent,
I guess a *crise des nerfs*, I must go over,
she wants me there."

"But Harlow's back again?"
"No, at the Westerns', Jerome found him lying
by the road in Olney, over near his place,
and took him to his own house."

"Did he now?
And why not to the Lamys'?"

"I don't know.
I'll find out when I get there, but I gather
that that's what's troubling her. I think the boy
is ill or something. Anyway, I'll go."
"Yes, do," he said. "Do you think that you'll be long?"
"How can I tell, dear? I shall have to stay
as long as she may need me. If this makes her
ill or brings on the pain . . . I just don't know.
Don't wait up, Roche. There's nothing you can do,
not at the moment. Go to bed and rest,
I'll see you in the morning. I expect
she just needs comforting, a woman near.
Jennifer'd be no use. Perhaps herself
upset by this too. Sleep well, I'll be home
as soon as possible. I'll telephone
if I need your help."

"All right, do that," he said.
"It all sounds screwy to me."

"Doesn't it?
But let's wait till we know."

And she had left.
Not hearing from her, he had gone to bed,
read there a little, but still she'd not returned.
So he'd put out his light. Sleep had not come

soon to him then, too many threads, too bright,
for the busy mind to weave: they would not make
coherent pattern.
                 Nor would they make it now
in the cool overcast of a grey morning.
So he rose, eager to meet his wife, to hear
the story of this complex, a little angry
because it threatened to upset his day,
the anticipated, the wanted day. Would he
be caught up in all this? Would Jennifer
come as they'd planned? How many damnable
small accidents upset the careful schemes
of one's intelligence!
                      Serena sat as always
at the breakfast table, but he saw she looked
tired and drawn. And old. Hard age for women,
where looks no longer could withstand the lack
of sleep's good restoration.
                            "Well," he said,
"good morning. I hope you finally got to bed.
I was awake till half-past one myself
and hadn't heard you then."
                           "Oh, no," she said.
"I got in about half-past two. I stayed
till the sedatives took hold. Virginia slept
well after that. I've called the house already,
she's still asleep, thank goodness."
                                    "Good," he said.
"Well, what went on? My curiosity
is at the boiling point."
                         "Of course," she said.
"I'll tell you all I know. It isn't much,
whole gaps of knowledge yet.
                            It seems Jerome
came home by Cross Bridge—on that road that runs
by the Standeven place?"
                        "I know," he said.
"I know it well."
                 "He came there after dark,"
Serena said. "His headlights caught the color

231

of something in the ditch outside the place,
by the road's edge. He found it was the boy,
Harlow, he lay there, deep in the dry leaves,
almost invisible. Jerry said he thought
at first the boy was drunk, had just passed out—
though God knew how he'd got there. When he shook
       him,
Harlow awoke at once and spoke to him,
and Jerome said he thought he spoke Italian,
but couldn't understand it."
                  "He was dreaming,"
Rochester said.
              "Probably. Then he sat up
and seemed to make an effort and he called
Jerome by name. Then Jerry helped him up,
he said that Harlow had no strength at all,
but there was not the faintest smell or trace
of alcohol on his breath. Then Jerry got him
into the front seat of his car and said,
'I'll take you home to Lamy's.' But he said
the boy awoke then and said, violently,
he didn't want to go there, he'd get out
before he'd go there. Then, more quietly,
he asked Jerome to take him to the Inn,
the Maple Inn at Cottrellton, and he said
he was all right, he simply would not go
back to the Lamys'. Then Jerome suggested
he'd take him to his own house and the boy
seemed very pleased and finally agreed—
and, Jerry said, passed out again at once,
leaning against him. He didn't move or speak
the whole way home."
              "Most curious," Mallin said.
"No smell of liquor? None?"
                  "No, none at all.
And listen, Roche, Jerry called Quintus up
and told him. Quintus said to call the doctor,
get hold of Fanshawe. Fanshawe came at once,
he said the boy had better go to bed
and stay there for a bit. He said he thought

that it was simply weakness, lack of food,
that Harlow looked like someone who had gone
long without eating. Beyond that there was nothing
wrong with his body. They put the boy to bed
and fed him some clear soup, and then he slept.
Harlow is there now. He is still in bed.
I called up Millicent this morning early.
That's all I know."

    "Well, it is damn peculiar,"
Rochester said. "Didn't Jerome find out
where Harlow'd been?"

      "If he knew he didn't say."
"Funny as hell," said Rochester. "Bears me out
when I say the boy's unbalanced."

      "Maybe shock?"
Serena said.

    "Then long delayed. What shock?
He just came down from Cambridge, went to bed,
and left there early. No, the boy's unbalanced,
he's like his mother. Tell me, did this upset
Virginia—and the others?"

      "Yes, Virginia.
She seemed to take it hard. She really was—
I hate to say hysterical, but at least
she took it awfully hard, the pain came on,
and Quintus had to telephone to Fanshawe
to get him there from Westen's. But it was
hours before the sedatives took hold.
Oh, poor Virginia!"

    "And Quintus?"

      "He's so tired
he's nothing left to show. He moved around,
kind, sober, thoughtful, but in a sort of daze.
You'd speak to him and get no answer. He,
the responsive Q!"

    "I'm not surprised." Within
the recesses of his mind he suddenly
saw the whole bright-lit image of the knoll
under the westering sun, the kiss.

    "And Jenny?

How did it hit her?"

"That is hard to answer.
She seemed a cross between two moods at once:
annoyance at her mother—but then that's
nothing unusual—and a cold, detached
amusement about Harlow. Oh, she did
the things she had to, helped about Virginia,
got me a drink, and Quintus, but she said
practically nothing. But she's young. The young
are often cruel."

"Yes, I see," he said.
"Well, quite an evening. And what do people
do in the country to amuse themselves?"
He laughed. "And you, you ought to be exhausted."
"No, I'm all right," Serena said. "For me,
nothing that sleep won't cure."

"And I?" he said.
"Can I keep out of this? I do so want
to work this morning."

"Certainly," she said.
"There's nothing now. If there is anything
for us to do, I'm sure that I can do it.
The work comes first."

"Good, then," said Rochester.
"But call me if you need me."

"Yes, I will.
The only thing, you'll be alone for lunch.
I'm going to take Virginia in the car
straight up to Providence, to the hospital,
we leave at twelve. Fanshawe has ordered her
a few days' observation there, a check-up.
I shan't be back till just in time for dinner.
You'll be all right?"

"I'll be all right," he said.
"That's nice of you."

"Rubbish," she said. "I need
to do some shopping. And poor Q is busy,
he's got contractors coming."

Mallin rose.

"Till dinner then. Don't get too tired out."
He left at once. There was a pleasure in him
he didn't want to show.

☐☐☐☐☐☐

PLEASURE, indeed! Oh, yes, warm to the mind, held warm
in the body's cavern; you walked with pleasure
all the way to the studio, and the dove-grey iridescence
of the quiet sea and the warm grey of the high
clouds over lost blue like the dead flowers of autumn asters, the
sound of the soft sweet small waves and the redolence
of the sea-smell, rock and weed smell, salt air,
added to pleasure and became pleasure by kinship
with the warmth within. Cool air
made warmth seem real again. Rhythm now
altered and made a music.
      But the bare, orderly
desk and the blank white sheets of the too-attendant paper,
the pen and the many pencils, the idle, accusing
typewriter with the little white rounds of the letters
saying Q W E R T Y U I O P—what
magic turned these to words? A S D F G :
symbol, the cabalistic, the secret sign
of a comprehensible something to tell a comprehensible
something to someone?
      Yes, if you know the secret to loose
comprehension: unopened seasame.
      So he sat down at the desk:
you call on habit, you pose
body and mind in the habitual pattern of doing:
and nothing, nothing.
     And the warmth of pleasure—
it comes and disturbs and goes and disturbs and comes;
and where is the work now that was once clear,
that excited and flamed and was?
      There is only pleasure
that comes too strongly and going is turned to grief
and the grief's illogical, wrong, anticipated

before existence: the White Queen.
                                    The minutes, the creeping
        minutes,
the arid waste of the vast crawling minutes,
the hours dashing past, the waves of the hours
blown by the wind of self to crash and crash
on the barren shore!
                        Work? What is work?
There is only the one coin held in the greedy fingers, one
small and gleaming coin, with its shiny obverse,
its corroded reverse—the fingers of the poor mind
turn and turn the coin.
                        One side says Jennifer, says
alone, alone, all the long afternoon alone, none
now to disturb—if: the little giant
to stick a knife in the soul. If. No one knows.
Or she knows, but not Rochester. Ah, if—
if she comes, then alone and none to threaten, the waited,
the wanted?

In God's name, Rochester, what do you want?
And what will you do?

But if destroys the answer, and answers must
lie in the black of the mind now.
                                    But if:
then pleasure, the feeling rushes through you, the warmth
floods and floods and excites and this side
of the coin shines like light—oh! the young loveliness,
the unattached, the detached, the eager . . . and wanting?
Have you forgotten signs seen once so clearly?
Were they not clear?
                        Yes, clear as crystal.
There is only an if to attend. It is nothing, nothing,
keep still, let the thoughts be quiet, send
no long waves of doubt to the air about you, sit
still in the pleasure: alone, the studio
softly and privately enclosing, the shared art, the words
still to be spoken and just you two, the young thing,

the beautiful thing. Alone.
                         And the nervous fingers
turn the small coin:
                    Alone? Ah, after
she leaves you, yes. And where is Virginia?
And the long, oh, the desirable night
flows by alone, and there was the kiss and there was Quintus,
and there is Quintus, will be, and there's the alone,
and the long night and another and another and what
is the studio now? Or you?

In God's good name, Rochester,
what do you want, where are you going?
Do you see the road ahead?

I can only see
to the afternoon—the flying hours of work undone drag by
till the if is over and the alone becomes
something, something—this is the needed, wanted,
the huge want beyond reason or reason's willing,
the blind, the importunate need.
                         The white pages
lie still, lie still. The coin, bright, bitter,
turns and returns.

▣▣▣▣▣▣

RETURNING after lunch, he lit the fire,
the room seemed chilly and unwelcoming
in the grey afternoon. Then there was nothing
further to do—but wait.
                    To wait for something
that might not happen? He made himself sit down
once more before his desk. He forced himself
to write some letters urgently required.
He was immersed in this at four o'clock
when Jenny knocked. His heart beat hard, his whole
body twitched at the tentative small sound.
He rose, walked to the door and opened it.

237

She stood there, beautiful. Under her arm
she clasped a big portfolio.
                              "Well," he said.
"Welcome. I'd given you up."
                              She didn't move.
"Oh, dear," she said. "Perhaps I am too late?
Better if I come back another day?
You're in the midst of something?"
                              "No," he said,
"not in the midst, but just beginning something.
I couldn't be happier you are here. Come in."
She entered and he closed the door and turned.
"Let me take that," he said. He reached his hands
for the portfolio, took it, and walked across
to set it on his desk. "No, I was doing
only some stupid chores. You must be chilly.
Warm yourself at the fire."
                              "I will," she said.
"Where shall I put my coat?"
                              "Give it to me."
He took it from her. Taking it, he smelled
the perfume of her. As he hung her coat
beside his own on the row of metal hooks,
he was aware again of the faint, exciting
scent of herself it held.
                              The girl walked over
and stood before the fire.
                              "How nice!" she said.
"I envy you this studio. You're alone here.
It must be good for work."
                              "It is," he said.
"No one disturbs me here."
                              "Oh, lucky you!
Maybe some day I'll earn a place like this.
To work alone—bliss!"
                              "Yes, you have to earn it.
You will in time. I'm so glad you have come.
I'd really given you up."
                              "You had?" she said.
"But why?"

"Harlow, your mother, all those things.
I thought you'd be disturbed or have to do
something about it."

        "No," she said. "Not me.
Your wife took Mummy up. Quintus is working,
Eddie's at school, he won't be home till six,
and as for Harlow! What a comic business!
He really must be nuts." She paused, and said,
"He's left, too, in his car."

        Rochester came
near to the fire and stood beside her.

        "So?
You take it with detachment, I must say.
A pose, or truthful?"

        Jenny turned her head
and smiled and said, "It's truthful. Do you know
anything deader than a dead affair?"
"Oh? Then I'm sorry for him."

        "Why?" she said.
"It wasn't dead for him," Rochester said.
"I can imagine one could find oneself
very involved with you. Or are you still
too young to know your power?"

        She smiled again
and made a tiny curtsy. "Thanks," she said.
"You say the nicest things. Such a good moment
to hear them, too."

        "Easy enough," he said.
"You just say what you think instead of trying
to dress it up."

        "It's all long gone," she said.
She wasn't smiling now. "You know, the glamour,
he'd just come back, the uniform, the ribbons,
he seemed—experienced. I let it get me,
it was so . . . look, I really didn't come
to talk of Harlow. Can I show the pictures?"
"Yes, do," he said. "But still I'm interested
in what you're saying."

        "The novelist?" she said.
"Probing the motives and the odd causations

of young love and its physical attractions
and its decline and fall?"
                    He laughed and said,
"Let's see the pictures. I guess it's why you're here.
Stick to the script, then. And I'd like to see them—
though there's a part of me would always rather
probe into physical attraction. Writers
are only men. Even when they have lived
as long as I have."
                    She said, "Where shall I put them?
Here on the sofa? Can we turn the lights on?
What's age to do with it? Do you think you're old
or still feel as you did?"
                    "Who's probing now?
Males go on being males for quite a while.
I'll put the lights on."
                    Rochester went round
and turned on the big lamp behind the sofa.
"Is that enough light?"
                    "Yes, that's fine," she said.
"Good. Then go to it. I'll just pull the curtains.
I hate the feeling of unshaded windows
with dark outside and lamps lit up. It makes me
feel like an actor."
                    "Would that be bad?" she said.
"Not always, no. I guess we all are actors
at certain moments, happily. Just now
I'd rather not feel viewed by an audience—
even imaginary."
                    "Oh." Her voice
was blank. She fetched the big portfolio
and set it up against the sofa's back.
He drew the curtains on the three big windows.
They were of soft and patterned stuff, their color
a lovely salmon pink. It made the room
suddenly warm and most enclosed, the single
bright lamp shone on the yellow of the sofa,
a pool of brilliance, all the rest was touched
by the half-light reflected and the moving

240

color of fire-flame.

"Lovely!" said Jennifer.
"Did you choose this—the colors and the curtains,
or Mrs. . . . or Serena?"

"Mine," he said.
He heard his voice give too much emphasis
and could not help it. "It's all mine. It's me.
I built it and designed and furnished it.
It's what I like, it's really wholly mine.
Even Serena can't come into it
unless I ask her."

Jennifer was bending
over the sofa. She had loosed the ties
on her portfolio, one cover fell
flat on the sofa-seat, the other rested
against its back.

"I see," she said, "I see.
That's probably why I've never been allowed
to come before. It's funny, isn't it?
In all these years." She laughed and said, "At that,
I never wanted to, till now."

"Till now?
Well, there's a reason now." He walked around
and stood beside her. "Let me see," he said.
Jennifer straightened up.

"I've just brought ten.
That's why I was so late. It took so long
to choose the ones to bring. Six drawings, brush
and ink, four water-colors. Five of these
were done for Mensinger—you know, my teacher?
Five are my own, I did them for myself.
Mensinger hates them. What I want to know
is what you think. I won't say which is which,
they're not in order. Will you tell the truth?
There's nothing else will help me."

"Yes," he said.
"Of course I will. But why can't Quintus help you?"
"I don't know," Jenny said. "He can't, that's all.
Too close, perhaps? The family. And he has

241

a queer conventional streak. You'll see, I think,
after you've looked at them. Shall I begin?"
"Begin," he said. "I shan't say anything
until I've seen them all."
                              Jennifer bent,
reversed the big white blank of drawing paper,
and the picture showed.
                        So one by one she'd reach
her hand out, flip the paper till it fell
face downward to reveal the next. She said
nothing but "Ready?" Rochester replied
only with "Yes."
                  When they had reached the end,
he said, "Now put them up and start again.
But this time, leave them, will you, till I say
to show the next?"
                    "Yes," she said. "Yes. I will."

So it began again—once more the ten
pictures succeeded each other, one by one.
They were the same size, all. But beyond that,
Rochester found it hard now to believe
the same hand did them.
                         He could see at once
the ones that grouped together. It did not matter
whether they were in ink or water-color.
Five were precise and beautiful, with line
living and color rich, harmonious;
descriptive of a scene—two landscapes here,
three still-lifes. They were skilful past the point
one would expect of her—not once conventional
except in that strange, over-all conception
that seized a subject's beauty to convey
the essence of that beauty. It was easy
to see that these were the five pictures done
'for Mensinger,' as she put it.
                                 Yet of these,
what could one think or—harder still, what say,
except foresee potential excellence,
a fruitful promise? And like all promises

242

of talent showing, where the talent led
remained a query more deadly dangerous
than any other. Was not all art filled
with broken promises? Here was skill and talent,
technical excellence, the observant eye,
the will to seize an essence, to abstract,
to state a condensation of a fact
till it was more than fact—but yet a promise
that this might lead to art, that well might turn
at last to doing.
     Now, and for the moment,
Rochester had forgotten Jennifer,
himself forgotten, almost, in the compelling
need to respond.
     Oh, but the other five!
Incredibly different!
     To be sure, he saw
the same live line, the same maturity
of color balance—only the one hand
could state these similars. But beyond that bare
and technical sameness, there was nothing same.
Here color flamed or clashed or harmonized
or shocked—on purpose. Here the lines and strokes,
the very washes of the monochrome
of India ink cried passion—to depict
something so abstract, so immensely grown
within the shell of person that there showed
only the mood that saw, the need that joined
this mass to that, this color against this,
to move the beholding eye, to beg the eye
to search its own beholding for the cause
of these conjunctions, dissonances.
     How
did youth create such passion or such lust
in forms and colors alien to all
objective life, drawn from an inner world
that had been where, known what, had felt (and when)
how strong an urge?
     So now he stood to view
the tenth, the last, in color. Purples here,

violent greens and crimsons, forms that groped
to enclose each other, perhaps to swallow up
other's identity?
                    How old this girl?
No: woman. What were years to measure by
in such a revelation?
                         Oh, toward what
secret and almost terrible dark worlds
would years accreted lead? And every form
of the five pictures was so utterly
female, as though they cried out to betray
all wanting, all desire—what would they cry
if want were filled?
                        He drew a breath, expelled it,
noisily, like a sigh.
                        "Quite wonderful.
The five you did," he said. "Quite wonderful.
The others are just damned skilful, let's forget them."
She looked at him and he at her. He saw
a flush of pleasure mount to her whole face.
"Truly?" she said.
                     "Truly," he answered her,
but felt his voice grow thick.
                                  "You knew?" she said.
"You saw the ones were Mensinger, those were mine?"
"Too easy, not a question. God, I haven't
anything I can say."
                       "I think you've said it."
She looked back at her picture briefly, then
turned once again to him. "Go on," she said,
"as I am going?"
                   "I don't know," he said.
"Now you're beyond me. All five of these pictures
frighten me, just a little. I can't see
to what new worlds they lead as you increase
in understanding. That's so personal.
No one can tell you—perhaps not you, yourself.
Looking at them I only know they move me—
move and excite me terribly."
                                "Oh," she said,

"oh, do they really move you?"

                                        "Yes," he said.
"They move me as you move me."

                                        Jennifer's
eyes widened suddenly, the smile she'd worn
faded to nothing. She stood there, motionless,
unspeaking.

                    "As you move me," he repeated.
"I can tell now the way the pictures move me,
how they excite, how I should like to have them
near to observe, to see, to try someday
to understand a little, perhaps at last
to cherish and make mine—as all art lives
finally in the beholder's loving eyes,
their emotion so translated to his own
till both are indivisible. I could tell you
that these are products of a female soul,
not youth's, but woman's, there is nothing male
in any of them—some day, God knows when
or even why, you will add in, perhaps,
something to balance—because some man has crossed
the passage of your life. And when that comes,
you'll be an artist grown.

                                   But do you know
of your own power to move—to move and shake?
Will you hoard this, or use it? Will it be
allowed to be the touchstone to a knowledge
that will give balance to both life and art?
I wish to God . . ." He stopped, and turned away,
walked to the fire, stood there with his back
turned now to Jennifer.

                              She said, so softly
that he could hardly hear her, "Yes? You wish
to God—what?"

                        Without turning then,
he said, "That I could be the one to lead you,
however briefly, toward it."

                                    There was silence.
It seemed to last forever, but was not
an empty pause. He turned his head around

till he could see her. She was motionless
where he had left her, looking (so it seemed)
still at the picture, at the passionate thing
propped to the brilliant light.
                              He left the fire,
stepped swiftly up behind her, laid his hands
down-pointing, fingers touching on each other,
flat on her thighs. She did not move at all—
she stood, not tense, without response. He felt
fierce passion rise and sweep him, knew his hands
were trembling as they touched her.
                              When he spoke,
his voice was husky.
                              "You do not know your power.
But I have seen it. I have seen it clearly,
it shook me to my roots. I want to teach you
the knowledge of that power, its release."
"Release?" she said. "Or else captivity?
I must be free."
                              "With me you would be free.
Are we not artists? Do you think I want
captivity to chain you up because
I hold a captive? Is the slave less free
than the slave's master?"
                              "Oh. You said you'd seen
my power clearly. Now? Because of these?"
She gestured briefly to the painting shown,
but still she did not move away.
                              "Yes, there."
He thought, it can be done, no risk's too great,
you're on the edge now. Through his hands he felt
the warmth of her. He pressed them harder then
against the flat and terrible straight thighs.
His hands were steady now.
                              "Yes, there," he said.
"But yet not only there."
                              "Where?" in a whisper.
"Now you must tell the truth to me," he said,
"as you exacted of me. Yesterday
I stood in the grove at the Standeven place.

246

I saw you, Jenny. Tell me. Does this mean
I may not have the way to teach you, show you
the way ahead—the whole? You wanted that?
Or did not want? Tell me the absolute
whole truth." The pressing of his flattened hands
pulled her back now a little till she stood
closer against him.

              "Say it out," she said.
Her voice was cool and clear. "Just say it out.
You saw what?"

              Voice still husky said, "The kiss."
Jenny said nothing. She stood rigidly,
and he could feel the faintest trembling shake
her erect stillness. But what caused the trembling?
"The kiss," he said again. "Where did it lead?"
A briefer silence, and he felt her shoulders
move in a shrug, and then she spoke, her voice
incredibly detached. "Nowhere," she said,
"though why I answer you, I just don't know.
Nowhere at all."

           "By your will or by his?"
"You ask too much," she said. But still she stood
motionless, pressed against him. Then he felt
her body shaking, and he knew she laughed,
though laughter was so silent.

              Laugh? My God,
it was too much!

           He seized her roughly then,
whirled her around, drew her close up against him,
and kissed her mouth.

           She did not try to move—
stood there, accepting, giving nothing back,
till, from the frantic searching of his hands,
she suddenly relaxed her body wholly
and melted into him and the kiss grew
to a full passion.

           Soon, oh soon,
after the endless time, clock so betrayed,
beauty so young and fresh fully replying,
lamp is extinguished, pictures upon the floor,

light of the fire only and all enclosing,
bodies stretched out in passion upon the yellow
dark in firelight, seizing and ever yielding,
hands and fingers skilful on lover's mission,
flesh that is touched to flesh and the lips to flesh
and the blind need that is seen for all its blindness—
oh, never before, oh, never before to him
this grasping, clutching, God-give-it-me response of
flesh beneath that cries from an aching flesh
its palpitating language of whole desire . . .
and now too much, the youngness, new perfection,
unspoiled and the terrible closing grasping
now no longer to wait but to culminate
fierce moment and the whole-absorbed relief
and then . . . the knowing, the cruel, the hurtful knowing,
not the shared but the had. Alone.
                                    Oh, God! for youth
and the soon recurrence to double the impact needed,
to seize and own by the given, the not single
divisive reception. No. It was gone and gone,
over the time, the endless that was too soon,
the want that had proved too much, the barren
satisfied all unsated.
                          But still she lay
recipient—and expectant?
                          Were there words
made to make good the lack? The words like sorry,
darling and Christ! how wonderful, you are wonderful:
dust in the mouth.
                          A log broke in the middle,
fell and the flames rose and the fire flickered,
small explosions of light and the crackling sound
of the flames consuming.
                          The flames consuming what?
Time and the need for time? Where were the words
to save, to prolong?
                          She said, "I can't breathe, darling.
Do you mind moving?"
                          He moved and lay beside her,
stretched out on his back. She pulled her clothes to order.

248

"Have you got a mirror? Is there a bathroom here?"
"Yes," he said. "Oh, Jennifer, I'm so sorry,
you were too much for me."
                                    "It doesn't matter."
She rose up and climbed over him and stood
and shook herself. "Let's hope there is no baby.
That would be hard to handle. Where's the john?"
He pointed to the door. She went to it
and disappeared behind it. He lay still,
hoping he knew not what, and feeling still
a strange confusion—a wanting without passion,
a need beyond experience, a regret
bitter to pride, a sense of stupid failure,
a feeling that he did not know his way
with such as she in spite of what they'd had,
in spite of yielding to him. They had had
what? Was it nothing?
                          When she came again,
he moved his body over to make room.
She sat beside him. He said, "Lie down here, darling,
you are so lovely."
                          "No," she said. "Not now."
"It was too much," he said. "You were too much—
your beauty, what I wanted. Let me learn."
"Learn? You don't need to learn. You're great.
In fact, terrific."
                          "Next time I'll be better.
So it will grow."
                          "Next time?" she said. "We'll see.
No use to plan it, is there? It was fun.
We both had need. And if we do again
make love together, we'll be even then.
Quite even."
                  Rochester said, "Even? Even?
How do you mean?"
                          "The kiss," she said, "and Q.
Now you have Q and I—I have Serena.
We're really even. Unless I have a baby.
Then we're both in the soup."
                                    He felt a chill

striking straight through him, and a sort of anger
that she could be so cool. He cursed himself,
knowing his own fault. Beauty sat beside him,
young beauty, everything one could desire,
and he'd possessed it and it was not his,
not even faintly. Good God, he thought, she's cold—
except her body. Cold and cruel too.
And calculating. Yet he wanted her
now more than ever—what a paradox
of cockeyed wanting!
                        Well, then, play it so.
"No, don't go having babies. I agree,
we'd both be in the soup. Very hot soup."
"You more than I," she said. She laughed a little.
"You see, you should know better. I'm so young,
so inexperienced. Poor Rochester!
How they'd come down on you for knocking up
poor little Jennifer—a married man!
And she—perhaps a virgin too?"
                            He tried
to smile—it was a poor attempt. He said,
"Well, it was lovely. Jenny, would you meet me
somewhere one day soon, let's say in New London,
and we'd go on a trip, two or three days,
just you and I—pretend it was New York—
something like that? I want to sleep with you
and wake with you and let you see at last
what I can give you—and all the lovely hours
to talk and to explore—the world and art,
and no one in between. Will you do that?"
She looked down at him and she ran a finger
lightly across his forehead and she said,
"I'll think about it. You want me for your mistress?"
"My lover, not my mistress. You're too free
to be a mistress."
                    "Yes. I am too free.
You see that, don't you? And what could I give you,
dear Rochester, fast lover, except my beautiful
white body?" Then she laughed and rose again
and said, "I must be going. I'm so happy

you liked my pictures, mine, not Mensinger's.
No, don't get up, don't move. I like to see you
stretched out, unbuttoned. It is so unlike
the Mr. Mallin that I used to know.
You must have had a lot of women, dear,
to make a girl so fast." She leaned down then,
picked up the pictures scattered on the floor,
stowed them within the big portfolio,
tied the strings neatly, smiling all the while,
walked to the corner and put on her coat,
and started for the door.
                              But then, in panic,
Rochester rose and said, "Don't go like that!
When will you come again? Don't leave me so!"
He went up to her, would have taken her
into his arms, but the portfolio
blocked him completely. "Kiss me, kiss me, Jenny!"
"Another time, another kiss," she said.
"The mood is over now. Don't force me, Roche,
I must be in the mood. Good-bye for now.
I'll see you soon. Forget about the kiss—
all kisses—that is best."
                              She turned away,
opened the door, and vanished in the darkness,
and the door closed and clicked.
                              Now there was time—
oh, hours and hours of the deep sea of time—
to taste the bitterness, to learn the taste,
to make it all your own.
                              The words she'd said
flashed through his mind again: "Perhaps a virgin?"
Not true. Not true by whom?
                              The bitterness
grew deeper, deeper.

Part Four

JENNIFER MESSLER

□□□□□□

LEVEL light of the lifted sun,
eyes to open and close again,
eyes to open to see the day
sun suffused, and the eyelids close,
close to taste the delicious, ripe
fruit of the time that is still to come:
sweet, sharp taste of the perfect, rounded,
misted vision of yet to be. Vague,
lit with the color of closed eyelids.
Move a little, the warm, soft movement,
pull of the sheets, the gentle turning,
side to back, stretched out, the long straight
legs to the cool of sheets, the delicate
felt warmth of the body's night nest now
holding, enclosing all the length of the back.
Oh, the sweet act of living! to feel the sun
that is not yet felt, to know
hours of sun ahead and the swift, graceful,
grateful movement of muscles, of fresh feel
of October air on the hot cheeks of sleep.
Stretch a little, the arms flat at the sides,
the body flat and known: the transient touch
of sheets on ankles, sheets on the silk of gown,
silk of gown on the skin of legs and breasts,
the rested, welcoming, taut skin
wanting the day!
                    Delicious and undefined
joy of the body's need and the yet uneager
purpose of flesh, now only the awakening

full of delight and feeling, the suffusing
warmth and coolness, the quick soft
dear response of the skin, the gentle flooding
sense of the need and the power, the lovely
fulness and weight of the young, wide-spread
breasts that the silk caresses, the almost
known and defined sharpening and arising
of the tips of wanting.
                    The hands must
know and discover, move, the infinite
delicacy of the long, graceful fingers
once touch, light touch, drop now,
lie by the flanks, the knowing
is all a part of the joy of the wanted
day arising.
                    Different the own touch!
Light and passing, the undefined, the clever
swiftest passing and not there, all
still to be in the not known, the not spoken,
the vague of wakening in the act of being
and the perfection of own.
                    Now
let the eyes open, and the mind too.
Ah, it's Sunday.
                    God! let's hope
Harlow is still away! Eyes hurt:
eyes that possess and know. The stupid folly
leading to nothing—except the harsh, unwanted
memory of his flesh. Why, oh why? Put
all aside, to bury, the page is clear now,
there is today and tomorrow, all fresh tomorrows
and the life to do and to be.
                    And Quintus
this afternoon? In the still woods, in
the forest of colors, in the intimate
search of the small plants, sweet shared
peering and searching.
                    Looked at me. He looked . . .
it is not to be thought of, felt now . . . later
to feel and to know.

Oh, lovely body!
Straight and firm and strong and the power to use,
the looked at known and felt and the brought about
look of the other eyes! Oh, God, not bent,
not crippled over, not always now unable,
the undesirable thing. There must be
no complaining, a sweetness and a willing,
and the soft movement and always
grace of the step, the bending, the
lithe and the supple shown, shown and seen. Sun
pours on the good day! And tomorrow?
Rochester is tomorrow. Rochester.
                      Looked too.
So to arrive and to be, to be now, wholly,
me, myself, the pictures, the act of being
not the thing of another but the creator
in her own right.
             And looking? Looking always?
Pictures—or me? or both? To know,
to feel the power released in the whole sense
of self, of Jennifer!
           Oh, the good
times of the days ahead, the quiet
exciting doors to open if they will open—
by me, by me. Myself!
           The sun now
calls to be at the act of life, the lying
was sweet, was grateful; no longer, be
up to the joy of moving, the richer
sense of the power to be.
            Oh, God, please,
fix it that Harlow has left for California,
keeps out of this, this sweetness, this
lovely excitement of the pursuit of life
always ahead. Today, tomorrow—
and the uncrippled body, the power
to sweep and to claim.
           My own!

Part Five

QUINTUS LAMY

🔲🔲🔲🔲🔲🔲

SO HE AWOKE and the clock said six-fifteen,
the pale clear day foretold its brilliant unfolding,
and life and its many problems at once and heavily
descended upon him: the sense of the weight to lift,
the confusion hard to clarify.
                              Almost forgotten
the sense of the welcome of the new day's good advent:
one was accustomed now to the sense of something
always impending heavily.
                              Now his mind,
awakening a little more, remembered yesterday:
work unfinished, behind time, Virginia, Hearing,
the drive home, the sudden clarity of ideas
born in the car's motion, Jennifer.
                              Oh,
too many things to sort! Too different, mixed
in an amalgam of his weariness. Nevertheless,
must be sorted out.
                              So, rise and descend
to the still deserted kitchen, and make some coffee.
One didn't have to think of the things to do,
it was all postponed. The smell of the coffee making
was good and cheering. He poured himself out a big cup,
added the cream and sugar, and walked up slowly
back to his bedroom. The big cup rattled faintly
no matter how hard he tried to steady it. Tired.
Hand reflected the mind. He smiled a little.
I'd better watch out, he thought, or first thing you know,
I'll add self-pity to all the rest of the problems.

Virginia . . . no, that a little later. First
back to your bed.
                    He set the coffee down
on the bedside table. The whiskey glass was there,
empty but smelling faintly. He moved it away
to the bureau top. Jennifer . . . no, that later too.
Lie down, Quintus, relax, man, let the coffee
start the true day going. This was the false
time between sleep and waking.
                              He propped the pillows
comfortably upright, climbed back into the bed,
and drank the coffee. Strong and hot, delicious!
The heat runs through you, the body's tension slacks,
the mind begins now clearly. The coffee finished,
he lit a cigarette.
                    Now. One could think again,
set facts in order. Saturday: that was one fact.
Work to be done, too much, and none to help him.
But still to be done. If Rochester should succeed
and the hospital came in, he'd hire another man,
or maybe two. Wonderful. Things would hum
if he could let someone else do half the tiresome
chores of the work. A man for specifications,
another for full-size details. Oh, good—but if
the new job came. Now, for this very morning,
no help, the work to be done and it must be done.
So I shall do it.
                  And doing it get more weary?
And coming home to discover the hospital lost,
and perhaps Virginia ill or perhaps in pain?
With what will you meet this? Never mind, I'll meet it,
somehow, some way. Does anything guarantee
rest in this house today?
                          Queer life, odd life.
A wife and a no-wife. Puts things out of balance.
Better alone? And how would you be alone,
what would you do? Run off? To what, with whom?
Rubbish. Life always laid on you what it laid—
they were your doing too, not wholly come
as the arbitrary acts. If you ran away,

if you put your single self as the single standard,
and so avoided them, were you then not left
poorer and thinner?

               Oh, I know all of this:
I am enriched, like all men of my kind,
because I accept the things my life lays on me—
these are the bounds and the rules, they make the richness.
Could one design great work where there existed
no binding limitations?

               But a wife, yes,
and a no-wife. Hard. Perhaps if I were older,
I'd adjust easier. Chastity is so difficult
for a man like me.

               Harlow was having a bad time.
He was in love, poor boy. And Jennifer? No,
not even a little returned. But he played it badly,
he came too often, he mooned, and he was always
so accessible. Never a chance to miss him,
to let her see for a moment that she might lose
so much devotion. Should I say a word to him?
What was the use? Jennifer didn't want him—
she didn't want him at all, it was just a fact,
it was too easy to see. Or not as a husband.
Or not as a lover, either.

               Had they been lovers?
When first he came back? Always together then,
for the first few months—and off and alone together,
and late at night—and the rest—the usual signs,
and Jenny prettier than he'd ever seen her
and suddenly not a girl then, but a woman.
Being his lover would do that. This generation
took things like that so easily.

               Ah, but now,
it was all over. Perhaps she liked to have him
tied to her as a beau, or maybe something
similar there, or perhaps for her vanity.
What did she really want?

               There came a sudden
sense of unease (that yet was touched with pleasure,
a quick hot pleasure, the body suddenly well,

257

the bed so comfortable) as he recalled the image
of Jennifer standing and the light behind her
and the thin gown.
                    Jesus! the loveliness
of the young beauty!
                        What did Jennifer want?
The answer came, quick, flashing, the curious touch
of truth to it: Jennifer wants you, Quintus.
And before God, for my sins, I want her too.
Want her—and I can have her.
                            The single room,
the sleeping apart from the wife who was the no-wife,
the pain of loneliness, of the always empty
jar of desire—suddenly turned to fulness,
to joy accessible, to a life fulfilled,
to rest and sleep and to wake to a wanted day
with another night ahead, alone, and free—
and only the barest risk!
                        The planning mind
planned into pattern the whole intoxication
of sweet release . . . till it suddenly shut with a snap
and he cursed himself.
                        Will you make your daughter your
        lover?
God, man, what are you thinking?
                                But not your daughter—
somebody else's . . . not your flesh and blood,
simply the proximate, the attainable thing
wrapped in beauty.
                    What evil quality now
seizes and moves me? Will you not think at all
of what you're doing, of where it leads, of all
that this might do to Jennifer?
                            But to teach
love to a youth? For someone else, at last—
only a temporary thing for you, no lasting.
For her, no lasting, only a while, a while:
and richer then?
                    This is a sophistry.
You rationalize your illness, it is your age

258

has made this hunger—not to be satisfied
at the cost of evil. Evil to think so, too,
evil to feel so—the terrible, overwhelming
grasp of desire last night, the memory still
holding and cherishing all the sweet and healing
of the ride home, the stimulus of attention,
of good affection—and then the blinding light
of the body seen, and the pose of youth, the hunger
suddenly shown in her—in her, my God!
as well as you.

        All right, said Quintus then.
Face it, my friend, for you must face it fully.
First, that it cannot be, not ever be.
If you were caught—just think of that to start it:
Virginia ill and waking, wandering maybe,
as once in a long while she had strength to wander
into your room for help—and the bed empty?
How much further and where would Virginia wander?
The sweat came out on his body.

        But still face it:
what was the hope left then? Was the illness, pain,
the rapid ups and the soon-coming downs,
apart from the mind? What hope for the final healing
where the steady love, the steadiness of devotion,
the patience long maintained, were changed at once
into the shock of horror: to find devotion
to bed with youth, the well, competitive youth
whose health and beauty now was the cruel mirror
to your own age and failure? Had she not failed
once already?

        I thought it was Messler's fault:
the love denied, the fidelity soon withdrawn,
the hard indifference—blows on a tender thing
to warp and bruise. God! but I wonder now!
Yet still one hope, will you destroy it so?
Deny the mature conception of love given
wholly and long and steadfast?

        Could there be
ease for the body where mind must find unease
and the long, self-inflicted, self-made doubt

259

to grow with the day on day of the everlasting
single search for a peace?
                    But still to face it:
nothing is wrong in the want and the desire:
what is man but animal? What is Jenny
but what the animal wants and always wants?
Of course you want her.
                    And why does she want you?
But still, all natural, the unpredictable thing:
desire mutual suddenly, arbitrarily,
happening like the clouds or the fall of snow
or the swift heat of spring. It's what you do,
not what you feel, that matters. Starved, you feel
drawn to the proximate, to the obtainable—
and do not touch it. Never.
                    Oh, deadly word:
never—the cold, the final, the terminating!
Poor, poor demanding flesh! To be denied
for sake of the whole!
                    But nevertheless, denied.
So! done and over.
                    Up now, the work ahead:
old Doctor Work. And let the fatigue and chance
of disappointment, Virginia, and the evening
come as they would. There were other things to do
with the whole of living. And at the end, maybe,
something fine and wonderful, a reward,
a wholeness gained.
                    So he arose and dressed,
rapidly, almost hurrying; soon descended,
cooked his breakfast alone in the still deserted
kitchen, sun on the table; ate with speed,
got in his car and drove up, swiftly, swiftly,
to the empty office.
                    There was the work: it came
alive as he entered.
                    Just the long day to fill
with something new created.

◨◨◨◨◨◨

WEARY NOW, afraid by anticipation
of what he would find at home, he thought of Harlow
as he and Jennifer walked in the cold, clear dusk,
the first stars pale, from the Mallins' house toward home.
Virginia would be upset by the boy's absence.
Poor boy, upset too, doubtless. Oh, Quintus thought,
I hope that he's back now, I don't want to cope
with another damn thing. Where could Harlow have gone?
Funny performance . . .
                              "Darling, isn't it wonderful!"
Jennifer said.
              It took him a couple of seconds
to see what she meant, that now she wasn't referring
to Harlow's absence.
                      "Wonderful, yes," he said.
"It's going to make a difference."
                                  "Oh, I know."
The young voice, clear and eager. She took his arm
and squeezed it hard against her. He felt the soft
firm shape of her breast, and a prickle ran up his spine
and suddenly, unexpectedly he knew
he was less tired.
              "I know," she said, "I know,"
the eagerness and the words and the hard squeeze
now repeated. "It makes me very happy.
The luck's changed, Q. Now everything will go right—
go right for all of us. Darling, I just know it,
know it all through me."
                        "Rochester turned the trick,"
Quintus said. "It's great."
                          "But he couldn't have done it
unless you'd been so good. You're wonderful, Q,
and don't belittle yourself. Oh, I'm so happy!"
"I'm happy too," he said. "And it's nice to know
your daughter thinks you're wonderful."
                                        "Oh," she said,
and she dropped his arm. "And don't belittle me!
I'm a big girl now, and I'm really not your daughter,
and what I think is not just family feeling
or anything dumb like that. And I am an artist,

261

at least inside myself, and I see you are
and a really good one, too. So don't belittle
the praise I give you. And don't you try to put me
back in the nursery, darling. I'm too big."
She took his arm again and squeezed it to her,
and her giggle came through the dark like water flowing,
and she said, "At that, you're just like everyone else,
you want it both ways. Remember the verbal spanking
you gave me last night? I was a big girl then.
The big girl says you're wonderful."

                                                    "Thanks," he said,
and he felt the blood run hotly into his face
and was glad for the darkness. "It seems the spanking
    took."
"Yes," she said. "It did. In a way, it did."
No, he thought. I decided no this morning:
nothing has changed.
                    "I wonder will we find Harlow,
when we get home? I hope so."
                             Her voice had altered
when she answered him, but this time she didn't
let go his arm. "I really don't care," she said.
"Except for Mummy's sake. If it wasn't for that,
I'd really be glad if we found he was still off
with whoever he's with."
                        "The boy's upset," said Quintus.
"What's he upset about?"
                    "For you, for one thing."
"Upset for me?" she said. "Why?"
                      "Come along, Jenny!
Isn't he still in love with Jennifer Messler
who used to like him too?"
                    She shrugged her shoulders;
he could feel the movement.
                    "Oh, goodness, that," she
    said.
"That was a long time back."
                    "When you were young?"
She laughed and said, "Well, before I learned to know

what a grown man could mean opposed to the dull,
the sort of childishness of a man like Harlow."
She laughed again and she said, "And Q, don't ask
who the grown man is, either."

"All right," he said,
and he felt the blood in his face grow hot again.
"But anyway, home or not home," Jennifer said,
"I shall not trouble about him now, at all.
I really shan't. Oh, Q, you have got to do
something with me tomorrow! Tomorrow morning?"
"I can't," he said. "I've laid on a shooting lesson,
Eddie, and the young Carpenter boy is coming,
and Charlie Davis."

"Then the afternoon," she said.
"You'll simply have to give me the afternoon!
Look, I looked after Mummy the whole damn day—
and you know what that means, don't you, particularly
when she's upset? She's really psychic then—
think of a thing to do—I wanted to paint—
and that's the moment she has to have your help,
or is just so obviously in need of company,
that you can't leave her. God! I wish she was well!
But anyway, darling, I want to go west to Olney,
I want pipsissewas and some pitcher-plants,
for the rock garden. I want some help, and more—
I'm sick of being alone. I'm always alone here—
except for Mummy. Come along, darling Q,
you'll have to keep me company, it's my turn
to be looked after."

"Well, we'll see," he said.
"I'd love to, Jenny. I'll go with you if I can.
Leave it like that."

"O.K.," she said. "That's fine.
Something to look towards. Oh, Q, did I tell you,
Rochester wants to see the paintings, mine,
and swears that he'll tell the truth. I'm going to show
some of the ones I did by myself and some
I did for Mensinger, and I'm going to mix them,
tell him nothing, and ask him his opinion.

263

Isn't that grand? Isn't he pretty good
as a judge of that sort of thing?"

"He is," said Quintus.
"He's very good indeed, and he knows a lot.
Yes, that should help you, Jenny."

He felt a sudden
pang of dismay and doubt. But now they stood
before the door of the house and there was no time
to probe or question. Rochester? But for art,
or for something else? And you? he thought. And you?
A big girl now—and what was that to you?
Well, now go in. No time now—maybe never
time for such thoughts.

■□■□■□

THE TROUBLE that evening began as soon as he entered
the rooms of his house. There was tea in the living room,
but cold now, and the fire, which had been started,
smoked without flame. But hadn't Virginia known
he was to go to Mallin's? Of course she knew!
He'd called from the office.

He heard the radio on
loudly in Eddie's room.

"I'll go up now,"
he said to Jennifer. "See how your mother is."
He found his wife in bed, she was looking pale,
and her face was drawn—the signs, the usual signs
of her troubles brewing.

"Oh, Q," she said at once,
"I am so glad you're home! Did you just get in?"
"Yes, just this minute. I went direct to the Mallins',
I worked till late. How are you?"

"Oh, dear," she said,
"then you didn't get the tea? I had so hoped
you'd come for tea and then go over, I knew
you'd be so tired. Oh, Q, I was so sorry
not to be there with you! But tell me quickly,
what is the news?"

"The news is fine," he said.

264

"Rochester did it. I have the hospital job.
That's wonderful, isn't it?"
                              "Oh, yes," she said.
"That's really wonderful! Now you can get the men
to help you out. You can really have some help—
I hope it means that you'll now be able to work
less long hours, dear? You will really hire
the help you need now?"
                              "Yes. I'll get two men.
I'll have to have them. Sorry I had to stay
so long today. I worried about you."
                              "Did you?
I wish you didn't have to. I worried too—
about my tiresome health—and about Harlow.
Oh, darling, I am so troubled. The boy's not home,
there's been no word. It really isn't like him.
Jennifer says his car is here, still here.
Where could he go?"
                              "Don't know," he said. "Don't fret.
There's not a damn thing to worry about, not one.
The boy's O.K."
                              "I hope so, oh, I do hope so,"
Virginia said. "But it's all so disappointing!
I was so happy knowing that he'd come down—
someone for Jenny, someone of her own age,
there's nobody here now, it must be hard on her.
And she's so against me now, and I can't reach her.
I feel so awful in asking her to help me,
knowing the . . . almost hostility she shows
whenever she's with me now. I did look forward
to a nice week-end, the beautiful days, October,
and Jennifer occupied, and you at home,
and a chance to rest, and the cook now, and me well
and able to get about—as I got down yesterday,
the tea, such fun, such a good change. Oh, I hate
this room, this life! And awful to lie abed
and not be there with you and with Rochester
and with Serena to hear the exciting news!
What is it, Q, that makes my daughter hostile?
What have I done, and what can I do to stop it?

It troubles me so, I can't now even tell her
the things I ought to. Tell me, what is the matter?
Did Jenny go over with you, go to the Mallins'?"

He could feel the weight descending on his shoulders:
it was almost physical, hard to stand up straight,
one wanted to sag down. The effort. He drew a breath,
said, "Yes, she went. She's come to the cruel age.
We all go through it, the ruthless search for self.
She's simply discarding you—not you as a person—
you as a parent. You know that, Virginia.
It's what we all do at that cruel age.
It's utterly normal. Forget it. When she finds
the self she's after, this will be all forgotten,
and love—that's there, as always it has been there—
will flow toward you again. Her sort of love—
the child's love, not the parent's. They can't be equal—
folly to think so or expect it. Now
she's after Jennifer, crying, 'Who is Jennifer,
placed in the whole big world?' That you're a woman,
and Jennifer now a woman, this makes it worse,
as it always does. But all these things you know.
So just forget it. And just don't worry for Harlow.
Be glad of the new job."
                              "Oh, I am," she said.
"Good. And yourself? How are the aches and pains?"
"Stupid and there," she said. "I'll stay in bed.
I've ordered supper for four in the dining room,
send Jenny up with a tray for me, not much,
I couldn't eat much tonight. And come up later,
after you've had your supper and had your coffee,
I long for company. It's so hard alone.
And I'll try not to worry."
                              "Good girl," he said.

He brought the tray himself and he propped her up
and fixed the pillows. He came up just as soon
as supper was over, and brought his coffee with him.
It hadn't been easy. He wanted to stay below
and talk to Eddie and—he had to admit it—

266

be with Jennifer; there was something, something,
an undefinable current that flowed from her
and wrapped him warm in comfort. There was no comfort
in seeing Virginia now.
　　　　　　　　　He first began
to try to distract her mind by recounting to her
the beautiful, clear idea for his Thursday meeting,
the thought born on the ride home, the exciting
excellence of it. But soon he became aware
that she wasn't really listening, was too restless,
couldn't absorb it. The whole idea grew muddy,
dead in his mind and dead in his mouth. He said,
"I think you're worrying."
　　　　　　　　　　　"Oh, God, I am, I am.
I feel so awful!" Then she'd begun to cry,
not sobbing, but just slow tears and a face of pain.
So hard to take, to see!
　　　　　　　　　　What could you do?
What could you do but follow the only lead
that she could follow? To do the smaller things—
unreasonable, maybe unnecessary too,
that eased her mind? The endless telephone calls:
"Have you seen Harlow?" Something embarrassing
about the whole of it. Hating to call the Messlers—
getting Jimmy. There wasn't anything there
to trouble about, Virginia and Jimmy'd divorced
before he met her. But something still stood between them
a sort of barrier. Perhaps it was Jennifer,
who rarely saw her father, and held him now
in a contemptuous scorn. Ah, stupid of her,
the man was excellent, liberal and successful:
but not to Jennifer.
　　　　　　　　　Then the illness grew,
and a sort of fever descended on Virginia—
until the Mallins came. They all had sat,
grouped in the bedroom, talked the whole thing over,
and she'd grown calmer, and smiled, and when they left,
took her pills and was sweet, and said, "I'm sorry
to be such a nervy creature. I'm really sorry.
I just make trouble." But she knew she'd sleep now,

267

three or four hours at least, the blessed little
white sleep inducers from the pallid bottle
that was herself extended now—in glass,
fragile, enclosed.

And the evening was over then,
and the door shut and the whole deep fatigue
worn like a too tight garment, and Eddie asleep,
and Jennifer and he were to go now soon . . .
to separate rooms . . . to sleep? The single rooms
that need not be? The no-wife of the sweet
oblivion glass-contained, the counted-on,
the single certainty: now the four absolute
hours of . . . what? Of safety? And if you say
safety, then save from what or for what purpose?
Too complex and too hard. Or just too simple?
He said within his mind then, "The hell with this!"
and went downstairs. But there was no one there.
He found a glass, he got some ice and water,
he picked the whiskey up to pour out a drink.
One part of him said, "No! go up to your bed!"
The other said clearly, "But just a drink, relax,
sleep better." "No," the harder voice cried out,
"to bed!"

He put the glass down, it was empty
of all but ice-cubes, and he turned again
and mounted slowly up on the lonely stairs,
through the deserted hall, to his own room.
"Ah, sleep!" cried out the undefeated hunger,
"Ah, sleep, alone!"

He hurried to his bed,
fearing himself.

□□□□□□

THIS DAY the clouds sang and the air said welcome
and the morning was new. Then the clouds disappeared
and the whole Sunday sky was the vast deep
of the autumn blue, and under its infinite
purity the sun-warmed earth said peace

268

and the time for rest.

All thought postponed then,
or put aside. Perhaps there were times that came
when thinking was too much, there was only space
for the act of being, the paradox of the passive
held in the active.

All the morning long
Quintus was with his son and the two boys
shooting at targets with a little rifle,
and with a gun at the black clay-pigeons hurled
from a hand trap out over the ruffled mirror
of the scented water. Something of the excitement,
the whole delight, the delicious seriousness
of the boys' preoccupation and happiness
communicated its happiness then to him,
and the thoughts were buried so. He found himself
sorry when lunch time came, and he had to walk
with the three boys (who babbled a noisy joy)
back to the house again. Within the house
lay the taut web of life.

Jenny was out—
and lunch was ready. Quintus began at once,
served the three children, put food on a tray,
and took it to Virginia, who'd kept her bed.
He placed the tray for her, propped her up with pillows,
and said, "Where's Jennifer?"

"I don't know," she said.
"Isn't she in? She ought to be. She knew
lunch was at one. Oh, Quintus, still no word
at all from Harlow!"

"No," he said. "Not a peep.
Well, I hope he's having a good time."

"I'm still
worried.
It seems so strange he hasn't at least called up
and told us something. Q, do you think that I
should call his room-mate, Levering, on the phone,
and ask him if he knows?"

"What could he know?

Up there in Cambridge?"

"Darling, oh, I don't know,
but maybe Harlow said something, gave some hint
of some plan, something. It's just the sheer not knowing
that worries me so. An accident, a smash-up,
the mind imagines things."

"Forget it now."
He smiled at her. "Let it all go, Virginia.
It'll all come out in the wash. No use to worry.
He's old enough to look out for himself, that man.
Now I must leave you, the boys are at the table,
I'd better police them before they get in trouble.
I'll see you later. You're going to stay here, aren't you?
Rest for the afternoon?"

"I must," she said.
"And you? What are you doing?"

"I take the boys
over to Carpenter's. After that, well, perhaps
I'll drive toward Olney, look for pipsissewas
and try to find some pitcher-plants for the edge
of the rock garden."

"With Jennifer?" she said.
"If she still wants to go." He heard his own voice
produce the half-lie.

"Pipsissewa won't live
in the garden, Q. You know that. They need the shade
of the oak trees, and their leaves."

"I know," he said.
"But sometimes you have to find things out for yourself.
She wants to try. And it's such a lovely day,
it will be pretty there."

"I used to love it,
looking for plants," she said. "I miss it so!"
Then suddenly changing, she smiled at him and said,
"Go get your lunch, and have a lovely time,
it's good for Jenny to be with you. It may be
good for her, too, that Harlow has gone off—
just all a little too easy, and too devoted.
You have to learn that too. Now get your lunch."
"I shall," he said. "Good appetite!" He turned

swiftly and left her.

He had helped himself to food,
had almost made up his mind (while part of his mind
attended the children's chattering) not to go
over to Olney, when Jennifer finally came.
Her face was flushed by the cool autumn air,
her hair was beautiful in the wild disorder
that only youth affords.

"Sorry," she said.
"I *had* to finish."

"What were you finishing?
A picture, Jenny?"

"No, I'm an outdoor girl.
I dug the beds, I got the whole thing ready.
I've put in some moldy humus, some of the sand
from the little sand-barren, and some rotted oak leaves—
I know I've got it right. I dug it deep.
I'll bet pipsissewas love it."

"Oh, that," he said.
"Well, maybe they will, though I've never seen them last
more than one season."

"You say that every time.
But did you prepare like this?"

"To tell the truth,
I didn't, to that extent."

"So there!" she said.
"Wait till next year then! We can dig them up,
take a big lump of their own earth with each—
I'll take some paper for that—we'll wrap them up—
and before they know they've moved, they'll all be placed
in the proper beds. You'll see, they're going to last,
they'll love it there. And let's not start too late—
the days are so short now."

"All right," he said.
"We'll take the boys here over to Dickie's house,
and then go on from there. Is that O.K.?"
"That's wonderful," she said. She caught his eye
and smiled at him—but she didn't drop her eyes,
but went on looking.

He felt his heart pound hard

and he forced himself to look down at his plate:
too hard to support that look: it said too much.

They had dropped the boys off at the Carpenters' gate,
they were alone now.
                            "Where shall we go," he said
"to look for your plants? Have you got a place in mind?"
"Oh, yes," she said. "We'll go by Indigo Mill
and toward Cross Bridge to the old Standeven place.
There's a fine bog there, and it's full of pitcher-plants,
and the oaks grow near and under the oaks we'll find
lots of pipsissewa. I spotted it all before.
I can go right to them."
                            Quintus began to drive,
but he drove on slowly.
                            "Does Harlow know you're going,
you're digging his plants?"
                            She looked at him and she
            laughed.
"He said take anything that I wanted, darling.
Oh, just anything at all." She laughed aloud.
"And he was so keen to go, to help me get them!
Well, we'll manage without his help."
                            "All right," said Q.
"As long as he knows." It was odd: he had a feeling
he shouldn't be going there. "Jenny, my dear," he said,
"it's none of my business, but what has happened to change
            you?
Once you liked Harlow. I think you liked him a lot.
And now—what's happened?"
                            She didn't reply at once.
"That was a long time back," she said. "It's gone.
You grow and you change." She paused. When next she
            spoke
her voice was a little hard, her words came fast.
"Have you ever been pursued to the point where, well,
there's nothing to do but run, you have to escape,
for fear you'll be captured, or else be swallowed up
by something too much to take? Pursue, pursue!
There's nothing easy, no humor, no relaxation,

272

it makes you into something you aren't at all,
and you don't want to be." She made a sharp
and a cutting gesture with the palm of her hand.
"For God's sake, let's not talk of it any more.
I'm sick to death of it, sick of the way my mother
looks her reproaches and doesn't dare to say them.
I want to be me, be happy, and be with you,
and drive toward Olney and dig up the little plants,
and feel the sun and the air and see the colors,
and be, and be! Not think, I'm sick of thinking—
is there never a time to be?" She laid her hand
lightly upon his arm. "So, please," she said.
"This is our afternoon, don't spoil it, Q,
don't make me your little girl, but let me be
grown, a companion, will you?"

                        "Of course," he said.
"I'll turn off the parent now, for a little while.
It's a habit is hard to shake."

                    "I'll bet," she said.
"But when you do, then those are the heavenly
times I adore you." She took her hand away.
"Look at the colors! God, but they're beautiful!
I wish that I had the art to paint in the way
they make me feel."

                "That's what you want to paint?"
"That's what I want. And if I painted it,
I think it would frighten you."

                "Why should it frighten?
I might not like it, but why the idea of fear?"
"The way I feel," she said.

                There was silence then.
They drove in the clarity of the afternoon,
through the crystalline contradiction of golden haze,
the trees surrounding, enmeshing them in the old
brilliance of the year's dying.

                Within himself,
Quintus said, it is true, there is a fear,
even to ask more.

            "Now," said Jennifer,
"slowly, go slowly. There is a little road,

273

it is still open, it comes soon, before we get
to the place itself. It opens up on our left.
We can drive the car in, leave it. There is a path,
it leads on up and along the eastern edge
of the big Standeven bog. Look! There it is."
He slowed the car and turned it into a narrow
grass-grown road that led between maple trees,
winding and rutted. The road they had travelled on
was soon concealed from sight, but they still crept on
a hundred yards or more, to an open glade
where the car could be turned.

                               "Stop here," she said.
"Isn't it lovely? It's such a secret place,
you feel as if it belonged entirely to you,
that no one, not any one, could find you here."
The car had hardly stopped before she was out,
her face alight with happiness.

                               "Oh, Quintus,
I hope you like it here! It is such fun
to take you on to my secret place, to share it,
but yet not lose it!"

                             "It's lovely," Quintus said.
Her happiness was contagious, he felt himself
joined to her mood and glad of it, all else
willingly now forgotten or else removed
into a distant future.

Swiftly time passes so in the sun-drenched, sun-warmed
hours of occupation, the gentle, the engrossing
work of the eyes to peer, to search out the soft red
cups of the pitcher-plants, sweet-grouped, tall
nodding of leathery flower shape holding
seed for the future, cups full
of a death-in-water, the down pointing easily entered
hairs of the inner surface, traps
for the insect food.

                        Sun beats
deliciously on the neck and shoulders bending,
warm on the hands that dig in the cold, wet
soil of the bog's edge, fingers busy to part

274

stems of sheep laurel, or the tiny wood stems
of the low huckleberries still
flaunting their blood-fired leaves.
Words,
small and unimportant, soon forgotten, not needing
the act of memory, soft sounds
of companionship, flutter and die gently
in the still and enfolding air of October day.
Blue haze over the hours, blue haze binding
multitudinous clashing colors together in
moving harmony, the antiphonal voices
of the green and the yellow and the scarlet turning
hours to the precarious
mutable beauty.
Northward always the thin
leading of path by maples, to bog edge,
into and past and around, the twist of the natural
way of the ground and the growth, so
one by one, to lead, to be led, to follow,
to follow grace and the smile and the backward look,
the sharing look, the one that says, see and see?
Nods are answers and being there is an answer.
Silence hangs over the whole of the afternoon
like a warm mantle to wrap and to keep safe,
silence too is precarious, like the moment:
perched in perfection to fly off and away and never
again to be seen.
Northward and always northward:
maples to jack pines and pines to oak and to birch and soon
the white pines, scented, the carpet
of flawless brown and the aromatic.
And passing,
look to the bog and color, the haze of blue and then
the far sky, remote and still, and here are oak leaves,
and here the sharp spear-shaped leaves with
the white stripe, the pipsissewas thrusting
out of the crumple of oak leaves.
Shadow of crimson
leaves for a canopy, bend and the skilful,
tender fingers, the sharp trowel glinting silvery

in the coins of light, the shared
and the silent sharing, the moments go
dancing sedately, generously by you, asking
no attention of time they pleasantly reckon,
only the sun to creep in below the spreading
branches of oak trees, and your two figures, bending,
bending, softly and deeply uprooting the little
tender wild plants in the shared and the sharing
with them and the hours moving.
                                        Done now. Baskets
heavy and full and the smell of the moist earth,
and the deep greens and the soft reds of
plants packed safely, wrapped up.
"That's enough now," says Jenny.
"Good. We have done well. Now we had better start
back toward home," says Quintus. "Sun's low."
There is no pressure: the time stands
still as the air. They stand
still as the day about them, easy, the feel
of the work done delicious about the shoulders
in the chill of the afternoon, the low sun
no longer warming. It is still shared and sharing
in the spell of the October.

        Jenny said, "Come with me, for I want to show you
        my favorite oak. It isn't far off. And then,
        we'll go back by the road, it's easier with these plants."
        "Good," said Quintus. "Lead on."
                                        The heavy baskets
        dragged at their arms, but the drag was purely pleasure,
        the thing accomplished, the thing they had done together.
        The path led down again to the edge of the bog,
        skirted the low ground and then suddenly rose
        onto a steep knoll, an island hill surrounded
        by the low watery land. Upon its crest
        stood a great spreading white oak, its wide limbs
        stretching in knotted strength until the eye
        marvelled at strength that held the horizontal
        so long against earth's pull. Beneath it grew

in a sparse grove a group of stunted birches
like chickens underneath the spreading wings
of an old gray hen.
                              "This is my tree," said Jenny.
She set her basket down and stretched her arms
and smiled at Quintus. "Lovely, isn't it?
Lovely, and lonely too. When I am here
then there is no one in the world but me
and the great oak—unless I choose to bring
someone to life here—but it's by my will."
She laughed a little. "How does it feel to you,
existing by my pleasure?"
                              Quintus too
set basket down, straightened, and smiled at her.
"I like it, Jenny. It's a fine old oak.
It's wonderfully placed."
                              "The view," she said.
"The bog, the maples, the beech grove to the south.
Look hard, you'll see the glint of Naius River—
all perfect, except one small thing."
                              "And that?"
"The house," she said, and pointed.
                              Quintus looked:
one saw the edge of the Standeven house,
the white of cornice and the grey of wall
protruded past heavy leaves.
                              "Why do you mind it?"
"It is not mine," she said.
                              "It could be yours—
or I'm mistaken," and he smiled at her,
teasing a little. But she was serious now.
"Not ever mine," she said. "It is not old.
It's just a copy of the old, a fake house,
a Mensinger house. I would not have the thing.
I could not live in it, I could not ever
make the house mine. There's only just one thing
could cure it for me. That one thing is fire,
I'd like its ashes. Then I'd build again
and build for something real that didn't try

277

to be what it is not, can't ever be.
Do you understand?"

"Perhaps I do," he said.
"But perhaps Harlow loves it?"

"Yes, he does.
And that's the trouble, too. But now," she said,
her voice grown gay again, "let's just forget it,
we'll turn our backs, and make a little spell—
I always make it, when I'm here alone—
I exorcise it. I become alone,
the place is mine again, the house forgotten.
I'm just the oak and me."

"What is the spell?"
"Cry 'Harlow' loudly. You must call it, too.
Your voice will echo, as will mine, and so
we call it twice for once—that's magic, Q.
And when the echo's gone, and the world's still,
and there's no answer—then it is all mine,
all secret and enclosed. You'll see. You'll try?
You'll make the magic with me?"

"Yes," he said.
"I'll make the magic. And I'll have to laugh—
and you'll forgive me—if we get an answer,
an answer not an echo. And what then?"
She said, "Oh, there's another magic then.
We put our feet into our seven-league boots
and fly, we fly! Come on then, dearest Q,
make magic: call!" She took his hand in hers,
said, "Call now!"

Her hand was warm. He turned
his head toward the far distant glint of water
beyond the beech grove and he called aloud,
"Harlow!" The echo answered softly, pale,
his voice transmuted by the evening air.
"Again!" she said, her voice imperative now,
and he called out the name and heard the echo
once more come drifting without resonance.
Even as he listened, she called out the word:
"Harlow!" Again the distant pallid echo,
then silence: silence deeper, more profound

because they'd shattered it.

                               "It's worked," she said,
in a soft whisper. "Now it's mine—and yours—
my secret place is ours. We are alone,
and the whole earth is vacant as the sky
except for us, for us, for you and me
together and alone." She paused. The silence
wrapped and enfolded them. "Oh, I love you, Q!"
She turned on him and faced him, flung her arms
about his neck, pulled his head down, her hands
grasping his head, and kissed him on the mouth.
Beyond himself, beyond shock and surprise
(that was not quite surprise), his lips responded,
and a small voice within him, something separate,
removed, observing, said, "Go on, go on!
It's what you wanted, it has come to you,
it's not your doing, take it, it is yours,
there's nothing filial here."

                               The kiss went on.
How long? Oh, measureless, there is no clock
to measure passion.

                        Then, beyond his will,
his arms went round her, held her close to him,
feeling her body against his. The force
of all desire beyond the force of willing,
beyond the wanting or the good or bad,
took hold and moved him, and his hands began
to explore her body.

                     Oh, the terrible hands!
Force beyond force, beyond the power of lips,
the mute, the blind, the knowing and the known,
transmuting and transmitting.

                           Oh, poor starvation
that must be fed even upon the poison
it knows, it knows!

                      So for the time that was not
time but was endless, these two clung together
committing love.

                    It had to stop: they staggered
in this intensity, grown so dizzy now

that the solid ground was heaving, moving, swaying
under uncertain feet.

And stopped. And drew apart.
And Quintus knew then. There were but two things
and only two that could be done. He chose—
but not by will, by something else within him,
some deeper instinct.

"No," he said. His voice
was low and harsh. He clenched his hands, hard, hard:
they held the memory of the shape of her,
the thighs, the breasts, the willing shape of flesh
given to his fingers. He opened them
as though to let the thing his fingers clutched on
fall to the ground. "That's all, and never more!
You understand? Not ever!"

He bent at once
and picked his basket up.

"Quintus," she said.
The one word, pleading, crying out to him,
offering.

"No," he said. "Now home. It's late.
Your mother's ill. I must go back to her.
Forget this, Jenny. It's deadly wrong—for us.
Pick up your plants."

He turned away at once
and headed east, half blindly, toward the road
he knew was there, pushing past twigs and shrubs,
whipped by the branches, clawed at by the briars
he did not see, nor wanted to avoid,
not looking back, not caring if she came,
but urged by the whole need for an escape
back to the known, the tried, the way he'd lost
for just those minutes. Anger filled his heart—
oh, not with Jenny, with himself. His mind
said, "This you did, you made it, it all lay
long in your thoughts."

A wall at last,
stone upon stone, a solid, ancient wall,
a wall to climb, surpass. He climbed the wall.
The road lay brown below, the welcome road;

the road was sanity.
                         Standing now upon it,
he turned and looked. The girl was following,
her face was grim and cold. My fault, he thought.
What can I do to cure it?
                         Nothing now.
Nothing but cruelty was any good
to cure a cruelty.
                         They walked in silence
down the straight reach of the oak-bordered road,
under the passion of the red and brown,
in the cool onset of the coming dusk.
Silent she followed him the long return
to the concealed car on the secret road,
the shared place. Silence, silence as they drove
the known road home.
                         But as they neared the house,
saw the great sweep of bay, the eastern sky
pierced by the evening star, Jennifer spoke.
Her voice was cold.
                         "I shan't forget," she said.
"I know now what I should have known before.
I won't forget—nor you forget it, either.
Thanks, dear, dear father, for helping with the plants.
They'll be so pretty in the spring. Each year
you can look at them and remember how
you helped your daughter dig them up to plant
in cute, conventional beds."
                         He made no answer.
In silence then they entered in the house,
the usual and the known. But stranger now.

⬚⬚⬚⬚⬚⬚

THE EVENING passed in a haze of his fatigue
and his deep disturbance. But now both of these
were the background to his acts, and the acts dictated
by the events that were well beyond control:
Virginia's illness, the news of Jerome Westen's
finding and harboring Harlow, Serena's coming

(he was glad that Rochester hadn't come with her,
but glad without phrasing it), doctor, the hypodermic,
the presence of Jennifer, helpful and detached
and oddly neutral, not being warm or cold,
but simply there; and then at last wife's sleeping,
the drug-induced, and the planning with Serena,
and finally bed in the little room alone,
too tired to think, too tired even to be
relieved that Jenny had gone to bed before him
and he needn't say good night.

       Too tired to sleep
except in a fitful dozing that woke and woke
to a sense of sorrow, the feel of something weighing
heavily on his life.

      And all next day
the work at the office and the men to see
and the mind to whip to attention while the flesh
cried out for rest, and the sharp, persistent thought
that when evening came and he could go home at last,
there would be the house and Virginia would not be there,
but only the small boy and—beyond thinking of—
Jennifer too.

      But it didn't turn out that way.
There was only Eddie; and Jennifer wasn't home,
there was just a message: she wouldn't be home for dinner,
she'd be back late—only that.

        He found himself
greatly disturbed—though part of him felt relief:
something had been postponed that he had no strength
to cope with now.

      He managed to be himself
with the small boy at supper, and read aloud
for an hour afterwards. But when the boy was in bed,
Quintus went to his room.

        I'll get in my bed,
I'll read, he said to himself, I'll read for a while
till the mind lets go and then, pray God, I'll sleep.
He thought of the little sleeping pills, he almost
went to Virginia's room for them. Then he said,
I'll wait a little, I'll see if the sleep won't come

without their help, the book will maybe do it.
He took off his clothes, he took a long, hot bath,
he got to his bed and settled himself to read:
a murder mystery, something to fill the mind
with a credible unreality detached
from all the use of the day and the day's binding
problems, confusions, hurts.
                    He was almost ready
to turn off the light and risk the attempt to sleep,
when he heard a knock on his door.
                    He said, "Come in,"
but the words were a reflex, habit, not a willing:
indeed, they denied his will.
                    The wooden door
swung slowly open and Jennifer entered the room.
She closed the door behind her. She smiled at him,
and said, "Good evening, Q." She was dressed for bed—
surprising, he'd heard no sound—but she wore her wrapper,
a thick and quilted covering. Her dark hair
shone as before. He noticed that her lips
were still made up with the flamboyant red
she'd favored recently.
                    He said, "Hello, there.
You came back early."
                    She said, "I was too weary
to stay up late. After last night. I see
you're drugging yourself. You must be weary too."
"I am," he said. He lowered the book to the bed,
face down and open. "I'd rather take this than pills."
"Of course," she said. She moved up closer then,
stood by the bedside. "I just came in to say
good night, sweet dreams. I'm weary, but I'm wound up.
I think I'll read too. Maybe then I'll unwind."
"Yes," he said.
                    "I had a terrific time
with Rochester, Q. A really terrific time."
"Did you?" he said. "What way?"
                    "I showed the paintings,
some of the drawings. He liked them, really liked them,
you could tell by his voice, his manner, it wasn't merely

being polite or helpful. He liked my own—
not those for Mensinger. God! it was exciting!
He's really clever, isn't he? And he knows—
he knows his stuff. He certainly knows his stuff.
It's done me good."
                              "I'll bet it has," he said.
He watched her face. It wore a secretive smile,
an inward look. He saw, with a sort of panic,
a hurtful feeling, how beautiful she appeared,
her face so young and flushed, her cheeks so full,
the eyes (withholding) brilliant with something hidden,
some joy enclosed in her.
                              "Clever," she said.
          "Accomplished.
I'm going to see more of him. Funny, you suddenly
make a new relation with someone known
always so differently before. Oh, yes—
so very differently. I thought I would tell you,
before I went to bed. I knew you'd be glad
to hear about it. It's given me confidence—
in many ways. I guess that I needed that."
She smiled at him now directly, she almost laughed.
She said, "I got the plants in, too, they're happy,
each in their beds. They'll grow. You'll see them grow.
I can hardly wait for spring. Good night, dear Q,
I'll pop along now, you'll want to get your sleep.
Don't read too late. Tomorrow's another day.
Good night." She waved her hand and turned at once,
and walked to the door and opened it. She said,
"You know, when we left, when we crossed the wall to the
          road,
at Harlow's place—poor Harlow!—there was a car,
the taxi, Asa Congdon's, parked up the road.
You saw it, didn't you?"
                              "No," he said. "I didn't."
His mind recalled the scene with a clarity
brilliant in all details: the road, the trees,
the violent leaves, the color of greening sky,
the young girl following with the heavy basket,
the long road back to the car, the empty road—
284

no taxi in the memory.

                   "What do you think
Asa was doing there? Oh, I have to laugh
when I think of you and me and the way we called
Harlow to rid ourselves of Harlow then!
Well, I thought I'd ask. I hope poor Mummy's O.K.
The house seems empty, doesn't it? Well, good night."
She left and she closed the door and the closing made
its cruel, dividing sound.

                   He lay quite still
till he heard her door close too. Then heavily rose,
put on his dressing gown, walked to Virginia's room,
found the sleeping tablets, took two of them,
and returned to bed. The bed in the single room
with the door shut and the house empty.

                       Some way
you had to have sleep, you must have sleep. Indeed,
tomorrow's another day. And you mustn't think
of Rochester Mallin, the skilful, the accomplished,
nor Asa Congdon, nor of the unseen taxi—
nor of Jennifer.

Part Six

MILLICENT WESTEN

FIRST LIGHT coming and the bed warm and remembering;
    Monday.
Freddie curled up in a ball, deep in the child-sleep, thumb in the
    mouth, so sweet,
warm on one side, Jerry warm on the other. Oh, lucky
to wake so!
                No hurry, almost an hour
before rising and children, breakfast. Soon the soft whirr
of the thermostat and the heat on.
                         Poor boy! Do hope Harlow
got some sleep, Freddie so cute and excited, lending
his bed to him. Small bed, not
really a man-size. But the boy, exhausted, the small
sedative pills, how nice and kind dear
Dr. Fanshawe, probably slept, he'll be
hungry, some oatmeal, eggs this morning the doctor said,
something solid, but young, they pick up, get over soon, young.
Warm bed, warm nest, me
and my males, nice. Poor boy!
                    Don't move, lie still
yet a while, my men deeply
sleeping.
          Sky's grey, the spell of the
clear days gone now, oh well, they lasted, lucky
for poor Harlow.
              Fasting. Curious. Something
hard to get hold of, hurts and something
looked for, run to, run from? Strange strong
passion to not go back to the Lamys'. Remember
what he said, late, but remember more

286

the way he said it, something like, 'Not now, later.
First to digest it, make it mine, then
it can be faced, do you understand? The facing
is too soon now.'
            No fever, yet
something like fever, not normal, the brightness
of the grey eyes, the funny hard, not young, thin drawn
line of the mouth, not hating and not caring but
wilful? or what?
            Queer thing to happen to
Jerry and Millicent! Maybe
that Jerry found him, only that, or maybe the warm
voice of Jerry, still sleeps, so does Freddie, curled
in the arch of my back, warm, so dear, so small, will he
go through this too?
            Woman? The pretty
Messler girl, such lovely clothes, they were
together so much then, spring then, she looked
in love then. Maybe only
in love with in love and spring, but he's so
good-looking, Harlow. Poor boy! Turned off? All of us
go through something, I almost
didn't take Jerry, imagine, no, can't imagine, not
lying now in the warmth between him and Freddie, the cool
day beginning, the sense of
the wanted and the secure.
            Better maybe
to get it over, to start fresh. Hope
I can help a little, woman, clever of Jerry saying
you do it, he'll be easier, to you, not me, a man, see?
Jerry's a man, mine, he is kind, oh!
the cool and the welcome coming of the many-demanding
day, the Monday feeling and school and the young
voices, ours, all ours, poor Harlow, he
is nobody's but his own, it will
have to be later, but the pretty young Messler, Jennifer,
looking for trouble or freedom, and what is freedom, are you
free as you lie between the man and his child and the
day and its tasks for a blanket?
            I am warm. Is not

287

the warmth of my making too?
                              Oh, I do hope
there's enough oatmeal, I gave the kids that, let's see,
only two days ago, but ought to be some, the kids
can have dry cereal. Sure there are lots of eggs,
and tea, the doctor said tea, don't give him coffee, give
tea tomorrow. And milk. Monday, the man came
Saturday, good, this morning again. Soon now
up and about.
                The thing
is to listen, listen, be kind to listen, to hear, let
the boy talk if he wants to talk, or else be silent,
be welcome, easily, no demands, let him
go or stay or anything. Will he go
back to the Lamys'? To get his things or will Lamy
bring them over? It's awkward, I don't
know what to say to him, good man, I like him, but
different, they're all different, what is
the difference, cook in the kitchen not hers, or
the way of speaking? But happiness from the difference?
Here is happiness.
                    Move now, closer, touching, the warm
body against his body, so warm, saying (he stirs now), nothing,
it's me, dear, sleep again, just want
closeness. And the soft sigh saying, Mm—hmm, and
the little movement of settling, the even
breathing of sleep again, close now.
                                      Soon
up and about, but now
taste comfort, briefly, it is always
there for the tasting.
                       Oh, good, the little light
body of Freddie pressing into the space left
vacant for my own comfort, good, oh,
all of us.
          Monday, mustn't
forget the laundry today, grey, hope
that it doesn't rain.

Part Seven

JEROME WESTEN

□ □ □ □ □ □

LATE in the bright-metalled morning that held indefinably
smell of a Sunday, Jerome took the two youngest children
and they walked peacefully, happily (the steady and firm
pace of the man, the rolling, on-the-toes jiggle of Freddie, the
hop and scamper of eight years uncontrollable in Justine)
to the small grey pebbly beach south of Little Rose Head.
The yacht club turned its blind, green-shuttered eyes seaward,
closed now, unsocial, the gulls stood
puffed and motionless on the wet stretch of the muddy
sand of the lowering tide. Off to the southwest
the bay was a deep blue in the gentle riffle
of the light northwest breeze. The land smells, bayberry,
cedar and warm earth flowed out and over them, mixed
with the dry pungence of the drifts of seaweed
curved into windrows high on the neap tide line.

The children
played in the sand and dug and resurrected
a horse-shoe crab, foul smelling. He didn't care:
there was nothing that just a little
soap and water wouldn't take care of. Jerry just sat
and let the sun sink into him and allow him merely
to be, most peacefully and contentedly aware
of the sense of the flesh of him. Warmth on the back,
hotness on skin of the neck and the cool, comfortable
feel of the sand and the sun on the bare feet.

Justine and
Freddie
now had the giggles. Nice sound. Good kids, fun
to sit and be near them, nothing

to worry about. How good was last night!
He stretched his body and felt his muscles moving
and remembered Millicent. Good, even after having
the four sweet kids. Not as good as Loretta Messler,
she was terrific, but then, just the one child, and all
that sort of woman seemed to know how to fix it
so nothing was lost. Money, I guess, he thought. One child.
She wasn't married then, it was just after the second
divorce, she married Messler later, a nice guy,
stiff and a little pompous, but a nice guy. I guess
he had a rough ride the first time round, Virginia,
and why the hell did Lamy hook up to her? Well,
she was a hot-looking babe back in those days, and glory,
she has a hot-looking daughter! That Jennifer! Someone
was going to be lucky who got to lay that body, or maybe
someone already was. But lots of trouble.

                         In two years
I'm going to be forty, I'm a kid no longer, I wouldn't
mix myself up again with a number like Jenny,
and I wouldn't get tangled up with Loretta now, funny,
you could remember, the memory was pure pleasure,
but it was just memory, it was better so, better
to sleep night after night with a woman like Millie
and the hell with a little better, a little hotter, there was
plenty of heat yet, and you knew
you'd wake up and be glad and not start sort of wondering
what the hell you'd say or maybe would have to do
when you didn't really want it.

                          He stretched again,
full of well-being and knew he was getting hungry
and food would be ready soon. Ah! Sunday dinner,
it was going to taste good, life was good, no worries,
the sun delicious.

                "Hey, kids!" he called out to them,
"I'm getting hungry."

                Freddie stood up at once, he dropped
all the shells he was holding and walked up toward him,
saying, "I'm hungry too."

                "Oh," said Justine, "oh, Freddie,
you're always hungry. But I'm not hungry. It's nice

here on the beach and as soon as it's nice, then always
we have to go home and eat."
                              "Poor you," said Jerome.
"It's a hard life. And you with no appetite
and steamer clams coming up."
                              "Oh, clams?" she said.
"Oh, good!" And she too stood, and she brushed
sand from her clothes. "Oh, I love clams," she said.
"I hope there's lots."
                              "There's lots," her father said.
"So let's get moving." He got up slowly, feeling
the skin move on his sun-warmed legs. He looked out then
over the water. The northern tip of the curving
of Sickle Island loomed and the tide had made
triple the long curve of glass in the riffled blue
of the wide Sunday water.
                        The tide still ebbs, he thought.
It'll begin to flood about three o'clock at Cross Bridge,
and the wind will freshen, there ought to be a good chance
for catching the skipjacks. The girls might like to go,
or some of them, but say nothing in front of Freddie, the boy
is still too young for that. It's going to be fun
to teach him fishing. Now lunch. A lovely day, home,
home to be fed, and home to Millicent, you were
fed by someone like Millicent more ways than one.
"Come along," he said. "I'm happy."
                              "I'm happy too," said
     Freddie.
"But I'm hungry. I don't like clams."
                              "Good," said Jerome.
"Then there'll be more for the rest of us."
                              The small boy
looked startled at his father. Justine said, "Pop,
do I have to put on my shoes?"
                              "Lord, no!" he said.
"I'm going barefoot myself."
                        The three began
their various gaits toward home, and happily home. The day
still smelled of Sunday and all shadows
were small under the high noon.

□□□□□□

EDYTH, who was fourteen now, pretty like Millicent,
beginning to show what she would be as a woman,
drove over to Cross Bridge in the soft Sunday
afternoon with her father. They took their light rods
and the red and green floats and the long ten-foot seine
and the two pails and an empty coffee can with holes
punched in the top.

The breeze was fresh and blew clean
out of the northwest. Under the narrow
constraint of the old wooden-span bridge and the long
stone embankments that led to it over the shallow
flats of the tidal river, the current, flood now
just beginning to strengthen, began its ancient
war with the wind. Soft green opaque water pushed on
hard to the northwest and the wind attacked it, pushing
hard to the southeast and the small, troubled chop-waves
stood and wavered and frothed, unable to move save
up and down in a sort of permanent joggle of
light-filled miniature hills whose miniature valleys
bloomed into white lace flowers, sown by the wind on
field of water and flowing
over the hills like clouds, the unharvested.
Off in the distance, lost
to the eye in the intensity of the luminous air,
a winter yellowleg called and called, renewing
his five-note, chrome-steel cry of the lonely places,
and the marsh grass flowed in the wind.

They leant their rods on the solid wood of the bridge's parapet
and Jerome rolled up his trousers above his knees and they took
the pails and the can and the seine and they walked together
out to the shallow water on the west side, defined
by tiny beaches of curving muddy sand, the stiff
bristle of water grasses. Back and forth
they hauled the seine, top cord held in one hand, the bottom
cord held in other after it had passed under
their sneakered feet, backward and forward, slowly
in the warm riffled water; landing
the seine in a swift movement on the small sandy

beaches and hearing the good
splash of the multiple and various
tiny fishes within the brown and close-meshed
strands of the seine. Happily, laughing, Edyth
saying, "See this one! Oh, do look! It's got
prickles all over it," they sorted the
catch of the draft, the flipping, slipping, glistening
richness of water-harvest.

Off in the northeast under
the blue of the deep sky turned now
away from the sun's passion, the yellowleg
cried out his metal lonely
O! where are you, O! where are you now?
Drift of the plovers flying
close, close to water, long sharp
wings in the rhythm of conflict with
wind to be glad of, cried back, impatient,
We'll *be* there, we'll *be* there!
                              Tide rip
north of the bridge kept winning and losing
bright green inches and growing the unending
flowers of foam-white, foam-grey, lace-grey.

They put all the big shiners, that were more than two inches long,
the narrow, translucent fish of the backs enamelled in silver
and the green stripe like a boat's neat water-line running
from gills to tail, these
went into one of the pails in water. These would be bait.
The littlest shiners, the tiny oyster crabs, two could fit
to the little finger's nail, and the grey and very small
shrimps, into the second pail with its salty water. These
to be fried in the deep fat and eaten.
But the big crabs with fierce blue claws were urged
to their swift escape, and the multitude
of the brown barred mummiechogs with the big mouths and the
          fierce
will to live in the air, and the many late-spawned, tiny
white perch, yellow perch, blue fish, needle fish, flounders,
striped bass and the ones with odd prickles all over, these

293

were thrown back into the water save for a few of each in
the coffee can, to take home for the great delight
of small Freddie.
Edyth giggled and jumped and
poked crabs out with a stick and said, "Oh, Poppy,
the jellyfish are disgusting!"
Jerry just laughed. He said,
"Nothing but phosphorus, honey, they can't hurt you,
it's what makes the shine in the dark water at night."
"I know," she said, "but they're all so goozly awful."
He laughed again and he thought, she's growing up, two years ago
it didn't faze her, a tomboy then.
It was fun to do,
a pleasant thing, unthinking, the sun still warm,
the breeze cool, and the feet wrinkled and white in
the warm of the shallow waters.
When they'd caught enough,
they fished from the bridge; the little floats ran with the tide
and bobbled up and down. You could simply stand
unthinking, silent, and watch the float on the water and
hold the rod and feel the drag of the tide
and the joggle of waves of the little rip,
and nothing else at all was needed. Time flowed
smoother than water, unhurried and unperceived, it ran
like the deep flow
of the green dark water below the planks of the bridge,
but it made no sound.

Off to the south in the woods of the reddened oaks
a crow cawed and was answered and cawed again
and the harsh sound mellowed in the deep air flowing,
and the yellowleg cried in his wild and steely
voice saying, I am alone all
alone alone here, and the west wind
brought the hoot of an engine four miles away, soft,
deep and usual, deepening the afternoon, the silence
flooding in after to the undemanding
water sound flowing below the cool-felt
pressure of wind flow.

294

There was almost no fishing. They didn't really care, or certainly
Jerry didn't, he was simply happy without
necessity of more than the act and the place and the presence
of pretty Edyth, so cheerful.
There was one flurry when
a small school of the skipjacks came and they did catch three,
and the floats bobbed under the water, and the shiners
were snatched clean off from the hooks. But it was over
soon and the sun sat redly
above the trees of the hill to the west and the dropping wind
felt suddenly cold and it was time to go home.
"It's getting chilly," said Jerry. "It's late, too. You'd better
put on your sweater, and I guess we'll stop now."
"But I'm not cold," the girl said. "It's not really late."
"Put on the sweater," he said. "We've got to stop.
The tide is slacking, the wind has dropped, there'll be
no more fishing." He reeled in his long, green line,
cleared the hook of the eel-grass, took off the curving shiner dead
      now,
fastened the hook to a reel-stay. "Just three fish. I'm sorry
we didn't get more, but we got a load of the whitebait, a fine
collection for Freddie."
"We did," she said. "Oh, Pops, I wish
I knew what they all were, do you know what they are?"
She began to reel in her line.
"Not all," he said. "No. Just
some of them. Never did know."
"I wish
we could just show them to Freddie," she said, "and then
let us have them, he'll spill them out or something, so we
could take them to school and ask."
"Why, sure," said Jerry.
"We'll do that. A good idea." He took her rod
and he said, "I'll finish, put on your sweater, the sun's
down and the air's cold. Your mommy will skin me alive if
I bring you home with a cold."
She did what he told her,
and they packed the things in the car and began to drive
toward home and supper.

295

The bridge, alone now,
spanned the tide that had given up its conflict
with the fled wind of the north, and the glaze
of the blue dusk covered the
whisper of easy water.

░░░░░░

JERRY was happy as he drove home. It was good
to be full of the sun, to be pleasantly, gently weary, the legs
tired a little from seining, from the long, peaceful
standing to fish. It was good to be with Edyth, to have her here,
to see her so pretty, so grown, to be going home to
the others, the kids, to Millie, to supper
and the enfolding lights of the lamps, to sleep. He didn't
think about it at all, it was all there, like the three small
blue fish and the good mess of whitebait and crabs and shrimps;
it was, and it needed no thought.
                                    It was like loving Millie:
you did or you didn't. No use to think about it.
A good day.
                    Then he noticed the car parked
by the side of the road—he was driving very slowly, the road
was full of stones, small holes—and he knew it, Asa's taxi.
What the hell was Asa doing to haul somebody—who?—
to the old Standeven place?
                                    A funny one, that. Oh, well,
easy to find it out. His mind leaped then, at once
to the Hearing and he laughed to himself and thought,
I'll bet old Hetty Browne's burnt to a crisp with Ted Gross,
and she'll lose her petition too. Just all too smart.
This wasn't the sort of place—and Christ knew they
ought to have known that—where you could get by
with that sort of a too smart deal. Ted Gross should have known
it never would work like that. People like Mallin.
And Ledbetter on the Board.
                                    He switched his lights on, the better
to spot the bad holes, ruts. Almost at once
he slammed on the brakes, his right arm flinging out in
a reflex motion to guard Edyth. The car squealed,

296

the tires scratched on the gravel-dirt.

"What is it?" Edyth said,
her voice a little frightened.

"Nothing," said Jerry. "It's only I
saw something by the side of the road. I'm sorry, honey,
didn't mean to scare you."

"It's O.K.," the girl said,
"it was just so sudden, Poppy."

"Sure was," he said.
He backed the car up and turned it a little sidewise until
the lights shone on the ditch by the roadside, its depth
filled with fallen oak leaves caught in a drift
by the brown bare stems of the sparse sweet-fern.
He opened the door and got out and walked around
the back of the car, and forward again, seeing now
the body that lay in the ditch.

A man.

A drunk,
he thought at once. He went to kneel by the body. He heard
the car door open.

"Get right back in," he said in a voice
he didn't often use, hard and peremptory. He didn't look round.
He heard the car door close and click. Fourteen. You didn't
know what a drunk would say. Inside himself a swift
irrelevant voice said, 'What could the poor drunk say that she
wouldn't have heard, at fourteen?' And he giggled silently
and bent to look at the man.

He knew him at once, it was
young Harlow Standeven. The boy
was asleep or passed out. He lay half covered over
with the crisp curled brown of
the oak leaves. His face, uncovered, clear to be seen in
the beam of the headlights, was uncommonly pale, his breathing
shallow, irregular, hard to hear. There was
none of the stertorous breathing of the unconscious
drunk by the roadside.

Jerome reached out and touched him:
his body was warm under the jacket of rough, torn tweed,
his heart beat, weak and irregular, was faint under
the blue cotton shirt. But touched so, the young man

297

stirred not at all.

    So then Jerome shook him, roughly.
Harlow moved a little, stirred slightly, his eyes kept
closed, his hand brushed once, lightly, over his face as though
a fly had troubled him, and he sighed, and he said,
clearly but ununderstandably, in a whisper,
"Lupo mi ha mandato, vuole
inviare il vino."
Foreign, thought Jerry, it maybe could be Italian. Vino,
that was the wop for wine. He said,
"No more vino, brother, maybe too much of the stuff."
The young man didn't move but he opened dilated eyes wide
and he smiled, looking at Jerry, and he said, more
incomprehensibly than the Italian, "I knew
God damned well that you'd come. Let's go. Andiamo."
He rolled over then at once onto his stomach and began
carefully to rise, first to his knees and then, slowly,
up to his feet, swaying a little. He said,
"Weak as a kitten."

    Jerry got up with Harlow,
he put his hand below the boy's elbow to steady him.
"Good now," he said. "I'll help you
into the car, and we'll go home."

      "No," said Harlow.
"Not home. Not home again. Never home again. No.
It's over and done with. Been there." He made then
the immemorial gesture, as he swayed, dusting
his palms together, dismissing, and he said softly,
"Well, that's that. I have buried my father."
He swayed again violently, he almost fell, he reached out
and clutched at Jerry's shoulder, steadied himself and
looked at Jerry again. He said, "I know you,
you're Jerry Westen." He smiled. He said, "It's good
to get it all straight again, to remember their names.
There was Mrs. Browne and old Miss Hall and Asa
and Mr. Lamy and Jennifer, and there was also
Rochester Mallin's horse. I saw them, but nobody saw me,
though I thought they did during all the time that
I didn't know them." He smiled again. "Didn't see me,

298

none of them. Only the horse."

Standing beside him, so close,
the boy's breath in his face, Jerry
was sure that he wasn't drunk. Harlow's breath
was fresh and was clean.

"Sure, the horse," said Jerry.
"Let's get in the car, O.K.?"

"O.K.," said Harlow.
"Better if I sit down."

Jerome called out, saying,
"Edyth, get out now, open the door and hold it, I'm going
to put young Standeven into the front seat. You
had better ride in the back then." Without turning
he heard the door open and the girl's voice saying,
"It's open, Poppy. Is Mr. Standeven sick?"
"He's feeling weak," said Jerry.

"Weak as water,"
Harlow said in a whisper. "Like being frightened, your
knees feel watery, except that I'm not frightened,
not a bit any more."

"Come along, then," said Jerry.
"Easy does it." He put one arm round the boy's waist,
the other under an elbow. The boy walked
with surprising steadiness, climbing
slowly out of the ditch, slowly across the deep
swale of oak leaves, over the rough
edge of the road and up, almost unaided now, using
both his hands, into the front seat, sitting down,
heaving a big sigh, saying then, "Ah, that's good.
We did it. We made it."

Jerry, watching him closely,
saw the pallor increase to a pasty whiteness on
Harlow's face, the sweat start
out on his forehead.

"Move over a little," he said. "Move
toward the middle, you can?"

Harlow moved over, his
mouth was a thin line, lips bloodless.

"Get in beside him,"

Jerry said to his daughter. "Brace him, honey, he's feeling sort of weak, I guess."

The girl got in,
Jerry closed the door gently and walked quickly around to his own side. He climbed in, shutting the door.
"O.K.?" he said.

The boy nodded only.

"O.K., then."
He put the car in gear. "Just lean back, son, I'll drive her slowly, hang on to Edyth, she's strong. We'll go back to the Lamys' now and you'll be fine."
Harlow spoke then and his voice was surprisingly strong, he said, "No, not to the Lamys'. No. Not
to the Lamys'. Anywhere. Maple Inn, anything, not to the Lamys'."

"You're staying there," Jerry said.
"Was," said Harlow. "Not now. Inn, please. You understand me? I will not
go to the Lamys'. Christ sake. *Claro?*" He swayed sidewise, straightened himself again, and his voice blurred, and he said, "*Lupo ha dice . . . treno . . . Svizzera.*" Then he fainted, slumping
down in his seat.

"Hold him up, honey," said Jerry.
"I guess that we'll take him home, we'll take him to Mommy."
The girl put her arm around Harlow's sagging shoulders and Jerome drove slowly over the bumpy road in the soft autumn dusk, toward home and Millicent Westen and the sure things.

HARLOW came out of his faint as the car pulled up in front of the Westen's house, and Jerry said to his daughter, "Run in, tell Mommy, honey."

The girl got out of the car quickly
and ran to the house.

"Where is this?" said Harlow.
Jerry looked round at him. Even in the increasing darkness the boy seemed less white.

300

"Good. You've come to. Hang on to it. We'll have you in bed soon."

"Yes," said Harlow. "Where are we?"

"My house, at Chogs Cove. My daughter's gone in to tell her mother. Sit easy now, wait till she comes."

"Shouldn't be here," the boy said. His speech was clearer, but still blurred. "Should have taken me to the Maple Inn at Cottrellton. They know me."

"Sure," said Jerry. "Sure. It was just too far, I wanted to get Edyth home for her supper. It's late."

"Oh," said Harlow.

"Oh, yes. I see. I'm sorry if I've delayed you. Stupid. I guess I'm weak. I haven't had food since . . . since . . ." His voice trailed off. "Hard to remember. Time," he said. He smiled. "Old Anachronos. You know, it was damn funny, but I heard the clocks tick."

"Sure," said Jerome. "Sure. Where was all this ticking?"

"And all the, all the flowers, the ones that were not there. Funny. I'd like to tell someone about it. Iris Osiris. I thought of a lot of things. Like Romeo wasn't built in a day. I ought to tell someone about all this."

"Sure thing," said Jerry. "Just hang on to it now, you can tell Millie later. She likes to listen. Right now, just save up the strength, you'll be sort of heavy to carry in all the way to the house if you pass out, faint again. How would hot soup sound?"

"Soup," said the boy, and paused. "Yes, some soup. It sounds good, delicious. It's queer, I'm not really hungry at all, but I'm very empty. It makes you weak. Long time." He paused again. "What day is today?"

"It's Sunday. Sunday evening."

"Oh. Sunday evening. Oh, yes. I see. He used to come home on Sundays, always, he was punctual in his habits. That's all over."

"Sure," said Jerry.

"Just hang on now, they're coming." He felt his spirits
rise as he saw his wife come out, and Edyth with her, and
Emily too. There'd be lots of help to get this
boy to the house, to bed, to get him
where Millie could care for him.

☐☐☐☐☐☐

IT HADN'T been hard to do. Harlow had walked in, under his
own power, just steadied a little, and he had sat, quietly, pale,
in the big overstuffed armchair with the three children
gathered around him, looking, but kindly, with the child's
endless interest in novelty.
                    "I guess that we'd better put him
in Freddie's room," Jerome said, "the only single one, the bed
isn't too big but it has no footboard."
                    "Yes," said Millicent.
"Edyth is making it up now."
                    "You don't mind, Freddie?" Jerome
asked his son.
                    "Will he sleep in my bed with me?"
"No, he's too big, but you know what?"
                    "No, what?"
"You lend him your bed and you can come in with us, and sleep
with Mommy and me, for a treat."
                    "Oh, yes," said Freddie.
He went a little bit nearer to Harlow, said, "You can have
my bed to sleep in and I'm sure
I'm very, very welcome."
                    "Thank you," said Harlow faintly,
trying to smile.
                    "And I'll come in after I've had my supper,
and you can read to me."
                    "Fine," said Harlow.
                                        "Emily,"
Jerome said, "why not take Freddie now, along with Justine,
and start your supper. It's late, and Mommy's busy."
Emily nodded and smiled and the three children went out
to the kitchen next door.
                    Then Millicent and Jerome

sent Edyth in to look after the other children and they put
Harlow to bed.

The boy walked in by himself, but as soon
as he lay down, he fainted again. Together they stripped him.
It was odd, his clothes, though ripped in innumerable small
tears as though by briars, were clean except for the dry mud
caked on the front. The toes of his shoes, his elbows,
his hands, were muddied too. In a clean pair
of Jerome's pyjamas they tucked him into the bed and he lay
inert and pale, unconscious. Millicent laid
her hand on his forehead, shook her head, said in a whisper,
"He has no fever, or at least, I don't think so," and together
they left the room and closed the door to a thin crack, one lamp
lit against waking.
"What is it all about, Jerry?"

"Tell you later. I think
I should call the doctor. I guess I better call Dr. Fanshawe,
looks after the Lamys."

"Yes, that's next," Millicent said.
"And afterwards, call the Lamys?"

"Yes, I guess so, Millie.
Can't say I want to."

"No," said Millie. "I'll put the baby
to bed now, settle the others. Then I'll be back."

He got the doctor, that was simple enough, and Fanshawe
said he'd come down and look at the boy. Then Jerry, neither
worried nor happy about it, called up the Lamys' house.
He got Jennifer Messler.

He said, "Can I speak to Mr. Lamy,
it's Jerome Westen, Jennifer. Is your pa at home?"
The girl's voice said, "Yes, oh, hello, Jerry. Sure, he's here. I'll
call him for you."

"Don't like to bother him, this time of a
Sunday,"
Jerome said. "Tell him it's about Harlow Standeven, the boy's
here at my house."

There was only the slightest pause.
"Really?" she said, without emphasis. "I'll tell Quintus.
How is Harlow?"

303

"Not too good," Jerome said.

"Pity,"
said Jennifer. "Give him my *best* regards. I'll go get Quintus.
Hang on a minute."

Jerome chuckled, thinking, she might
as well have said it, she really meant
the son of a bitch. The whole thing's funny, there's something
complicated is happening.

Lamy's voice said,
"Hello, Jerry. I hear that you've got the boy."
"That's it," said Jerry. "I've got him here at the house, he's
in poor shape. In bed now, sleeping."

"Sleeping it off?"
"Don't think it's booze," said Jerry. "Found him unconscious
in the ditch by the road to Cross Bridge, by his own place,
he was unconscious. No smell of liquor at all. I
brought him here, I had Edyth with me, we've put him
straight to bed. I've called up Dr. Fanshawe, and he's
coming down soon. I guess he's the right man?"
"Yes, that's dead right," said Quintus. "Yes. Dr. Fanshawe.
I guess he knows him, too. From the old days."

Jerome waited
then,
it seemed a long time, for the expected question. It didn't
come. "I tell you," said Quintus then. "Ask Fanshawe
to give me a ring when he's seen the boy, been over him,
I'd like to hear what he's got to say. Odd. I figured
he'd been on a binge."

"All pretty funny," Jerome said.
"I sort of gathered he hadn't had much to eat, and seemed
pretty weak in the legs, kinda white. Yes, I'll ask the doc
to call you up, he ought to get here pretty soon. I got him
at supper at home. I was scared I'd have to chase him
all over town."

"That's good," said Quintus. "I'm glad
he's safe with you and Millicent, he couldn't
be in better hands."

Well, O.K., thought Jerome then,
I'll have to say it. Sooner or later.

"I tell you,

304

he seemed in poor shape, sort of a shock or something. He
was upset, some, he didn't want to be taken
back to your house. Wanted to go to the Inn,
up at Cottrellton. I had Edyth along, getting kinda late, so
I brought him here, and Millie. He wasn't
making too much sense."

"Yes. I see," said Lamy.
"Well, thank you, Jerry. It's good of you. I'm relieved
he's turned up. My wife will be relieved, she's worried.
I'll wait till the doctor calls. Thank you for calling me."
Different, thought Jerry Westen, as he hung up the telephone.
Different. They never say
just what they mean, they go around it with all sorts of
words and politeness, you have to guess
what the hell they really think. And a good guy, too, a good
guy and a friend. Why wrap up life in a fog of words
when you could say it out flat? Well, it was just
a different system.

Millie came into the room. She said,
"Did you get them?"

"Yes, I did, and Doc Fanshawe's coming,
and I spoke to Lamy." He grinned. "He's a nice guy.
He was very polite. And Millie, I got, first off,
Jennifer on the phone. She was polite too, all her
words, and what they said, and the voice, was actually,
well, the son of a bitch, I hope he rots. That's
quite a babe, that Jenny."

Millicent sniffed, softly.
She said, "What happened, Jerry? Tell me."
He said, "It was funny, I found him by the roadside as
Edyth and I came back from Cross Bridge. Golly, I clean forgot,
there are fish in the car, three skipjacks, and whitebait, I'll
get them later. Anyhow, he was lying, he was half covered
in leaves by the roadside, right opposite
his old place. He was unconscious. I thought, sure as hell,
he was drunk or passed out. Until I smelled
his breath there. I shook him. He said
something I couldn't get, I think it was in Italian, I got
one word, *vino*. Anyhow, I don't know. While Edyth and I

305

were getting him in the car he said some funny things, he
spoke of knowing some people now, he called off
Asa and Hetty Browne, and Anna Hall, and Lamy—"
he was ticking them off on his fingers—
"and Jennifer and Rochester Mallin's horse. No
kidding, he said that. He even said
nobody saw him except the horse. It wasn't
funny at all at the time. What's funny, Millie,
was Asa's taxi was parked up the road a little, near
the old entrance drive of the house. His taxi, mind you,
and not his own car. The whole thing's
queer as hell. Well, we got in the car and I put
Edyth in front to hold him, he looked so white, exactly
as if he was going to faint, and he did too, but before
he fainted I said I would take him back to Lamy's and
he said, out loud and clear, too, no, not to Lamy's,
he wouldn't go there, not for nothing, to take him
to the Maple Inn. He meant it. He sounded half way
between a sort of panic and a kind of
determination. Hard to describe. It was getting
late, and Edyth, and so I brought him
here and to you. I guess
that was the best to do?"

       "Yes, that was the best," said Millie.
"We can care for him here. Gee, it's a queer story, I
hope he don't go crazy, the kids. But he seems
a gentle sort of a boy."

      "Upset," said Jerry. "It's maybe
that baby Jennifer. Well, we can wait for the doctor, he's
a good doctor, he knows those sort of people, they're
different from us. Everything's complicated. There's nothing
is ever simple and straight. Listen, I'm hungry, all day
in the open air, let's eat now while we're waiting, you
start some supper and I'll bring in the fish and
the tackle and put the car up. Jesus, some days
I'm glad I'm married to you."

LET US GO lightly, quickly now over
the mere events, we know them already a little,
they are only
the acts, the things done that form
the map of the land where the heart dwells. We shall pause,
scrutinize through the strange magnifying
lens of words when we come to the place
of the heart's dwelling, abiding. Oh, strange,
oh, fearful (be fearful) this abiding
within the heart of another to know
the cause of the blood's
crafty and punctual flood. But now
be fearful, but with a humility until
(discerned through the lens) it becomes
yours and your own. Now
lightly and swiftly a space and a space.

The Doctor:
"No, no. Nothing really wrong. I judge it's
from lack of all food, mostly. And maybe shock, it could be
emotional shock. No injuries, anyway, there are
no bruises, there's been
no concussion or anything. Temperature
a little subnormal. Just soup and tomorrow cereal,
and tea, better tea than coffee. The boy's
young, youth is on his side still, the body is
the mind's master. Feed him, and sleep will
finish the rest of it. Then
we can look to the mind, a little.
Only a little. We all
have the right to be crazy, at least a little, and
now and then. Good night. I'm off now,
poor Mrs. Lamy. I wish
she had youth on her side. 'Night, Jerry, 'night, Millicent.
No coffee at all in the morning. I'll call in
tomorrow sometime."

The Plans and the Daily:
He said, "I won't go up to the office tomorrow, Millie. I'll call
Henrietta and tell her, if anyone comes she'll call me. I want
to be here."
                    She said, "There's no need, look,
I can look after him."
                             He said, "Yes, I know.
But something's happening. Maybe none of my business, only it's
made my business now, in a way. I want
to find out what cooks here. The boy, I figure, didn't
just make up the names, Hetty and Anna Hall, and then
there was Asa's taxi. There's something. If I'm here,
with the girls at school, I can take Freddie, and leave you
clear to look after Harlow. You talk to him, Millie, he'll
talk to a woman, I figure, more than a man, and I want
to find out about it. I'm just
the cat that curiosity killed. You just do it
easy and natural, like always. He'll talk. He's bound
to spill it to someone, it hooks up some way or other
with something else. I want to know. It's my business.
Is that O.K.?"
                    She said, "That's O.K. I guess
you're right, dear. We better
go to bed now, tomorrow's soon, we better go
one by one, so not to wake Freddie, cute thing. His saying
'I'm very welcome.'"
He said, "Yeah. You go first, I'll sit a little while,
finish my pipe. You go now." Smiled.
                              She left him, closing
softly the door to their room, smiling.

The Sleeping:
So, one by one into the bed for two that
held three now.
                The one
and the one could be but one and one
   308

and thus be two, or become one and so make
three in the deep, the exacting science
of the mathematics of love. This
not his knowing or hers, but known
below the surface of knowing as flesh
is known in the darkness when
spirit transcends.
>   But now
peace in the simple, the bodily
three on the soft-sprung, moving
wagon that rolls over the timeless
leagues of sleep.

The Doctor:
"He's all right. He wants to drive back now
to Cambridge, I said all right, but after his
lunch, just whatever you have, nothing special.
He's slept well, eaten. There's nothing the matter now
that food—and a little peace of mind, maybe—
won't take care of. He's young and he seems
perfectly normal, just the average young man
after that damned war."
>   The doctor paused.
>   Inside,
his mind said, oh, normal, and what is
normal, for dear God's sake, a word made
to cover ignorance, to delude. It is normal
to be a little crazy, the abnormality
is to be sane. And the worse word's average, there
is no such thing. If you ever could really find
the average man you could close up shop, the race
would vanish away in a terrible panic of
its conformity.
>   He laughed aloud. He thought,
such thoughts for a country doctor. The local

309

physician's become the local metaphysician.
Aloud he said, "Well, I'll be off. So long.
Just make him eat his lunch."

The Morning:
Jerome took Freddie and together they walked up
the half-mile to the Lamys'. They went to the back door, knocked,
there was no answer, but Jerry could see Guinevere Lovelace busy
inside the kitchen, washing up. Deaf, he thought, she won't hear.
He opened the door and entered. He stamped once with his foot
on the linoleum floor. Guinevere turned. She smiled.
"Morning," she said. "There's nobody home but me, except
Jennifer's outside somewheres. The grip is ready, it's
all packed and a green bag with books, by the front door,
the car's in back. Key's in it. Morning, Freddie, he's
grown so, Jerome!"
                    "Morning. He has," Jerome said.
"Be a big man soon. Well, I'll take the bags."
"Boy is sick, maybe?" she said. She looked at him hard,
reading his lips.
                    "No, he's all right now. Just
felt sort of weak for a spell."
                    "You get Dr. Williams?"
"No, Dr. Fanshawe. Tended him when he was just a little
sprat of a boy. Seemed better."
                    "Surely," she said.
"Well, I won't keep you. Dishes," she said. She laughed.
"Sunday dishes, a pile!" She turned around and began
at once to wash them.
                    Jerome took Freddie's hand,
they walked to the front hall, got the brown leather suitcase
and the bag of books, went out and around to the car,
standing near the garage. They had climbed in, had started
the motor running when Jerry saw Jennifer coming
up from the garden. The girl had a trowel in her hand
and wore leather gloves. She waved, and Jerome waved back, and
let the motor idle.
                    "Hello," she said. "Did you get

310

Harlow's stuff all right?"

"Yes, I got it, thanks. It's all
in the back. The case and the books. There was nothing else?"
"No, nothing else," she said. "Nice of you to come. Is
Harlow better?"

"He seems so," Jerry answered. "Doctor says so.
He aims to leave after lunch."

"I see," she said. "But still
a little too weak to come round and get his stuff?"
Jerry looked at her and he thought to himself, oh, Jesus, what
a hell of a lay you'd be. "Could be," he said. "Or else
too smart, and wants to hang on to his hair, don't aim
to be scalped yet, maybe."

She laughed. "He can keep
his hair," she said. "Is the boy's name Freddie? I get
mixed up with all your children."

"Yes. This is Freddie."
"Good morning, Freddie," she said.

The child looked at her,
a long, unblinking stare; but he said nothing.
"He's beginning early," Jennifer said. "Well, anyway, thanks
for coming over. Give Harlow my best regards. And Jerry,
give him a message, ask him to give my best
to the Leftwell twins. Will you remember that?"
"The Leftwell twins, yeah. Well, so long, Jennifer."
He put the car in gear and he started off. She waved,
and he waved back. Freddie didn't wave, but turned
to look at Jennifer. Jerome thought, I'll remember
not to mention the Leftwell twins, she can do
her own hitting.

Freddie turned back to his father. He said,
"Are we going to Mr. Dexter's store now, Poppy? You said
we were going there."

"Yes," said Jerry. "Yes, that's right.
You didn't wave at Jennifer, Freddie."
"She was waving at you," the boy said.

Yes, thought Jerry,
right,
she was waving at me.

311

The Store:
"Morning," said Henry Dexter, and nodded his head once and then he nodded and smiled and he said, "Good morning, Freddie. You come for your mother's groceries?"

"Yes," said Freddie.
He felt in his pocket and produced a very much crumpled piece of paper and he gave it, importantly, to Mr. Dexter.

"Good boy," the old man said. "You didn't lose it.

I'll fix it
right up for you. Seems to me I remember you had a sort of a liking for lollipops?"

Freddie said, "Oh, yes, lollipops."
Dexter picked up a box and he held it out, and he said, "You choose.
Four or five different sorts."

The child took out a red one.
"And one for Justine," he said, and he took another one, "and one
for Emily and one for Edyth." He took two more.
"Right," said Dexter. To Jerry he said, "It keeps them quiet, except for that sucking noise."

"Say thank you, Freddie."
"Oh, thank you. We came in a new car."

"Did you?" said
Dexter.
"Standeven's," Jerry said.

"I seen it," said Dexter. "How is he getting along?"

"He's all right, Henry. We got
Dr. Fanshawe over. He's O.K."

Dexter began to collect
the groceries on the list. "That's good," he said.
"Is there any way I can help?"

"No," Jerry said. "He goes
back to his school this afternoon. I guess he
just got sort of upset, upset about something, didn't eat, and went without it too long. That's all there is to it."

312

"That young woman?" said Dexter.

"Dunno. It could be.
Anyhow,
just upset some."

"A lot of people's upset these days, seems so.
Maybe the war. A lot of 'em got together, pretty good, those
days,
and now that's over. Something like that. You feel it.
Looking for trouble now."

Jerry said, "Yes, I know what you
mean.
Like that meeting."

"Stupid," said Henry Dexter. "This place,
too small for that sort of monkey-shines."

"I guess so," Jerry said.
"But it's not over yet."

"No, it's not over. There's something
going to happen. You feel it."

"You aim to attend
Lamy's meeting on Thursday?" Jerry asked him.
"Expect to. Don't understand it, but you can always listen.
A good man, Lamy."

"Maybe could do some good here,
if it works as he sees it."

"Maybe could," said Dexter.
"I aim to attend. But everything
here hooks up with everything else. There's nothing is separate,
you see that as you get older. Bad feelings now. There,
I guess that covers it. In a bag or a carton?"
"Bag," said Jerry. "I'll put it right in the car there."
"You fetched it? None of my business, but
the whole thing's sort of curious."

"Yeah, I fetched it. Lamy
was gone to work, his wife's gone up to Providence, sick again,
gone to the hospital. Nobody there but Jennifer. I guess
she wasn't too keen to drive over."

"I don't wonder. She's
pretty.
Her ma was pretty when she was married to Messler. They
get to a lot of divorces, seemingly." He bent to add up

313

figures written down on an empty bag. He said,
"Thirteen seventy-six."

"With the lollipops?" said Jerry.
"Bribe," said Dexter. "I'm getting old. I like
smiles from that age now. Hark to him."

Both men stood
a moment silent to listen to the eager noise
of the child sucking the lollipop. Then Jerry picked up
the big, full bag and he turned to the door. As he did so,
Asa Congdon came in.

"Morning," said Asa and nodded
his head twice, and they both said, "Morning."
"She run?" asked Asa, and he made but the slightest
gesture of head toward the door by which he'd entered.
"Runs fine," said Jerry. He hesitated a second, but something
inside him said, not the time, and he said aloud,
"So long, Henry, and thanks for the lollipops, I'll just
run the boy home. 'Bye now. Come along, Freddie,"
and he took the boy's hand and he left the store.
There were times and places to talk to Asa Congdon
better than this one.

The Leavetaking:
"Good-bye," said Harlow. "I don't know
how to thank you."
"It's all right, we were very glad to have you.
Come again, any time."
"Come again soon," said Millicent.
"Good-bye," said Freddie. "You can come again
and you can have my bed and I'll have
a bed party with Mommy."
"Thanks," said Harlow. "I like your bed. I'll
read to you next time."
"Take it easy," said Jerome.
"I feel fine now," said Harlow. "I feel
ever so much better. I'll try
some time to tell you."
Chorus of good-byes then, in the four tones
and the four meanings over

the sound of the car, impersonal, creating
distance between: but there is
no distance from warmth to warmth.

□□□□□□

JEROME came to the kitchen and sat down there, while Millicent
washed up the dishes from lunch.
He said, "Do you want help?
The child is asleep now."
"No," she said. "Sit still."
"Maybe I'll take the car in a minute," he said, "and make a
quick run up to the office, look at the mail. It's funny,
haven't done anything, but I'm sort of tired."
"Yes," she said.
"I'm sort of tired too. Maybe Harlow."
"Maybe," he said.
"Did he talk at all, Millie?"
"I'll say he did. But Jerry, look,
it's all so queer. It's awfully
hard to repeat."
"Is it?" he said. "Well, anyhow, give it
a try. For I'd like to hear it. Unless
the evening be better?"
"No, now," she said. "I'll forget it,
evening and the girls home. And I didn't sleep well, I kept on
waking to think of Harlow, worried, the way at night, and
Freddie, he burrows, the cute trick. Jerry,
let's make another baby before he gets too
old, would you like that?"
"Yes," he said. "I'd like it.
I'd like it a lot if you're really sure you're willing
to go through all that again."
"I love it," she said, "it's nothing.
You know that, I never get sick."
"No," he said. "I know that.
O.K.
We'll start tonight."
"No, not tonight. I'm tired. I want
to be fresh, dear."

315

"All right," he said. "Tomorrow."
"Thursday," she said. "I've thought it all out."
                                                    "O.K.,
      Thursday."
He laughed. He felt himself want her now, this minute, the
      weariness
vanished away. It crossed his mind that the wanting was
needled by seeing Jennifer. Red hot. He put it aside,
and the wanting too.
                    "What did Harlow say to you?"
She said, "It's so hard to tell."
                              The images rose, clear,
the sound of the boy's soft voice, the accent not hers, the look
of absorption on his face. Mind held it,
but the tongue faltered.
                        "I went in and asked him, I guess
it was around half-past ten, while you and the little one
were out of the house, I asked him
if he'd like some milk. He said yes and I fetched him
a big glass, full. He was troubled, I guess, you know,
about being here, you and me, nuisance. He
said not to bother, I must be busy. I told him
I hadn't a thing to do, kids out. I don't know what
he thinks that I do in the morning." She giggled and
paused, the search for the words, the pictures so clear,
so bright in the mind:

      He was sitting up in bed, he looked rested, handsome,
      a beautiful aquiline nose. The uppermost buttons
      of Jerome's pyjamas were open, the soft blond
      hair of the chest was visible, the clear skin.
      She felt two things at once: an attraction toward him,
      a woman's feeling, the unexpressed, unexpressible
      knowledge it would be good to be touched by the long
      delicate strong fingers; a powerful, older-than-he
      desire to warm, to protect. She thought to herself then,
      what's the matter with Jennifer, something like this
      thrown away maybe?
                        She said, "You're looking much
            better.

316

Would you drink a glass of milk if I brought it to you?
Nice and cold, too."

He said, "Golly, Mrs. Westen,
it does sound good. But I'm being an awful nuisance.
This whole thing. I'd get up and get out, except
I promised the doctor. I really wish you'd ignore me,
just do what you want to do."

She smiled and said,
"My work's all done, it's nothing, the kids at school,
Jerry has taken the baby, to fetch your car.
I just came in to see if you wanted milk
and I felt sociable, too."

His hands moved slightly,
a little nervously on the blue blanket cover.
"Oh, well that's good."

She said, "I'll just get the milk."
She fetched it to him. "Would you like company,
or rather be by yourself?"

"Oh, company,"
Harlow said quickly. "Or that is, if you're really
free to waste time on me?"

"Sure, I'm free," she said.
"Nothing to do till noon, when I get the lunch.
I like company too, it makes a nice change,
Freddie's fun but he's only four." She pulled
a chair round, near to the bed.

The boy said, "Yes,
the little boy's sweet."

She could see he didn't really
want to talk about Freddie. He held the tall glass
steadily in his hand, but looked at it, didn't drink it.
"Drink your milk," she said. "That'll please the doctor."
"Yes," he said. He took a sip. "That's delicious.
There's really nothing like milk. You miss it badly,
when you can't have it. All those years." He took
another drink from the glass. "The entire thing's
funny, isn't it? It must seem terribly queer
to you and your husband. It seems queer to me now.
I don't understand it exactly. I guess some day
I'll sort it out. Clear. I guess I'll have to.

317

You stuff too much down in the old subconscious
and it socks you later. But I can't do it yet,
I've been thinking about it. Confusing."

"Yes," she
said,
"of course it is."

"I'm feeling so much rested.
I'm awfully grateful. I guess that I really went
a little bit off my nut." He looked at her then,
and he said, but smiling, "You know, I'm not a psycho.
I'd have found that out. They always find the psychos,
or about always, after a while in war."
"We know," said Millie. "We know."

"I thought of the
war,"
the boy said. "I think it was yesterday. It is all
a little too blurred now. I thought about Italy."
"Did you?" she said. "Jerome said he thought you spoke
to him
maybe Italian, when you were first waked. Do you
speak Italian?"

"A little," he said. "It seemed
stupid in all that time not to have learned it.
Tough to get by without it. Yes, I remember.
I was thinking of Piacenza, I guess I was dreaming
about the time I went there to get a train
up toward Switzerland. Funny to speak Italian,
me, in South County. And to him." He laughed.
"He must have been sort of stopped." He raised his glass
and took a long drink of the cool, rich milk.
There was a pause then.

"He's worried," she said. "He said he was kind of confused, you
knew what he meant. He said he wasn't
a psycho. I'm not sure I understand exactly what that means,
psycho, does it mean crazy?"

"Well, sort of crazy. It means
sick in the mind, I guess. No, he's no psycho, they
weeded those boys out fast, they'd break down
any old time, in war. They sent them home. Hell, no,

he fought a good war, Harlow."

"That's what he said, I mean
about their finding them out. He said, too,
he sort of remembered about the speaking Italian, he was
    dreaming
about it, something, was going
to Switzerland from Italy. Said that he learned Italian
while he was there."

Jerome said, "Yes. Sure. Lamy
told me the boy was taken prisoner in Italy, then escaped after
the wops surrendered some time and got
up to Switzerland. Nothing
a psycho could ever do. What else did he say?"
"He wanted to talk," said Millie. "He got sort of going then,
it's hard to tell it, wish
you'd been there, Jerry, except maybe
he wouldn't have talked like that. A woman, it's
sometimes easier. Awful queer story, all
mixed, it was hard to tell what part of it's real and
what part a kind of a dream or something. So real,
and then so crazy wild. And some of it, some of the things
right over my head. But a nice boy, he's real nice, Jerry, he
ought to be settled, a good wife. Anyhow,
he started trying to tell me what happened. He said it
like he was talking about another person entirely, and not
in a story way, but backwards and forwards, the
things he thought of. I still don't know, not really,
what he did do, Jerry. He said . . ."

The boy said, "It's all just a little like that, Mrs. Westen.
It's some of it true, things done, but it seemed like a dream.
Do you ever have that happen? Something comes clearly
into the mind, it's wholly and well remembered,
but you can't hook it into your life, you can't recall
the time it happened? You only know after a while
that you must have dreamed it."

She slowly nodded her
    head.
"Yes, I know that, it's happened to me."

"Well, this,"

319

Harlow said, "it is all a little like that.
Don't know the real from the dream and both seem real.
Later, I guess. I mean, if I hadn't waked up, if
Mr. Westen had found me and brought me back here
and I'd waked first here, right here, I'd still be wondering
if I'd gone over and tried to get back in my house.
My father's house." He paused and finished his milk,
and handed the glass to Millicent. "Thanks," he said.
"It was awfully good."

     She took the glass and said nothing.
"I've been confused for a long time. Ever since
I came back home. There didn't seem to be any
pattern at all any more, you didn't belong—
I didn't really belong to anyone, any place,
except here, arbitrarily, because once on a time
I was a child here." He frowned and said, "That may be
what I tried to do to the Lamys, to make them home.
. And I tried to make Jennifer . . ." He paused again,
and he smiled and said in a voice too low to be heard,
"Period."

    "What?" said Millicent.

      "Nothing, really.
It isn't important now. It's all over and done with."
His voice grew louder. It seemed to her that it held
a trace of defiance as he said, "All done with,
and I couldn't be gladder." Then softly again, "You see,
I guess I was pretty tired and sort of upset,
and I got a . . . saw . . . there was a thing happened,
or at least I think so . . . no, I saw it, it happened,
it wasn't a dream. But then I knew I had to
go to my home. Go home. Go home again. Really
I was running away, don't you think?"

      All she could say
was, "I don't know, Harlow."

      "No, but of course you
  don't.
How could you know? But I had to get back to my own
 house.
And I walked there in the darkness. Isn't it funny,
I wouldn't take the car. It didn't seem right,

the car had no place in it then. But the house, it had:
it was my father's."

"I thought it belonged to you?"
"It does," he said. "It's mine. Or rather, it's mine now,
it wasn't then. I wanted my house to be
the place I grew up in. The old place, something sure,
all the old things, certainties. For a little while
it seemed quite wonderful."

"Even empty like that?"
"Empty," he said, and frowned. "Yes, it was empty.
Of course it was. But it had to be furnished, the mind
took care of that. I furnished it, all but the sofa—
the sofa was missing. That's queer. Did you ever try
fasting? I mean on purpose?"

"No," said Millicent.
"I never did that."

"I did," he said. "It was part
of the whole thing. All that you see seems clear,   ·
you can understand. Oh, yes. I had almost forgotten,
I picked a rose there. I found a rose, the garden
was really shot to pieces, but I didn't see it—
that's part of the half-dream, which-is-the-true business,
but I had to pick the rose. It was a compulsion.
You do what you must not do. My father was always
strict about that, I was not to touch the roses.
You can see, it is why I had to." He looked at her then
and he said, "I really am awfully grateful to you,
this is so helpful, it's all getting clear in my mind."
"That's good," she said. "I'm so glad."

He smiled and said,
"I'll bet it's not clear to you. But anyway, then
was when it all caught up with me, and I knew
I had to get off, get out. I just had to run
before they caught me. You see, there were really people
around at the time. I knew them, too. But I couldn't
let knowledge in, or the whole dream, the illusion,
whatever it was—the thing you had come to find,
had fasted for—would go. So I had to escape.
It seemed like escaping anyway. Sort of confused.
Things ran together then, the place and what I was doing

and Italy too. You see, I escaped in Italy.
It got mixed in. It was the thing I saw."
He paused, looked down at his hands. He said, still softly,
"A double repetition. The thing that started it.
Funny, I don't care now. When I was going
down from the hills above, to Piacenza then,
I didn't want to be seen, it was important
not to be seen, and there were two people I came on,
awfully close. It scared me. But then I saw
they were a pair of lovers, they were so wrapped up
in what they were doing they couldn't have seen me if
I'd touched them, truly. I guess it was that put
Italy in the story. I had to go then
off my place to the road—you know, the Cross Bridge
road where your husband found me. The road belonged
to nobody, everyone. It was really neutral.
Like Switzerland. When I got there, I would be safe.
I was too. And I knew, not thinking, at all,
your husband would come along, like the man I met
who got me onto the train to the north, and so
that's probably why I said what I did. I guess
I slept on the road. I remember how tired I was
and how good the leaves felt. Sure, that must be it,
speaking Italian then." He stopped for a minute,
turned to look at her once more, smiled a little,
said, "It isn't too terribly clear to you, how could it be?
It isn't too clear to me. I've talked too much.
But it's helped to talk."

     "I'm glad that it's helped," she
  said.
"It must have been strange, and hard. But now it's over.
Won't happen again. It'll all sort itself out.
Would you like more milk?"

     "I really would," he said.
"I'm hungry again. I seem to be always hungry,
I'm eating you out of house and home, I'm afraid."
"Nonsense," she said. "And I've got a nice lunch for you,
as soon as Jerome comes back." She rose from her chair.
"Rest for a little," she said. "I'll get your milk."
"Thank you," he said. "Can I say one more thing?"

322

"Surely," she said.

"It's only that when I came here,
came to a little last night, you and the children
and Mr. Westen—I don't know how to say it.
You look for a pattern, something, war was a pattern,
or made one, while it lasted. Then no pattern.
There's the confusion. Well, maybe the best thing is
to say I am less confused. Just being here, something
simple and evident. I hope you don't think me rude?"
"No," she said. "That's nice. Now just lie back
and rest for a little. We like to have you here."
She heard the screen door slam. "Freddie," she said.
"That'll be lunch for us. I'll be back in a minute."
She giggled and said, "I'll bet you Jerome's exhausted,
that child!" and she left the room.

She told it to him in her own words, briefly. Over and over again
she said, "It was funny," or "it was so queer, Jerry," or
"I didn't know what he meant and he didn't explain, he
simply said it, so queer!"
Jerome didn't
interrupt her much, he let her go on at her own pace, telling
the curious story, nodding his head or
shaking it in puzzlement: hard thing to understand, maybe
no use to try, anyhow.
At the end he said,
"Well, that sort of explains the Italian business, though it is
certainly a queer explanation. Did he say
anything, Millie, about the people were there he saw, the
ones he escaped from?"
"No," she said, "not a word. Just said
he knew them but didn't let himself know them. Somehow
it seemed like the thing he said of the house, standing empty
all those years and furnishing it with his mind. But he
didn't name the people. He hooked up
the thing he said was a shock, what started it all off,
with something he saw there, at the place, I got the idea
it was the same of the same people. He didn't exactly
say so. He jumped then

323

right away to the story about the two people in Italy,
the lovers he saw that he didn't want to see him. As if
it had been the same, sort of."

"I see," said Jerry. "I see.
Well, it all hooks up, I guess, with the ones he named off.
Something went on there, Millie, but
I can't figure it out yet, it's too damned screwy. Yet—
he didn't seem off his head here. You think?"
"No," said Millicent, "oh, no. He was sweet. Oh,
Jerry, he said at the end he had liked it here, being here, it
had helped him."

"That's good," Jerry said. "I'm glad
you let him talk to you. Bet you
it did him good, too. Well, we'll see, in time.
It'll all come out."

The telephone rang. He reached out,
took the receiver off, and said, "Hello." He felt then
a curious prescience, as though he'd expected it, this call,
it would connect with Harlow.

Hetty Browne's voice said,
"That you, Jerome?"

"That's right," he said. "How are you
keeping, Hetty?"
"Finely," she said. "I thank you. I tried to call you
up to your office, the girl said
maybe you'd be to home."

"That's right," he repeated.
"You still got the Standeven boy? How is he feeling now?"
"He's fine," Jerome said. "Fine. He went back to Harvard.
What can I do for you?"

"Glad he's all right," she said.
"I'd heard he was poorly."

Jerry
made no answer, but waited, thinking, not from me, honey.
"I'd like to see you some time, some time it's convenient."
"Well, good," he said. "In a hurry? Tomorrow do?"
"Tomorrow be fine," she said. "Today's the washing. I hope
the weather don't break now, overcast. Seems like
the fine spell's over."

"Yeah, seems so. Anything special

324

you got on your mind, then, Hetty?"
                              "Never was one
to talk on the telephone," the voice said. "Party line.
If you take your dinner to home, tomorrow, why maybe
you could drop in, coming or going, it makes
no odds, Jerome."
                    "I'll come in after dinner. Round half-past one,
that suits you?"
                    "Surely," she said. "Well, thank you.
It'll be nice to see you, Jerome, I'll look for you. Well,
good-bye now. Say
hello to Millicent for me. The children well? They didn't
get too excited up, all these things?"
                              "They're fine," Jerome said.
"I'll tell Millie you called." He hung up.
"Hetty," he said. "She's got something up her nose. And
it's quite a nose too. Funny thing, Millie, I kind of expected it.
I guess I'll go up to the office now, open my mail. I'll
be home around six."
                    He rose then. He was thinking,
so it begins, yessir, so it begins. I better stop by
tomorrow and maybe I'll get a chance to see Asa. Yes. Do it
before I go there. Yep. Something is cooking. I wonder
where Mallin's horse fits into the picture, and
Quintus Lamy. Jennifer. Red hot.
                    He put it
all aside easily, thinking, time enough later on. Kissing
Millie good-bye he remembered and said, "Thursday.
Everything really starts Thursday. Good-bye, sweetie, you're
the hell of a woman."

BOOK THREE

Resolution

S INCE there's no height that solitary rises,
but must be wedded beyond all divorce
to its companionate deep that so comprises
the unshaken law's unalienable force;
since there's no coin that has a single face,
but is forever joined to its reverse
that even in blank vacuity's disgrace
yet must be paid for better or for worse;
since there's no goodness that is self-contained,
but needs an opposite concept's evil fact,
can only by that concept be explained
as goodness, never to be alone, abstract;
then love is to be seized on, soon or late,
unshaken by its paradigm of hate.

ALONE to wake, by choice to wake alone—
but call it waking, Rochester? or better
the termination of the fitful night,
the end of fretful sleep and frightful dreams
all unaccomplished and obscure, the act
of rising to unwanted day where night
was even more unloved.
                    The loveless night!
But make it plural, night or sequent nights—
how far into the future?
                    So he rose.
He breakfasted alone, not wanting alone,

nor wanting company. Serena slept.
He'd heard her enter to her separate room
past two o'clock, and so pretended sleep
lest she should enter to his room—while yet
aware he hoped for this, the gesture made
and the feigned sleep effective.

                     Heavy-headed,
depressed, he walked out in the chilly grey
and overcast of morning, through the garden—
whose flowers these and blooming there for what?—
and to his studio.

              The old routine:
drawers opened, papers slowly set in order,
last pages read, the clock that ticked away
morning relentlessly toward noon.

                     The words
say nothing, nothing, they cry out emptiness,
zero for the blank page. Zero and zero
still equal nothing.

                 So he rose and paced
the studio room. Ah, it was subtly changed!
Work room or room of love or were they not
the same, or should be? There: upon that couch!
The draught for thirst, the very end of drought,
the current to recharge the batteries—
and so they'd light his lamp until it cast
a beam ahead, the incandescent ray—
so shines a good lamp in a naughty world?
Must you not feed to do? No longer now
the doubled creature procreating self:
but man and woman.

                God! and what a woman!
On this to feed, to fill, to be recharged—
no naughtiness. What are you then while all
the work goes empty? If the work does not
contain importance, why, then, cut your throat,
old man who is not husband, is not father,
and is not lover—but would want to be.
Am I an immature and groping youth
to think the spirit lives apart from flesh,

that they're not interwoven past mean picking
to separate strands?

               Ah, and I acted! I!
I, I! it was not she: I moved and took!
I took and gained!

                     Looking, he saw the rosy
small square of handkerchief, crumpled and tucked
half between cushions of the couch. He bent
and picked it up. He held it to his face.
It still smelled faintly of her, Jennifer,
the clean, light perfume, such a strength to move!
So different from the heavy, the exotic
perfume Serena wore!

                  This scent I held
(as scent became the person and the whole)
warm in my arms.

             And failed.

                     And it was over.
I bred but passion and but want in me:
whose need for a return was—God! and is—
so deep and fierce. Failed: what is left to me?
What's left for me without it? Or what need
for me, as me, the failure not amended,
nor turned to a success?

                  The empty page?
Not husband and not father and not lover,
and yet not worker?

              The gun, the cyanide?
But would you drink the hemlock at the end?
or just decline into a cowardly
desuetude of emptiness and sloth
and too-admitted failure?

             Civic man?
Ah, yes, the Rochester who did this or that,
who got you this, arranged that that be done,
whose weight could count on the crass scales of all
the things done—and for what? To please a God
never believed in? To crawl weakly back
to false and feigned belief? To see an end
better than glaciers or the star's collision

331

to feeble man's endeavor? Man! since when?
There was no comfort there, there could be none.
But drink the hemlock?
                    Angrily he burned
the little handkerchief in the fireplace,
till it was charred and blackened like his mood—
and, being done, regretted instantly
and savagely defended.
                    And savagely
back to the desk, back to the long attempt
to let a lifetime's habits move his mind
in the routine of work.
                    Emptiness.
                              The useless
grains of the morning sifted to the cone
of useless afternoon.

                    Lunch with Serena
gave some distraction but could not heal his mood.
"Virginia comes back Wednesday. I shall go
to Providence late on Wednesday afternoon
and pick up Quintus and we'll drive her home
and put her straight to bed." Serena paused.
"They'll find out nothing new, or that's my guess.
They'll check her up, they'll give her shots, of course,
and say already several days in bed
and lots of sedative. But that's not it.
That's palliative, that's not a cure at all."
Rochester thought, it's Tuesday; one more night
alone with Lamy. "The trouble is," he said,
"she needs psychiatry, not medicine."
"Perhaps," Serena said. "You may be right.
I fear you must be. Oh, I do not see
what causes this! How can you be the wife
to such a man as Quintus and persist
in mental fretting, fretting into illness?
So good, so kind, so thoughtful of all others,
so steady too. A warm and loving man,
to her and to her children." The simple words

took double meaning to him. "Maybe so.
It could be that there's just too much of that.
Perhaps he spoils her. The American Plan.
Maybe a little selfishness might serve
to snap her out of it."
                    "Can any good
come out of selfishness?" Without a pause
she said, "Did Jenny come and show her pictures?"
"She did indeed," he said. "She did indeed.
They were remarkable."
                    "Real talent, Roche?"
"Real talent, yes. Strange sort of pictures, too.
The sort of morbid only the very young
can still afford. Or genius. Or the cynic."
"She's a cynic?"
                    "Only as youth invariably is:
the obverse of its passion to cry down
that which it has and does not recognize:
sentimentality. And as for genius,
I hate the word, it is so much abused.
Anyway, it's too early in the game.
In fact, it's still too early yet to know
if talent will go on. If it will lift
all the hard roadblocks, or just sit and weep
because the path has ended, and go on
all its long, static life saying aloud,
'I wanted so to paint, but yet you see,
life stopped me.' I have heard the cry so often.
Perhaps she will go on. The talent's there—
real, genuine, fresh. Her own. One wants to help—
but, God! no one can help you but yourself.
And—to your other point, dear Christian wife—
there must be selfishness. So very often
the roadblocks are another's shelter. Well,
I gave her praise and needled her a little.
All I could do, at that."
                    "Of course," she said.
"Roche, I called Dr. Fanshawe on the phone—
primarily for Virginia—but I asked
for news of Harlow. He said the boy's all right,

and has gone back to Harvard. I pressed a little,
and he said something curious. Said he thought
the whole thing shock—perhaps exaggerated
by what the boy went through in Italy—
but an emotional thing. He said he guessed
it might be Jennifer. Do you think that's true?"
Speaking now slowly, very carefully,
he said, "That's interesting. Very interesting.
I gather that there was no drink involved?"
"No, none," she said emphatically. "In fact,
Fanshawe said that he'd fasted several days.
I wish I understood it."
                              "Yes," he said.
"I wish you did. I wish you could find out.
Do you think you could? Would Jerome talk to you?"
"He might," she said. "Why are you interested?
Your book?"
                "My book," he said. "The whole thing fits
into a problem—things to do with youth,
the war, the aftermath. I'd like to know.
It might make something clear to me that now
seems partially obscure."
                              "And you," she said.
"With this new phase of yours with Jennifer,
mightn't she talk a little? You're a man,
it's so much easier that way, isn't it?"
"Sometimes it is," he said. He rose from table.
"Well, back to work," he said. "See you at tea.
Thank God there's nothing on tonight, I'm tired.
And you must be exhausted."
                              "I am," she said.

So in the studio again: the place
of absences, of voids. The endless thoughts
to set in order, that would not be ordered;
and work gone out of mind. The little, black
remnant of handkerchief in the fireplace.
He took the poker and stirred it angrily
into the ashes. And the colloquy

went on and on within his head, one voice
to question, question—but so hard to answer!

Where are you going, Rochester?

God, I don't know where I am going to,
nor why I'm going there if indeed I go.

Oh, yes. You surely know why you are going.
It is for work, for writing, for the filling
of the empty page with excellence, is it not?

Well, yes. It is.

And work is you, it justifies yourself?

It justifies. The only thing that does—
or so it seems.

And you're a grown man, now, and you're mature,
you know about the joining of the flesh
to spirit and to mind and, yes, to heart,
and all inseparable. Why do you then,
the civilized individual, the artist,
continue to avoid the one conclusion
as though it were a sin? Or has New England
at the last triumphed in your desiring blood?

I do not know. Perhaps. But see, be fair,
it is not puritanical. I have failed.
I tried and failed.

But yet she gave herself, quite willingly,
it wasn't hard. Will she not give again?

Do you think she will?

Oh, yes. The days go by. A girl remembers.
She wants and needs, like you. It's the same thing,

335

plus joy of conquest of an older man
who can be useful. Have you thought of this?

I'd like to think it true. I've thought of it.
But she was not aroused, not really so—
there was the failure.

Then if at first you did not quite succeed,
try, try again. Another time: success!
Ah, then the wanting shifts, it will come back,
it will come toward you, it will lift you up,
pack you in warmth and strength—try, try again!
What is this easy failure? Why give in?

And if I try again, I may succeed?

Oh, yes, of course—unless . . .

Unless? What's this?

Unless . . . oh, but a shadow, a mere flitting
of an idea across the mind, a thing
to brush aside . . . unless she truly
wants someone other, needs him, and so, perhaps—
ah, but a thought, a merest flitting thought—
used you for stalking horse, for compensation?

Who, who? What man?

Oh, come along, you know it.

I know it but too well. Alone, at night,
no one to interfere, proximity.

But this was but a thought. Dismiss it, man.
Are you not you? Did she not come to you?
Are you not skilful, apt? Try, try again.
You are a man!

I am a man. I'll try. I must, I must!
And must succeed.

So, think about it now. Think well, a plan.
Why else your cleverness?

I shall think a plan.
And damn Serena!

And, failing, you will drink the hemlock down?

I do not know. God knows what I shall do.

Ah, but though 'damn Serena!', she remains?
Never forget this, Rochester: always there?
And now to plan.

◰◰◰◰◰◰

QUINTUS was still at breakfast when the girl
came back from taking Eddie to the school bus.
"I'll have some coffee with you," Jennifer said,
and sat at the table.
                        "Good, then," Quintus said.
"Some things to talk about. Your mother is coming home
late Wednesday afternoon, and that's tomorrow.
That means a tray in bed. I have the list—"
he pushed a paper toward her—"it's her diet.
Ask Mrs. Lovelace when she comes at noon
to order what she needs from Dexter, will you?
If she can't get it, have her call me then
up at the office, I'll get it in Cottrellton.
And Jenny, I'll be late, or should stay late,
a lot of work and Thursday's meeting too—
Jeffers can't come to speak, I'll have to try
to dig up someone else."
                        "Why not yourself?"
"I'll do it if I have to, but only then.
Anyway, I'd be glad if I could stay on
and not be hurried. Can you look after Eddie?"
"Yes, I can do that," the girl said. "I'm going
this afternoon to Mensinger for my lesson,
but Tuesday's football, Eddie will come home

337

in the Carpenters' car, quite late. So it's O.K.
Anything else?"
                    "No, nothing else," he said.
"Call up if you need me."
                    "Yes," she said. "I will."
Quintus got up to go.
                    "Sit down a minute—
just for a minute, will you? I have something
I want to tell you. Must."
                    "All right," he said,
and sat down slowly. "Try to make it brief, dear."
"It won't take long," she said. She smiled, and added,
"Like the thing itself."
                    "What is this?" Quintus said.
She heard both weariness and a slight impatience
sound in his voice. She thought, he won't be like that
after I tell him. She felt a strong excitement
prickle her spine. After a pause, she said,
"Rochester Mallin saw us both on Sunday.
At Harlow's place."
                    The man—she could not then
think of him as step-father—had been looking
down at the table. Now he looked at her:
straight at her, merely looking, no expression
particular to his face.
                    "Oh, yes," he said.
"What did he see then, Jenny?"
                    "While we were—
we were together under the big oak tree."
He went on looking, but still expressionless,
a steady looking, and once again he said,
in a flat voice, "Oh, yes. Oh, yes, I see."
Then paused, and dropped his eyes. His fingers drummed
an instant on the table. Then he said,
"I take it this was yesterday afternoon,
while you were at his studio?"
                    "Yes," she said.
"I thought you ought to know."
                    "That's right," he said.

338

"Better to know, of course. And did you tell him
what happened, where it led?"

                               "I told him nothing."
The lie came readily. "It all came up," she said,
"because he was too curious about Harlow,
wanted to know—I use the words he used—
if I was 'still in love with him.' I didn't
give him his answer."

                     He said, slowly then,
"All pretty personal, Jenny, wasn't it?"
"Too personal," she said. "None of his business."
"Well, now he's made it his. Not good, not good.
I'll think about it, Jenny. See what's best—
to speak to him or to ignore it. Thanks for telling.
It's best to know. Pity, at just this moment.
So God damned easy to misunderstand.
Say nothing for the moment. When I've had
a chance to think it out, I'll tell you of it,
what I've decided. Don't worry too much, either.
He can't hurt you with this."

                        "Or you?" she said.
He stood up and he said, "Let's wait and see.
I must be off now. Give the list to her,
and keep an eye on Eddie. I'll be home
by six o'clock, more or less. You're in for dinner?"
"I'm in," she said. "I'm sorry if this upsets you."
She paused, in anger most suddenly aroused,
and said in a whisper he could barely hear,
"When nothing came of it!"

                      Without answering,
he left the room at once and she could hear
the front door close and latch on his departure.
It had not worked. But nothing worked with him—
or more than hinted working. Still in anger
she wondered what could move his sort of man
out of his . . . what?

JEROME drew up his car at the Esso station. He heard
the bell that rang inside as the wheels of the car passed over
the tube-wire on the ground.
He had only a moment
to wait, for Asa Congdon came out smiling and saying, "Hello,
there,
fill her up?"
"Fill her up," said Jerry. "I still
get a kick from saying that after the ration days."
"You bet,"
said Asa. He put the automatic
nozzle in the car's tank and started the pump whirring,
and came to Jerome's window. "How's the real estate business?"
"Can't complain," said Jerry. "It keeps you busy enough to feel
as if you were getting somewhere. Better than setting
around on your ass and moping."
"It surely is. You wouldn't
have heard of anything further about Sueton?"
"Nope," said Jerry. "Nothing. Except that Hetty Browne's
got something she wants to see me about. But maybe
it's just to tell me a little about how much
she don't admire me."
Asa laughed. "Maybe you sort of
stepped on her corns a little, Friday. Could be
she's got hold of a new idea. She seems to get them easy."
"Could be," said Jerry. "I'll find out soon enough, anyhow."
"The boy get off all right?"
"He got off O.K.
Drove back to school in his own car, yesterday, after lunch. He
seemed pretty good, the doc said he was fine."
"That's good," said Asa. "Sometimes
I wonder what he will do with that big place of his, the one
over to Olney. It's a fine house, too."
"Seen it lately?"
Jerome asked. "It's been shut up a long time. Must be
in poor shape now."
"No, it ain't poor," said Asa. "Good shape.
Took a drive over there on Sunday, hauled old Hetty Browne
and Anna J. Hall along. They wanted to see it. The house

340

stood open. Funny thing. Empty and pretty dusty, and a little
mold on it, here and there, but nothing, seems so, that plaster and
paint wouldn't fix. I dunno but what
it's maybe this that Hetty got on her mind to talk about.
Good sort of house. Well built. Roof good too, it's all slate,
don't seem damaged any."

     "Well, now," said Jerry.
"That's good that it stood up so well. Pretty big to live in,
these days, unless you were pretty rich."

       "Surely would be, too big.
Cost you plenty."

    "Sunday," Jerome said. "You didn't
see young Standeven there?"

     "Well, no. I didn't. No,
I didn't see him. Was he there too?"

      "Seems so," said Jerry.
"Thought you might just have seen him."

       The pump clicked off.
Asa went back to the tank and finished his job and hung up
the hose on the pump. "Your oil O.K.?"

      "O.K.," said Jerry.
"How're the tires?"

    Asa walked around the car slowly.
"They're good," he said. "You want me to check 'em for you?"
"No need," said Jerry. "Well, thanks then, Asa. Seems like
quite a few people went to Standeven's place on Sunday then."
"Don't it?" said Asa. "The Great Man, he was there too.
Seen him ride by on his horse. And Quintus Lamy, he was
there with that girl of his. She's pretty.
Would of liked to be there alone with her myself, comes to that,
I wouldn't be one to blame him any."

      "No," said Jerry.
"Out with his daughter."

     "Step-daughter," Asa said, "or so
I believe it is. And his wife a sick woman, pretty chronic.
Must be hard. I guess they enjoyed the outing, fine day,
Sunday, sort of a lonely place. You wouldn't really
reckon there'd be so many people suddenly come there
all to once, now would you?"

 341

                                    "Well, no," said Jerry.
"Well, so long, Asa." He started the car. He said,
"You'll be coming to Lamy's meeting on Thursday evening?
At the library?"
                    "Well, I dunno," said Asa. He grinned at Jerry.
"Maybe I ain't got the confidence oncet I used had, you sort of
change your opinions. Don't like evening meetings, anyhow, hard
to keep awake then, got to be pretty important, or the man,
you got to count on him plenty. See what I mean? I don't say
I won't come."
                    "You better come," said Jerry.
"All hands had ought to come. Well, I'll be off now.
See you come, then, Asa. Lamy's a good man, this thing's
interesting and good. Be seeing you, boy."
                                              He drove off,
troubled, to Hetty Browne's.

"Come in," said Hetty Browne. "Set right down, Jerome.
I know you're busy. This won't take but a minute, no.
I'll get right to it."

(The soft face, the pink
cheeks, the plump cheeks, the
eyes behind glasses, larger
than in reality, the soft, white
hands in the comfortable
lap, and the gentle, determined,
almost amiable voice.)

                    "Go right ahead," said Jerry.
"I'm here to listen."
                    "Well, it's this way," said Hetty.
"First off, I talked to Sueton, he's agreeable
to what I'm going to say. But you're free, Jerome,
to ask him, if you've a mind to. We decided
to try to pick up that offer. One Cullen Ryan made

   342

at the Hearing, Friday. We'll develop the holding
like they said, large parcels, and they'll agree
to let Kellam build his store. Better this way
than lose the whole of it, I know Ledbetter,
he'll side with the rich folks. There's the first part of it.
Except we don't want nothing to do now with Ted Gross,
he got us into this. We want you to handle it,
all the development part. Those folks got confidence
in you, Jerome, seems so. If you're agreeable?"
"Sure, I'm agreeable," Jerome said. "Though sorry
Ted gets to lose out. Sure, I'm agreeable—
if you're not too late. If the offer they made still holds."
"It's not too late," she said. "We'll see to that part,
and you can help us. I'm going to see Ledbetter
tomorrow morning, I called him, go with Sueton.
I'd like you there, you're free?"

       "I'm free," he said.
"What time?"

      "At ten," she said. "His store.
It's not too late. The Board don't meet till Thursday.
And as for the offer, I'll come to that in a moment.
But first-off, there's more to it. We went over,
Anna Julia, my cousin, we drove with Asa,
went to the old Standeven place, looked it over.
It's a fine property, fronts right on Naius River.
House is in good shape, Jerome, it was open—
though they say the boy had been there, and I guess
you'd know about that?"

      "Yes, he was there," said Jerry.
"Or that's what he said."

      "I reckon that he was there.
Anyhow, house is in good shape, just needs painting.
Do for a clubhouse—better these days, we figure,
than trying to use for a residence, too costly.
That land in Olney, I believe it isn't zoned.
We could develop it, maybe, if we could buy it,
and not hurt anyone. Well, we'd like it if
you got to work to discover will young Standeven
want to dispose of it, how much, what terms.

343

Seems he must have some sort of a confidence
in you, Jerome. We figure that you're the person
to sound him out. But we got to keep it quiet.
Don't want it blatted all over South County, no.
Raise competition. Don't know what it'd start.
How's that strike you?"

*(No change at all in the pose, the hands
lie still, the fingers idle, the plump
body composed, at ease in the
unmoving rocker, only
the eyes look hard behind the
lavender frames of the glasses against
the pink of the soft cheeks.)*

                   "Well, now," said Jerome.
"You move fast, Hetty. That takes a little thinking.
Couldn't say straight off."
                   "Take your time," she said.
"No rush about it. Think of it, think it over.
Seemed like a good proposition. If you think so,
we'll talk again about it. But just you keep it
all to yourself meanwhile. Don't want it talked of—
even to Millicent."
                   Jerome laughed. He said,
"Millie's the grave. She's had to learn to be, too.
But I don't talk, Hetty, where talk's not wanted.
I can't afford to."
                   "No," she said. "That's so.
You can't afford to, surely."

*(Now the short, thick-set body
begins to rock in the chair, slowly,
back and forth, but no other
change, not any.)*

"Only one thing more, then," Hetty Browne said.
"About the Sweet place and the terms they offered.
Ryan said it, he made it as an offer.

344

We was took by surprise in a manner of speaking,
and Sueton and Mitchell Crane—I give him no credit—
sort of refused. Well, I guess you better
say they just plain refused. But in the talking,
Lamy came back to it. Good as offered it over,
spoke as if it was a fine thing for the village.
I don't know what he thinks, a man like him,
or what his reason is, what is really behind it, but
anyways that don't signify. He said it.
Wasn't never withdrawn, and that's a fact,
Ledbetter'd have to admit that."

(Now she pauses, the rocker
stops its motion abruptly, the hands
that have lain so quiet go
up in a quick movement, adjust
the incongruous glasses, drop again
into the lap—but the fingers
are intertwined now, tense.)

                      "Thing to do, then—
hearken to this, Jerome—is see Mr. Lamy.
Ask him to call up Ledbetter, say he thinks
we'd ought to be given the right to accept the offer,
for the town's sake, or something, he'll think of it easy.
Jacob Ledbetter'll listen to him. The others,
even maybe Mr. Rochester Mallin,
will listen to Lamy he says he thinks that's fair,
fair and just, the offer was made in public.
That's the way to work it."
                  "I see," said Jerome.
"Only catch to it is, when you speak to Lamy,
is he going to agree? And suppose he don't, what then?"
"He'll agree," she said.

(Voice very soft now, clear but soft,
with a glaze of hardness,
like candy held in a stale
chocolate shell.)

345

"I've thought about all this.
You're the one to do it. You tell him, Jerome—
tell him we was to the Standeven place on Sunday,
Asa and Anna Julia and me. You tell him,
just use your own words, say we saw him standin'
up on the oak knoll, there with his step-daughter,
but figure he didn't see us. Tell him we didn't
holler his name or nothin', we sort of decided
he'd want to be undisturbed—at just that moment.
Tell him. He'll speak to Ledbetter."

(Pause again: silence
definite as a wound.)

                              Jerome sat
moveless and silent for a prolonged minute.
"No, ma'am," he said at last. "You do the telling.
This isn't mine to tell or mine to use.
Anything like that, you had best do yourself.
Not for me. No, ma'am."

(Rocker begins again, slowly now
an indolent motion, comfortable,
so assured.)

                       "Jerome," she said,
"you mixed up in this World Federalist meeting
Thursday night? Seems so I guess I heard it
you was in that with him, with Mr. Lamy,
I'm not mistaken?"
                       "Yes, that's right," he said.
"I hope you're coming."
                              "I haven't made up my mind.
Want a big turnout, won't you? All those notices,
my gracious, my mail's been full of it. You'll be wanting
many to come?"
                       "That's right," he said. "We do."
"Folks like you, Jerome, and your people been here
a right good time. Westen's an old name here,
round South County. But tell me, do you reckon

they come for you, or come for Mr. Lamy,
because they figure the man's a pretty good man,
built himself up that name?"
                                "Oh," said Jerome,
"there's no question. Nobody comes for me.
They come for him, of course. And, as you say,
because of his reputation."
                                "Well, think it over.
Reputations, they're sort of fragile, best of 'em.
Don't take much nor long to lose—supposing
anyone, any people, should know enough
and maybe care sufficient to take the trouble
to—well, do something about it. Myself, I pity
his having a sick wife, gracious, I never did know
good to come with a woman who'd get divorced
just to marry another. But that's beside the point.
I guess you'd better speak to him, you just tell him
what I repeated to you. I haven't aimed
to say it to nobody else."

*(Longer pause now. The chair
rocks easily back and forth, an escaped
strand of her white hair
waves to the motion of
the creak of the chair.)*

                                "No," said Jerome.
"I'd like to help out on this business of Sueton Kellam.
I'd like to take on—or at least I guess I would—
the Standeven job. That's real estate. That's my business.
The other isn't. I'd like to see this meeting
good and successful, see it well attended.
But say this? No. If anyone says it to him,
it's got to be you. Well, there it is. And now,
do you want me still to meet you at ten tomorrow?"
"Meet me at ten," she said and, as though to herself,
"no time to delay. Let the Standeven matter
run for the moment. I'll see. I'll see.
But don't blame me if the meeting's poorly attended,
you understand? Don't put the blame on me."

347

He rose up then and he said, "Who will I blame?"
"Lamy," she said in a whisper. "And his leman."

□□□□□□

ILLUSORY promise, infinitely repeated!
You see the range of lovely beckoning hills
which, though you conquered, you'd be as much defeated
as if you'd sickened in the lowland ills.
This high clear air so newly generated
(like energetic atmosphere of youth)
is but geometry once more calculated
to prove old theorems of the cynic's truth.
What view from such sweet heights (all heights being
                    sweet)?
The stretch of future, or present's vanishing fact,
or past reseen, or victory from defeat,
or the transcendant, the compassionate act?
Or just the repetition of the stale
and windy known within the usual gale?

JENNIFER Messler, the lesson ended, dusk coming,
drove toward Chogs Cove. Soft air of evening
smelled of the sea and rain. Jennifer's hair
blew in a dark wave forward, the open car,
the sense of free and alone, of being done with,
feel of escape in the wind, the dark wind blowing
dark of the gleaming hair.

Lesson was over, good! Oh, the hard learned
skills increased, the door to the use of color now
opened and opened: spirit and mind denied.
Not much longer, ah, not much longer the strictness
under the alien mind, but the free, lovely
pursuit of self, self-doing.
                    And the mind turning:
Rochester, praise, the seeing eye that made you

348

see for yourself anew, the confidence, wonderful!
Freedom ran in the blood, she could feel it, it ran
hot in veins. The sofa Two men now.
What was he saying, what did he mean by failure?
Better and more exciting, better than Harlow,
but always the same thing, really? What did it matter?
It was exciting—and being done, was over.
Where was the failure?

                          Men were curious, what
do they want to have or to get, to receive from love?
Give and take, and it's over. But two men now,
only a little different. It was so easy:
what you wanted you could have, as you wanted—
wonderful!

                Except Quintus.

                              Hadn't been easy.
Hadn't happened. You wanted and he . . . but he wanted,
and would not, no.

                    Thought flicked into the mind,
a connection here, going to Rochester Mallin
because of Q . . . but too hard, put it
quickly aside.

                The sense of freedom vanished:
home now to Eddie, home again to be near to
Quintus, over and done before it began. The depressing
sense of a failure. Me? Mother or me?
Puritan man? Inhibited, got-to-be-good,
and Rochester saw and saw nothing, the mere
abortive, the trial that failed. Ah, Rochester's mouth,
it was stopped now. Ever again, again with him,
in the wanting moment? Or was the fun only
in the getting-to-do—was it not ever the same
except for a different face, and the same words
and over, was done? Was there something more, some thing
he knew, you didn't?

                    And Quintus?

                            You go on wanting—
because the hard door was shut?

                    And having . . .

349

would it be still the same . . . except three for two?
And the harm done—but done already, oh,
nothing was done but the harm.
                                          A waste?
                                                    And mother
sick and sick in the mind, the jealous mother,
perhaps for that?
                        She didn't want to go home.
Drive in the night, drive in the dusk,
feel soft air to pull at the roots of hair,
fold the body in the cool smell of salt:
drive, and drive alone!

She saw old Miss Hall, alone, the monumental
shape in the dusk, by the road's edge, before her house,
standing immobile, silent.
                                    Beyond all reasoned
or reckoned purpose, she slammed the brake down,
drew the car to a sudden stop, opened the door,
leaped to the road within touching of the old woman,
and said, "Good evening."
And having said it, had then no more to say.
Why did you stop then, Jennifer, why did you stop?
What is Miss Hall to you on the dark road
toward an unwanted home—or is she only
symbol of the postponement?
"Good evening, Jennifer," said the incredible deep
beauty of voice in the darkness of
unseen, sun gone under.
                                    Silence:
silence to make you feel like a fool who
stopped to be silent?
"I have heard," said Miss Hall, "your mother's ailing."
Gush of words in relief: "Oh, yes, it's true.
She felt awful, the doctor had to send her
up to Providence, up to the hospital.
But she'll be back home tomorrow, Wednesday.
Isn't it horrid?"
                        Deep voice, warm, enclosing,
sounding out of the half-seen mass of huge

350

undefined face and neck in the dusk, says
"Illness is always a hard thing. Warps the spirit,
where it don't temper. Hard and long on the ones
has to watch it. I know. I tell you
I'm real sorry to hear this. Was a time
she was beautiful, healthy." She paused.
"Pray the Almighty." And again she pauses.
"Leaves you alone. Alone is a curious thing.
You got to look after him."

        Jenny said, "Yes,"
whispering only, not knowing why she whispered,
feeling afraid and excited all at the one time.
Fear from what? From what the excitement?
Now the rich sound again, but suddenly stronger,
unexpected: "Got to look after him.
No one to do it, the ailing can't look after,
spend their care on theirself. Don't never
waste yours thataway. Nobody ever knows
what it is till they lose it, until
they've threw it out and denied it, closed the door,
deadened theirself. Man needs a woman,
a woman lives by the need. I learned it.
Better go home, young woman, you'll catch your death
of a cold on October night, half dressed like this,
in one of them open cars. You'll need your
health to be any sort of a use at all.
Nobody never gave nothing while body was ailing.
Keep your health. I bid you good night."

          The big
mass of the old woman turned with surprising
speed and walked heavily, swiftly, with purpose, off
toward the large mass of the house.

         Jennifer still stood
frozen to motionlessness by the side of the road.
Voice in the deep tones called, body unseen now,
saying, "Don't never mind what they say,
so long as the thing ain't selfish. You go home now.
You hear me, Jennifer?"

         "Yes, and good night,"
Jennifer said as though it were not herself,

351

another to speak for her.

And she drove toward home
shaken, made breathless by something that lay within her
never was known before.

■□■□■□

ALL DURING dinner Eddie was there beside them,
with home-work, reading after. No chance to talk.
But Quintus became aware of Jennifer's mood,
the unusual silence, the silent helpfulness,
the kind, the short (and the unrevealing) answers
to questions asked: of the day, of food, of work,
of Mensinger and her art.

At eight o'clock
he said, "Jenny, will you be a kind girl
and go with Eddie and see that he gets to bed?
Westen is coming to see me, Thursday's meeting,
and I want to be undisturbed. He's got some news
he says is somewhat private. It well may be
development on the Kellam thing. He hears
most of what goes on here. Anyway, do this,
it'll help tonight."

She agreed at once and left him,
not even a sign of a possible disappointment—
which wasn't a typical act—and took the young boy
off to his room upstairs.

Something's got to her,
Quintus thought, but he didn't have time to pursue it,
because Jerry arrived.

Quintus said, "It's good to see you,
nice of you to come over. To tell the truth,
I'm dead beat, Jerry. I'm going to have a drink.
Will you join me? Bourbon?"

"Never said no to it yet,"
and Jerome laughed.

They got their drinks, settled down
comfortably in the pleasant big living room

352

in front of the lit fire, the door closed.

"Jennifer,"
Jerome said, "likely to come in here?"

"No," Quintus said.
"She's up with Eddie. I've said not to interrupt us.
She won't come in. Now. What have you got on your
    mind?"
Jerome lit a cigarette and he took a long pull
of the drink he held in his hand. He said, "I'll tell you.
I'll tell you in two parts—first, of a proposition
made me by Hetty Browne, just today she made it.
I'll tell you the facts. I'll tell you the price she offered
to me to handle it. Then I'm going to tell you
some of what else she said. She said to tell you.
I said I wouldn't, it was her business only,
to peddle such stuff herself. I reckon she will.
She might just call on you, up to your office,
and it could be tomorrow. I don't want to have her
take you all unawares. What's more important—
look, Mr. Lamy, we have now worked together
a mort of times, all sorts of different projects.
You've known me all my life. I guess you know
about how I feel about you. I figure you know
more of this world, the worldly, than ever I will,
we've been raised different. But the reason for telling—
let's call it right, let's call it the reason for warning—
is because I know you, and I know you'll never
give in to that sort of pressure because it's pressure
against you, personal. What I don't want to see
is to see you fall over backwards, let something good go,
because it is done wrong, evilly done. I hope
you half-way follow me?"

"Maybe I do," said Quintus.
"If you fear I'll suspect you of some rotten motive,
then just forget it. And let her rip. I'm listening."
The younger man nodded his head, and he said, "Thank
    you."
Then he told his story. He told about Sueton Kellam
and the offer to be picked up. He told of the offer

353

of the Standeven job, in confidence. Then he came
to the end of it, and he told about Hetty Browne
and her use for Lamy.
                    He said, "I don't really know—
and don't want to know—what she meant. She certainly
                    seemed
sure that you'd understand. And be maybe frightened,
and so would cooperate. The point I'm after is,
there's nothing wrong with accepting the deal that Ryan
worked up for us. There's nothing wrong, I reckon,
with the Standeven job—which maybe I won't get,
as I said I wouldn't play ball on trying to scare you
into an attitude. What you answer to her—
that's your business. You're older than me, you're wiser,
you been around the camp longer, a bigger camp, too.
I figure you'll tell Hetty Browne to go to hell
in your own way and words. I guess that I sort of hope
you'll tell her so, somehow—and yet agree to the deal—
agree on its merits. I hope to God you'll forgive me
for sticking my oar in like this. It seemed
kind of important."
                    "Yes, I see now," said Quintus.
"Anything more?"
                    "Yes, there is more," said Jerry.
"The meeting on Thursday night. It's hard to pin it,
what she said, it was just a sort of a threat,
vague and half-said. Who would come to the meeting?
I figure what she was saying was, who will come,
if this thing that she saw, and that Asa saw too,
gets known around. I don't know how it would work.
Or who'd believe her. The people hereabouts
have a good opinion of you, I guess you know it.
There's no love lost on Hetty. Well, there it is.
I reckoned you ought to know it."
                    "Yes," said Lamy.
"I ought to know it. I'm grateful to you, Jerry.
Only a friend would do this. As the thing stands,
it's just a crazy mare's nest—with just enough
of inconsequential truth to be misconstrued—
by someone like Hetty Browne. I'll think about it.

354

I'll try to be calm about it. We've fights enough,
and hurts enough without making up some new ones.
We're after something bigger. I'll let you know
what I decide, what happens. Now I'm too weary,
end of a hard day, to see it very clearly.
Let's have another drink. And let's just put it
all aside for the moment and plan the meeting—
if that's agreeable?"
                          "That'll be fine," said Jerry.
"The drink especially."

                              Jerry had gone home now.
Quintus put out the lights and went upstairs.
He looked in Eddie's room. The boy was asleep.
Jennifer's door was closed. He turned off the hall light:
there was no light came under the crack of her door.
Asleep? Avoiding? It didn't really matter.
Night was a poor time for such things as moved
inside his mind. Not yet digested, either.
Save till the daylight. Or, indeed, keep silent.
Better perhaps. The old saw: the least said,
soonest mended. Perhaps.
                            In bed, with the light on,
smoking a cigarette, he felt his anger
rise and choke him—and put it down then, thinking,
something wrong here. Something hasn't been faced.
Your anger reflects only the innocent posture;
the innocence is but superficial, only
the outward act, the refusal. If there is guilt,
it lies in the thought—or better, the thought revealed.
Are you not human? And being so, of a sudden
you saw her, truly, exactly, as a woman,
and in so seeing, you caused her then to see
you as a man. Child and father—vanished!
Why was the anger then at the too revealing
nightdress, the woman's body? Would not a soft word,
gently, impersonally said have served?
Would not a joke and a laugh have done the trick—
the father, mocking? But of your need, your hunger,
your long, unwanted celibacy that so

355

ill assorts with nature, you turned to man,
and man saw woman, and woman's beauty, all
beauty proclaimed and trumpeted to the senses
of hungry man—and so you turned to anger.
As a protection, yes, but a revelation.
Did she not see it, feel it—and respond?
Is she less human than yourself? Shall you
deny her right to appetite for life, love—
except yourself as the satisfying agent?
Showing your own, your inner, your intense
unsatisfaction—did you not invite her
into your mood, your need? And if she finds it
close to her own, the wanted, the desirable,
where was the wrong in her?
                                        Is she a fool
to keep child's blindness who herself's become
able to see? The barren, desiccated
shell of a marriage reduced to the convention
of an old affection?
                            Harlow. Harlow failed.
Too bad. A pity. It does not change the failure,
nor change it to assign to her all the reason,
the cause for failure.
                            Rochester. But a whip
to drive her forward, on past the blocks of all
the old restraints, the habits so deeply grown—
but reasonably grown? I do not know.
There's no unreason in the unreasoning urge
of man for woman.
                            So. And now let it go.
Sleep and refresh and wake and face the new day,
the harm is done—but more by you than her.
Face it and down it. It is not important,
your soul's the last importance. Think of this
when day is bright and clear.
                                        He turned the light off,
settled his pillow, stretched his long body out.
He was aware of the stillness over the house
as though it most proclaimed now that emptiest room

356

where no Virginia lay.
                    Across his mind
ran the swift thought, they'd hang you for the lamb
you but caressed. It might as well have been
the whole grown sheep of passion.

▣▣▣▣▣▣

WHAT! There's no separation? Must living mean
always dilemma-prongs of double strife:
personal, private, excellent or obscene,
and virtuous posturings of public life?
These must be married into unity
before the man is whole, the woman one?
Before the spirit with impunity
absorbs each right and wrong as it is done
so that the private failure or success
relates itself to all the outer world
where it must live, whose influences press
like wind on secret sails at last unfurled?
Bend strongly public rights and private wrongs
until you've made a circle of their prongs.

HETTY BROWNE entered the office of Quintus Lamy
at nine-fifteen on the morning of that Wednesday.
Quintus was in his shirtsleeves, perched on a high stool
in front of his drawing-board, laying out in pencil
a quarter-scale drawing of an elevation.
As he looked up and saw her, saw the well-fed
expressionless-kindly face with the lavender glasses,
he felt his heart pound hard. It reminded him—
with another, a very separate part of his mind—
of the days of his youth when he waited, crouched and
        ready,
for a starting-pistol to fire.
                    He said, "Good morning,"
and climbed down from the high stool. "Nice to see

357

the sun shine once more."

"Good morning, Mr. Lamy.
I'm sorry to bother you, you're a busy man.
But if you could spare me a moment?"

"Surely, surely.
Let's move to the front room where we can both sit down."
"Stay right where you are," said Hetty. "Just set right there.
I like to stand. And what I have got to say,
don't think it'll take long. I'm a little pressed myself."
"Then go right ahead," said Quintus, and he climbed back
to the stool again. "What can I do for you?"
Clutching her big black bag in both her plump hands,
standing solidly, she said, "I'm on my way now
to call on Mr. Ledbetter. I have spoken
to Sueton Kellam. I've also talked to Jerome.
I guess he told you?"

"I saw Jerome last night.
He said he'd seen you and that you well might call
to see me here, this morning. We talked of the meeting
we're holding on Thursday night."

"Uh-hunh," said
Hetty.
"I better tell you what I told him then. We decided,
Mr. Kellam and me, to try to take up that offer
Mr. Cullen Ryan made at the Friday Hearing.
That is, if it's still agreeable. We'd undertake
to develop as Mr. Ryan suggested, good size lots,
and Kellam could get an exception for his store.
Seems best to do it that way. You spoke that evening,
seemed like you thought Mr. Ryan's scheme was good,
and a good way out. I've called to see if you'd be—
well, willing to say so again. If you'd be willing,
maybe you'd call up Ledbetter at his store
and tell him so. That is, if you think the others
will feel the same?"

"Oh, yes," said Quintus. "Yes.
I suppose they would. We were all agreed at the time,
when we talked to Ryan. I don't suppose they've changed,
though I can't be entirely sure. As for myself,
I think you're sensible, Mrs. Browne. I'm glad

358

that you and Sueton have come to this conclusion.
He's a good man. I didn't like to oppose him,
or block his enterprise. Yes, I'll call up Jacob.
Though I can but speak for myself."
                              "That's nice," she
          said.
"We'll be much obliged. You think maybe Mr. Mallin
may have changed his mind, or his wife, or Mrs. Gosford?"
"Don't know," said Quintus. "Perhaps I could call them
          first,
and see how they feel. But of course, if I did that,
I'd have to report it to Jacob too—I mean,
if they've changed their minds."
                              The woman stood then
staring straight at him with the madly enlarged
eyes back of lenses, solidly and unmoving.
After a pause she said, "Well now. It might be
better to let that go. Just to call him yourself.
We'll only ask him, Westen and me—he's going
to see Mr. Ledbetter with me—to postpone it,
the Board's decision, until we can be quite sure
the opposition is satisfied. Guess it's better
to let the phone calls go. I'd rather just leave it,
let you talk to them later. I guess they'll listen,
you can persuade them. Better for everyone, everyone—
if this is done, if they let us pick up the offer.
Better for you, too. That's a fact, isn't it?"
"Yes, I'm a neighbor," he said.
                              "Well, I guess that's so,
but better in all ways." The plump hands shifted the bag,
her only movement. "Maybe young Westen told you,
my cousin, Miss Hall, and me, we went over Sunday
and looked at the Standeven place. A pretty location.
Interested us. I'd rather you didn't say nothing
about this, Mr. Lamy?"
                              "All right," he said.
"Might be, if things work out, we could try to buy it,
big house like that. Perhaps if we do decide,
you'd say a word there too. We liked the place.
We went all over it, Asa Congdon hauled us.

My, there was plenty to see, yes, plenty to see.
It was interesting. But I won't take your time up,
that's all in the future, likely, no need to bother
about that now. But a word from you would help
with Mr. Ledbetter. Thank you. I'll be going,
you'll want to get at your work."

                  Quintus felt anger
rising within and a sort of desperation—
but he strove to control both.

                    "Good," he said. "That's
good.
I'll give Jacob a ring. But I doubt, in the circumstances,
if I'm the person to speak to Standeven for you
now or later. I hope I am going to see you
this Thursday evening, that you are surely planning
to come to our meeting?"

                  Mrs. Browne had turned,
but she didn't turn back, nor look back.

                    "Well," she said.
"I don't know, truly. Dunno as I will. Don't reckon
too many is like to come, to that sort of meeting—
from our sort of village. Dunno as I care too much
for that sort of goings on."

                  "You'd better hear it."
He kept his voice controlled. "Good to be informed.
Anyway, do it for me. It's a quid pro quo—
I speak to Ledbetter, you come to our meeting.
That's fair enough, isn't it?"

                  "Well," she said, "it could be.
But maybe I see it different. Maybe I see it,
if there's anything owed, why, mostly it is owing
to me right now, the way things is, developed.
It's hard to say. Good morning. I'm sorry to hear
your wife's been ailin'. Please remember me to her
kindly. And to your daughter. I guess she's a real help
while your wife is absent from home."

                  She walked out then
but she still didn't turn to look back at the man
perched on his high stool.

SERENA had gone to Providence again,
wouldn't be back home until six o'clock
when she came down with Virginia.
                              Rochester
again alone in his studio, tried hard
to write on his book. It was exhausting work,
the words came one by one, each one was written
slowly and with an effort. It was not good,
what he had written: it must be done again
on another day; but at least it served the purpose
of surface industry, sop to the damned conscience,
and kept his mind—or part of his mind, at least—
from thought of Jennifer.
                              Up on his mantelpiece
the pretty Dresden clock rang out the musical
monotone notes of twelve.
                              That was the end.
He couldn't go on. It was just too difficult,
and he put the cap on his pen, shuffled together
the pages done, dropped them into a drawer,
and stared at his blank desk.
                              Ah, but the mind!
It was not blank at all. The devilish mind,
its currents hidden, had flooded. No need now
to think or wonder. It was all there, so clear,
and so imperative. There was one thing to do
and only one: see Jennifer. See her now.
Bring it up to an issue.
                              Right! he said.
There'll be no work until I have settled this
one way or the other.
                              Deeply within himself—
in the way one knows but will not yet acknowledge—
he saw it was but one way, and not another
that might now save him, and so save the work.
Being possessed now—oh, God! and how possessed
as only youth possesses!—one could not
admit foreseeable failure.
                              Outside the sun
shone silvery and remote through layers of haze

361

that fused all autumn colors. Perfect day:
perfect for lovers.
He rose quickly then
and left the studio, followed the narrow path
north along Whales Head till it joined the road
that led to Lamy's house. And all the way
he watched the placid mother-of-pearl of calm
bay water stretch out endless into haze
with no horizon.
Like myself, he thought,
save I'm not peaceful.
He found Jennifer
kneeling, a trowel held in her gloved hands,
by the side of garden beds. She did not rise,
hearing his greeting, but simply turned her head
and nodded at him, smiling.
Rochester
stood by her side. He said, "I want to talk.
I must talk, Jenny."
She turned back to the bed,
began to dig and weed. "Go right ahead.
I'd love some company while I work."
He said,
feeling an awkwardness to be just standing,
oddly kept at a distance by himself,
"I've fallen in love with you."
"Oh," Jenny said,
and kept on digging.
"It's awfully strong," he said.
"You are strong medicine."
"By whose prescription?"
He laughed a little. "You say delicious things,
it's part of all of it. By Dr. Eros.
I started taking it Monday afternoon.
Unless I go on taking it, I'll sicken.
It's quite as bad as that."
"Oh?" Jenny said.
"Someone like you?"
"Someone like me," he said,
in a reflective tone. "But you don't know
362

what someone who's like me can feel and be.
How could you know it? There is but one way
to tell you. That's the way I want. It might
surprise you, darling—surprise you and reward you.
There is no use to try another way,
words alone wouldn't serve."
                              "Even the skilful
words that you use, Roche?"
                              "The most perfect words
can only be a part of what they say,
and what they say of this is what they mean
about some actual thing. Listen," he said,
his voice a little deeper. "Listen, Jenny,
I need you terribly. My work has stalled.
My work is me, the man, the human being.
Without it, I am nothing. When I knew
only that you would come and bring your work,
and be alone with me, then, suddenly—
the endless miracle—everything grew clear,
the work began to move, the book took shape,
took life again. Only for that! And then,
for better or for worse, we both went past it,
carried it further. As for me, I know,
deep, deep inside myself, the profound, blind
knowing part of myself, that now, with you,
all can go on again, life fill and flow,
take meaning and have joy, be now regarded
ahead with happiness—out of things like these
comes the creative act. This is my need.
It is too strong to tell of. I could show it
alone and close to you."
                              "Well," Jenny said,
"we are alone now."
                              "Publicly alone.
Seen by a hundred peeping, peering eyes.
You know your village. Listen to me, love.
I must go to New York on Monday next,
my publisher, Authors League. I'll stay two days—
and for two nights. I'll motor up, come back
on Wednesday morning—or maybe afternoon.

363

I've got a tiny flat there, probably
you know that, we have had it many years.
There's no one there. A woman comes each day,
but in the afternoons, to clean and such.
Jenny, will you come with me? Would it be
too difficult to get off, invent a reason?
Is that too hard?"

                Jennifer set her trowel
deep in the dark brown earth, and brushed her hands
lightly together and sat back on her heels,
her eyes on her skirt.

                "No. Not too hard," she said.
"I go up now and then. That isn't tough."
"Then will you do it, darling?" He squatted down
beside her then.

                She said, "Is it quite wise
to be like this, the hundred peering eyes?
You even peered yourself."

                He let that go:
he had no ready answer. In his mind
he cursed himself that he had ever said it:
how stupid can a clever man become?
So he stood up again, but still aware,
though it was wise, he should not.

                "Jenny, love,
will you come with me? Will you let me show
what it could be? To let you so discover
true fire, true passion? Will you give to me
this huge and generous gift, to turn the love
that now is acid eating out my vitals,
into the heavenly, healing balm of love
shared—shared and practised? We, together! We!
And I might fire you too into creation,
the whole creative act. Oh, God, my love,
say you will do this!"

                She turned round her head
and looked at him, a quizzical expression
shaping her lips and eyes.

                She said, "I couldn't.
I couldn't possibly."

364

"Why not? Why not?"
"What you want isn't there. It's just a thing
you have imagined for me. What I want
isn't there either." Hastily she added,
with a small gesture of her gloved hand, "Oh,
as a lover, fine, or once was fine, exciting,
I don't mean that, Roche."
                    "Then what do you mean?"
"I must be free. I can't be free with you.
You've stopped that now."
                    He cried, "I stopped it, *I*?"
"Just what you've said. You say you are in love.
I'm touched, of course, that such a man as you
could be in love with me. But look, it's better
if I am blunt. I'm not in love with you.
I like you, you're attractive, you attract me—
obviously. Otherwise—" she shrugged her shoulders—
"Monday could not have happened. But you see,
I'm not in love at all, it isn't something
that you can say I'll be it and then be it.
It is or isn't. So we'd be unequal,
you having it, I not having. All I have
to give you is my body, then. I know
that's not enough. Oh, if you just had been,
well, say attracted, if it could have been
gay, sort of light, haphazard, now and then,
the spirit moving—maybe. Maybe then
we might have found, between ourselves, some time
a—golly, but it's hard to say, you say
things so much better. Is equality
the word I need? I guess so. Something like that.
Not now. Not anyway something like this—
I'd end by hurting you, and maybe hurt
myself too. Sorry. Sorry it is true."
"But for the rest?" he said.
                    "What rest is that?"
"You are a woman. Does it then mean nothing,
what you could give? You say there is attraction.
With this, there's nothing ugly, and the gift
you'd give, would that not feed you, too,

the woman in you?"
                              "It's not there to give.
It is too soon. I haven't found myself.
How can I help you find the thing you want?
It isn't there." She threw both hands up then,
a gesture almost of despair. She said,
"I want to find it for myself, I must.
And by myself. All by myself. I must.
I need it so! It is enough to do,
all by myself." She turned and looked at him,
a hard look, almost angry. "Let me be!
Don't heap your love on me. I do not want it.
I do not want it. Don't you understand?
What must I say to tell you?"
                              Rochester
drew back a step then and he said, "All right.
You've made yourself quite clear. Oh, crystal clear!
I might have guessed it—if I hadn't let
myself get so involved in you."
                              "Guessed what?"
"That you're involved."
                              "Am I involved?" she said.
"Of course. It's obvious."
                              "And suppose I am?"
"I don't suppose. I know."
                              "And if you know—
what then?" Now she was smiling up at him,
and the smile hurt.
                              He looked away from her,
out toward the nacreous beauty of the bay's
far timid waters, and he said, his voice
distant, self-questioning, "We'll see. We'll see."
Then, suddenly changing, briskly, pleasantly,
"Now I'll be off to lunch. I'd say good-bye
except we're not quite finished with each other."
"That's good," she said. "I'd like you for a friend."
"A friend?" he said. "That takes a lot of doing.
Try it when you have found this wonderful
goal of self-finding. Let it be till then.
Well, I'll be off."

366

So he returned along
the road, the path, and felt within himself
all bitterness flow over him, and the once
lovely and silvery day was turned to ashes,
but now in haze of hatred, and despair
was greater grown than his imagination
could once have told him. To himself he said,
"And now, my friend, where do you go for honey—
and without honey, what?"

□□□□□□

ROCHESTER dropped in late in the afternoon
at Lamy's office. He came to the back at once
and sat, as he always did, on one of the stools,
close to Lamy. They went through all the idle
motions of meaningless talk for a minute or two.
Then Rochester said, "I've several things to say,
to discuss with you."
                    "Go right ahead," said Quintus.
Inside himself he felt an uneasy quivering,
but he didn't show it.
                    "I've had a call from Ryan.
He said that Ledbetter called him up today
after a talk with Mrs. Browne. I gathered
that she had talked to you and that you had called
Jacob yourself."
                    "Yes, that is so," said Lamy.
"She asked if I'd be opposed now to Ryan's scheme
and I said I wasn't. I offered to call you up too,
but she said no, don't do that. I let it go.
I figured we couldn't get out of it now, we'd made
the public offer. How do you feel about it?"
"I'd like to fight, of course. Sorry she did it.
I think that we had them beaten, store and all.
That's what I'd want. But like you I agree
we're stuck with it. I called up Mrs. Gosford,
and Carpenter. Ryan called up nearly
all of the others he was representing.
They're all agreed. Some of them are reluctant,

367

as I am. Some sympathize with Kellam,
figured he hadn't known what was involved
when he hooked up with Hetty Browne. Of all,
no one opposed the scheme. If any had,
I might have joined them in it—I don't know.
At all events, by now it's academic.
The thing's done, in effect. Ledbetter meets
with his Board tomorrow. I guess we'd simply better
relax and swallow it. Ryan said that Jacob
sounded, as near as he could judge it, pleased—
but I guess he would be. Anyway, it's over.
Do you agree?"
                    Lamy said, "Yes. I do."
He lit a cigarette and puffed on it, waiting
for whatever more was to come.
                              "All right," said Mallin.
"That is the simple part. The rest is different.
It's my opinion, only that. It really
is not my business—except that we're old friends
and neighbors a long time, and married cousins.
It's about Jennifer."
                    Quintus produced the easiest
smile he could muster and said, "Yes? What about Jenny?"
"I want to tell you that I thought her pictures
out of the ordinary. Very far out of it, truly.
You know I've a flair for that."
                              "You have," said Quintus.
"I was glad she was going to show them to you. I hoped
you'd form an opinion."
                    "I have. I have indeed.
Genuine talent, entirely her own.
One doesn't find that often. As you well know."
"I do, it's rare."
                    "It's awfully rare. Now look:
no one can surely say where this will lead her—
or if she'll let it lead her. Or, sad to say,
just send her good talent to the guillotine
in the tumbril of a marriage, babies, washing,
making the beds and changing diapers,
being the Little Woman when *he* comes home."
368

Quintus laughed.

"Golly," he said, "but you make it
sound depressing! But aren't you judging it
a little too much by our own generation,
its habits and its upbringing, and not allowing
for the way they do it now? Their point of view,
the methods they use, they're awfully different, Roche.
Not that I say you're wrong. There's no one knows
if a young talent will stand up under the act
of all the perseverance an art demands.
I speak of marriage only."

"Perhaps I'm wrong.
Times change, have changed. It isn't too important.
The point I want to make is this. She needs
now to be on her own, to work alone,
or work with others who are of her choice.
Forgive me, Quintus, if I say she needs
to leave both home and Mensinger. She's had
enough of both. I think she won't mature—
or, put it another way, maturity
will be retarded here. You can't escape
your childhood easily—without violence—
if you're surrounded by the frame of it
day after day."

"I see," said Quintus. "What then
would you suggest for her?"

"Let her off the lead.
Let her go to New York and study there,
and paint there. Be there on her own, a young
artist at work, at last."

Quintus rubbed his chin
and said, "Pretty expensive, Roche."

"Wouldn't her father
put up the cash? Jimmy is fairly rich."
"Yes, he might do that. He makes her an allowance,
he might increase it. But look, the girl's nineteen—
that's awfully young."

"She isn't young," said Mallin.
"Not young inside. Isn't she almost twenty
in actual fact?"

369

"Yes," Quintus said. "She is.
But I don't know, Roche. Honestly, I don't know.
She's awfully pretty, and inexperienced too,
to take New York alone."
      "Rubbish!" said Mallin.
"Let her live at that thing the Allerton—
total immersion in a sea of young
women all busy trying out their wings.
Or let her stay with someone, Mrs. Gosford,
she'd take her in, she has got lots of room
in her apartment. Lots of ways to do it.
Doesn't Kay Messler live there, she's her aunt?
But let her go from here."
      "Man, I don't like it."
Quintus was frowning now, and he shook his head.
"Somehow don't like it."
      "Listen, then," said Mallin.
"Sorry to have to say this, but I must.
I stopped to fill my car at the garage,
and Asa Congdon did it. He was full
of chat, was Asa." He paused and looked at Lamy.
Lamy just nodded once, his face a blank.
Rochester said, "He told me he had gone
over to Olney in the afternoon
of this last Sunday, and that he took over
Hetty Browne and her cousin, Anna Hall,
to Harlow's place." Again he paused and looked.
"And so?" said Quintus.
      "He told me in the strange
and sidelong fashion that he always uses
that he saw you and Jennifer."
      "Yes?" said Lamy.
"That's it," said Rochester. "Quintus, I was there.
I rode that afternoon. I stopped a moment,
hitched my mare in that wonderful old grove
of beeches. I have always loved the place,
so full of beauty. I saw you too. And Jenny."
Quintus smiled wryly and said, "Well, we had quite a
      public."
To Rochester's great surprise he added, "I knew that.

370

Jennifer told me. I had meant to speak to you,
waited until I'd sorted it out a little.
It's taken some doing."
                    "I'll bet it has," said Mallin.
"But look—I don't know why, or where it went,
and I don't want to. It is not my business.
I only know two things. It's going to spread.
Asa has told me—indirectly, slyly,
but told. He will tell others, or he has—
perhaps less indirectly. There's no use
thinking a man like that will hold his tongue.
Did Mrs. Browne speak of it?"
                    "She did," said Quintus.
"But indirectly, as you say."
                    "I thought so.
Well, then the other thing I know is this—
the worst will be believed. You must know that.
There's only one solution: send her off.
Absent, the thing will die. If she stays here—
Virginia ill, occasionally absent,
hospital, all that sort of thing, the talk
will grow and hurt. Hurt her, and hurt you more,
and—ultimately, surely—hurt Virginia.
It doesn't mean one God damn thing at all
that it was innocent. True?"
                    "I guess you're right.
Afraid so," Quintus said. "I thank you, Roche.
Good of you to have spoken. I'll think about it.
Maybe I've been too tired to think it out clearly.
Maybe too angry. What a petty, a small world
we do inhabit!"
                    "Don't we just," said Mallin.
He got down off his stool. "All right, I'm off.
Just one more small thing, Quintus. If you can—
if there's a good excuse—call off your meeting
tomorrow night. I think that few will come,
and those that do—perhaps a little hostile?
If this spreads as I think. I know you know
I don't believe in your world government,
but I should hate to see you hold your meeting

371

in such an atmosphere. Well, that's about it.
I'm off. I'm sorry to have had to be
the one to do this to you. Give my love,
please, to Virginia. Hope she's feeling better.
You've had a lot to carry. Well, so long—
thank God the hospital came through at least,
just when it did."
                    He left then, walking quickly,
smiling a little (the smile would be unseen).
Jennifer in New York. If not for him—
then, by God, not for Lamy!

🔲🔲🔲🔲🔲🔲

*(MINERVA NORRIS, thin woman, in a brown coat and
a brown hat, walks across the Indigo Mill Road
to the Esso station. She opens
the door to the office, brightly lighted against the advent
of the night foretold
by the outriders of dusk.
She enters.)*

MRS. NORRIS: Evening, Asa. My husband ain't been by yet?
ASA: No, he hasn't. You expecting him here, Minnie?
MRS. NORRIS: Agreed to meet here. Ought to be along soon now.
Nice and warm here. Gettin' chilly outside.
ASA: Providence radio says frost tonight. Set down,
make yourself comfortable.
MRS. NORRIS: Thank you, I will. I
walked
clear'n down to the Westens' to give Millie
the things I borrowed.
ASA: You see Jerry there too?
MRS. NORRIS: No. He wasn't to home yet.
ASA: Seems he went up
with Hetty Browne this morning to see Ledbetter.
MRS. NORRIS: Really now? What they up to?
ASA: Dunno. I heard
though

                    they called on Mr. Lamy. Or Hetty did, anyhow.
MRS. NORRIS: She going to take that offer up, Cullen Ryan's?
ASA: Could be so.
MRS. NORRIS: Don't know why she'd call on Lamy.
ASA: Spoke for it Friday, as I recall.
MRS. NORRIS: That's so. Yes.
            I remember now. Still and all, I don't see
            where he comes in. There was a lot of others
            hired Ryan, wasn't they?
ASA: Yep. A lot of 'em. Well,
            might be to get him to speak to Jacob. Smart
                woman,
            Hetty Browne.
MRS. NORRIS: She's smart. She don't let any
            grass grow under her.
ASA: Smart. I took her Sunday
            over to Olney way. We was looking around. We
            saw Mr. Lamy there. Didn't get to speak to him.
            He was off a ways. He had his Jennifer with him.
            She's awful pretty, ain't she?
MRS. NORRIS: Pretty? If you think
                so.
            Wasn't that young man, Harlow Standeven,
            old John's son, kind of sweet on Jennifer Messler?
ASA: Guess he was.
MRS. NORRIS: Well, ain't he now?
ASA: He may be,
            for all I know. Or for all the good it'll do him.
MRS. NORRIS: She don't like him?
ASA: I dunno. She hasn't told me.
            But now she was with him—with Quintus Lamy.
            I figure they didn't know that we ever saw them.
            His wife's took sick. Gone up to Providence, seems
                so,
            been in the hospital. Bed-ridden home for a spell.
            There was just the two of them, Mr. Lamy and
                Jennifer.
            Must have left the small boy home.
MRS. NORRIS: Is that so?
373

	Well, they was out for a walk, him and his daughter.
ASA:	Step-daughter.
MRS. NORRIS:	What you trying to say now, Asa Congdon?
	You speak to them?
ASA:	No, never spoke to them.

Figured the way it was, they wouldn't be pleased
to be disturbed. Man with a pretty girl,
alone on a Sunday afternoon, a wild sort of place,
you wouldn't expect nobody, hardly. No, you might
expect to be sort of alone.

| MRS. NORRIS: | Asa! Up to no good? |
| ASA: | I just wouldn't want to say. But maybe Hetty Browne, |

thinkin' it over, that's why she called on him
to get him to say a word.

| MRS. NORRIS: | Him and his daughter! |

And his wife sick. I never would have believed it.
Seems like a steady sort of a man.

| ASA: | They do say |

still waters run pretty deep.

*(A big green pick-up truck pulls up at the pump,
and a man gets out.)*

Well, there's your husband.
He come as he said.

| MRS. NORRIS: | He better. I guess I don't |

want my man off in the woods with pretty young
women.
No, sir. Gracious! I'd never have thought it of him,
seems so steady.

*(Soon now—the lights have only just vanished
of the Norris's truck—Clifford Peckham pulls in
to the Esso station. He doesn't
go to the pumps; he backs his Chevrolet swiftly*

374

up to the wall where the compressed
air hose hangs with its meter. Clifford gets out and
        sets
the clock of the meter and begins without pausing
to check his tires.
Asa comes out and stands near.)

ASA: Oughtn't to let them get so low. You'll ruin them,
riding like that.
CLIFFORD: I know it. I asked my missus
to have 'em checked, she forgot it, way all women
do.
Never puts oil in, neither.
ASA: No, they don't. How's
Rosy
feel about Friday?
CLIFFORD: All right, I guess. The main
thing,
she don't say nothing, one way or another. I ain't
no quarrel with that, long as she don't go siding
with Father Dexter, she don't have to side with me.
People like him, they always seem to want it
to be like it is, no progress. Be like it was, that's
better.
Never no change at all.
ASA: That's it. I hear now
maybe Hetty and Sueton is going to compromise,
pick up the offer Cullen Ryan made.
CLIFFORD: Is that so?
ASA: Seems so.
CLIFFORD: Say, Asa—here, hold this a minute, will
you?
Valve is stuck—what is this going around now
about the Standeven place? All right, I'll take it,
she works now. Sunday, they say.
ASA: Dunno.
What'd you hear?
CLIFFORD: I seen young Raymond, today,
said he'd talked to you. Mr. Lamy and Jennifer—

375

(He laughs and moves on to the forward tires and unscrews a valve cap)

pickin' wild flowers. Wild flowers in October, never did hear it called so before this time, if what Raymond said is true.

ASA: Well, something like that.

CLIFFORD: You was there?

ASA: That's right.

CLIFFORD: Seen it yourself, so Raymond says.

ASA: That's about it.

CLIFFORD: They really goin' to it?

ASA: Well, that depends. They wasn't picking no flowers, Clifford.

CLIFFORD: Jesus. His daughter.

ASA: Not real daughter. She's Mr. Messler's daughter.

CLIFFORD: Well, sure, but Christ! Can't say it would pain me any to pick some with her. Pretty.

ASA: Sure is.

CLIFFORD: You just can't tell about people, can you?

ASA: No, sir. You cannot.

CLIFFORD: Well, that fixes it. Now she'll roll. I'll see you. Thanks.

ASA: You're welcome. Give me the hose, I'll hang it.

CLIFFORD: O.K. Going to this thing tomorrow?

ASA: Doubt it. You going, you and Rose?

CLIFFORD: Well, Gawd, I don't know. See what the missus thinks. So long now, Asa.

(He gets back in his car and drives off now, the car's speed says: oh, cannot wait.)

376

(Supper over, the dishes washed, her husband deep
        in reading
the Providence Bulletin, Minerva Norris
steps outside for a breath of air, to see
if the night holds clear.
                Over the picket fence,
Cecile Boulais is taking down her washing from
the sagging line. The jerky bright beam
of the flashlight held in her hand waves madly
to her busy motions.
                Minerva moves to the fence.)

MINERVA: Kinda late with the washing, ain't you, Cecile?

            (Cecile doesn't pause at all. She continues
            her rapid motions.)

CECILE: Radio says maybe frost tonight, and tomorrow, it
                says,
            maybe some rain.
MINERVA: Yes. So I heard from your
                nephew.
CECILE: Raymond?
MINERVA: No. Asa, up at the Esso station.
            I waited for Frank.
CECILE: Oh, yes, Asa. A good thing
            he seems to have settled into that job, he's steadied
            down a little.
MINERVA: Seems so.
CECILE: It's high time, his age.
            Dunno how Jeanne has stood it, I mean my niece.
            Chasin' around. His age.
MINERVA: That's so. But goodness,
            men, they settle hard. I guess that he ain't by
                himself
            around these parts, if the half of what I hear
            is anyways true.
CECILE: Well, that's a fact. I guess
            there's plenty is just as bad. But thing is, Asa,
            he, well, so open. Hard on his wife, on Jeanne.

377

MINERVA:	Maybe you're right. But gracious, hereabouts, it's hard to be secret, seemingly. There's this thing of Mr. Lamy.
CECILE:	Really? I hadn't heard nothing.
MINERVA:	Sunday, or so I heard it. Seems he was out there, over to Olney, over there with his daughter—step-daughter, rightly—the pretty one, Jenny Messler.
CECILE:	Up to something?
MINERVA:	Well, so the story has it. His wife been sick a long time.
CECILE:	Yes, so I've heard it said. Somebody seen them, maybe?
MINERVA:	Asa, he seen them.
CECILE:	Gracious. Well, he wouldn't be likely to be mistaken on something like that, I guess. You never know, do you? Man of his age.
MINERVA:	That's it. It's like I said to you, they settle hard. Well, gettin' to be quite chilly, I guess I'll go in to the warm. You want some help before I go, that wash?
CECILE:	No, thank you kindly.
MINERVA:	Well, I'll go in then.
CECILE:	You told Frank about it?
MINERVA:	No, I haven't. I'm waiting till he gets done with the evening paper. He'll certainly want to know, he works for Lamy, or on his jobs. Done plumbing up to Mallin's new job. Well, good night, now.

(She moves toward the house, her steps are purposeful, forward-looking.

Behind her the beam of the torch waves crazily in the darkness, hurrying, hurrying to be done.)

(Cecile Boulais, widow, picks up the heavy hamper of washing, with the extinguished

torch on top of the load, and
walks now into the lighted house. She sets
hamper on floor, closes the outer door, lights
the lamp by the telephone. Calls her niece, the wife
of Asa Congdon.
                    There is no one to think of—
alone in the house—except
yourself, your need for company, for another
ear to be hearing, another
voice to exclaim.)

CECILE: Hello, Jeanne. It's Aunt Cessy.
JEANNE: Hello, Aunt Cessy.
           How are you getting on?
CECILE: Oh, nicely, thank you.
           I didn't hang out the washing till yesterday, so
           I took it in tonight. I heard on the radio
           might freeze some, maybe a little rain tomorrow.
           I just come in. It's chilly, ain't it?
JEANNE: I guess so.
           I ain't been out of the house since noon myself.
           But I hear the burner working below. It makes it
           easier having oil-heat.
CECILE: Well, doesn't it now?
           You talked to Asa this evening?
JEANNE: No, still at the
               station.
           Don't close up till nine o'clock. Don't get much
               business,
           but he likes it. Various. Sees a lot of people.
           Likes to talk, does Asa.
CECILE: Yes. Well, I heard
           he'd been over to Olney, Sunday.
JEANNE: That's so. Taxi.
           He took Hetty Browne and old Miss Hall out
               Sunday.   .
           You heard what he seen?
CECILE: I heard it. He tell it to
               you?
JEANNE: He told it. It's really something, ain't it now?

379

CECILE:	Why didn't you tell me? Had to get it told me by Minerva Norris.
JEANNE:	It's just I couldn't get over. Don't like to say it out on the telephone, hardly, that sort of thing. A party line.
CECILE:	I know. Yes. Well, then it's true? What Minerva said. It's so?
JEANNE:	I dunno what she said—about Mr.—you know, and the pretty one who's, well, not his really? Over to Olney?
CECILE:	Yes. That's what she said to me. She heard it from Asa, she says.
JEANNE:	I guess it's so. I dunno why he'd invent it. A thing like that.
CECILE:	No, hardly. Well, thanks then, Jeanne, it was that I wanted to know. Good night.
JEANNE:	Good night, Aunt Cessy.

(The telephones hang up, each at the same time.)

(Clifford Peckham goes in to Dexter's store. There is no one there, so late, except Henry Dexter, glasses down on his nose, his head bent over his ledger, pencil behind his ear, pen in the fingers of his single hand.)

CLIFFORD:	Good evening, Henry. Too late for a loaf of bread and a can of baking-powder?
DEXTER:	No, it ain't too late. I'm here. You fetch it yourself, I'm sort of busy.
CLIFFORD:	All right, I will.
DEXTER:	How's Rose, and how are the children?
CLIFFORD:	Everyone's niccly, thank you.
DEXTER:	Glad to hear it.

380

CLIFFORD: I hear that Sueton and Hetty have asked to take up
Mr. Cullen Ryan's offer.

DEXTER: Yes, that is the fact.
Glad of it, too.

CLIFFORD: He'll get his store then, won't he?

DEXTER: Seems so he'll get it. Glad he's going to get it.
Hope he prospers.

CLIFFORD: Going to hurt you any?

DEXTER: Maybe. I dunno. I been established hereabouts
quite a while. I'm old now. Don't rightly care.

CLIFFORD: I got the bread. Is the baking-powder hereabouts?

DEXTER: One shelf up, boy.

CLIFFORD: Oh, yes. Thanks. I got it.
I guess that'll do it. That's all she said she wanted.
She said to give you her love.

DEXTER: Well, thank her
kindly.

CLIFFORD: You going to this meeting, tomorrow night?

DEXTER: Surely, you know that, boy. No need to ask me.
I trust you're going, and going to take Rose along.

CLIFFORD: Dunno. Dunno as I want to. About Rosy, well,
someone's got to set with the kids.

DEXTER: You bring
'em
over to our house. Mother don't aim to go to it,
first cold weather, it's give her the rheumatism.
She'll look after 'em.

CLIFFORD: Spoil 'em.

DEXTER: Well, glory, boy,
what's a grandmother for? No, you take Rose to the
meeting,
she'd ought to go and she'll like it. Interesting.
And good for the village, too.

CLIFFORD: Dunno as I'm going,
what I hear about Lamy.

DEXTER: What do you hear?
Who's been talking against him?

CLIFFORD: It ain't like that.
It's just he was over to Olney, over on Sunday,

381

took his daughter along. There was some seen him.
They wasn't up to no good. I guess they reckoned
they was nobody round, a place like that.

DEXTER: Who
says so?

CLIFFORD: Asa does. He seen them.

DEXTER: You believe Asa?

CLIFFORD: No reason not to. Why would he make it up?
Anyways, I don't aim to take my family
to any sort of a meeting is run by someone
does like that.

DEXTER: I don't believe in a word of it.
Known Mr. Lamy now for many a long year,
he's a good man. And what, just all of a sudden
makes you so choice? You speak to Asa, don't you?
You have him to your house, too?

CLIFFORD: Sure, I have
him.
Known him since we was boys.

DEXTER: And Asa, he been
pure as a lily all that time? You forgotten
the days he chased after Letty Hathaway—
and when he was first married to Jeanne Boulais?
You forgot that, Clifford?

CLIFFORD: No, I remember that.

DEXTER: Well, just remember it next time he comes to
dinner,
and sets with your family that is so awful tender
they can't go to a meeting. And what is more,
remember you don't do no good to this village
nor anyone in it by spreading that sort of talk.
It's what has hurt us, over and over again—
and held us back. You just remember that, boy.
And come to the meeting. If you don't come, I'll
fetch
Rose there myself. You hear me?

CLIFFORD: Yeah. I hear you.
I'll think about it.

DEXTER: Do so. Think clear about it,

382

as long as you're thinking. Thinking ain't going to
        hurt you,
good time to start. Good night to you.

(*Clifford Peckham goes out then, without
returning the greeting. The door
slams on his exit.*
                        *Henry Dexter shakes
his head once, heavily, sighs, returns
to the dull books of figures.*
"*Profit!*" *says Henry Dexter.* "*Profit and loss. They're
curious words.*")

So you may see it, hear it,
it is the small brook, running as it is
permitted by slope, by stone, by
the roots of the tree. Here a confluence,
and the run of the falling water
grows and hurries. Here a backwater
where the current, lost, circling,
settles to a stagnation.
                        Its sound
is the voice and the voice, the sharp
ring, one ring, or two or three, of
the telephone; the greeting that is only
a key to unlock a story; the names
that link together to manufacture
a chain of communication, a binding
of mind to mind: but now
in the misunderstanding of the terrible
half-known, imagined: it grows
to a deadly size—the little brook is
lost in the muddy river.

Mrs. Boulais to Carrie Lloyd, the wife
of farmer Lloyd: a confluence, the water
deepens and swiftens—no impediment here
to block or to hinder, a native, natural
ditch to carry such currents.

Mrs. Lloyd to Miss Dorothy Telford, spinster,
village librarian, eager mind, inquisitive; here
is a reservoir that feeds to a whole
tissue of channels, gently, a little
of the mud settles now, but the run
of the water's constant.

Clifford Peckham to wife to next door neighbor
to mother-in-law.

Asa Congdon to fill her up, to oil,
to tire pressure, to a new fan belt,
to fix this jalopy, will you?

Minerva Norris to husband Frank—and here
a dead end, water dammed, no matter
how you spell it.
                    Miss Telford to
Mrs. Henry Dexter and here
water is run off in the excellence
of the deep, hidden drain, unheard.

Oh, look and listen! There is not
always the babble of malice to this
run of the water-words, there is
the search for something too: some hint
of a meaning to the ununderstood, the grasping
at an answer suddenly reduced to
man-size, life-size, within
the simple comprehension. The waters
run as they must, although
the spate erodes and the good
earth runs madly, muddy and useless to a sea
salted to barrenness.
                    Soon
will be sun and wind, and the water will
dry and recede and the banks
again contain and harbor. Then only
the dried scars show, then only
the tree uprooted and undermined will

lie, still leafed and living, across
that which cut under
the good and the strong roots.
                              Who, hearing, seeing,
shall say they must be more strong?
Or why?

□□□□□□

THEY SAT together in the living room,
their dinner over. There Serena'd told
simply about her day, about Virginia,
home safely and in bed. They had their coffee,
black and in little cups—the usual,
the wonted, the accustomed. There was nothing
to mark it off, to make it different
from a thousand such.
                              And yet within himself
Rochester was in agony. Tearing now
hard at his vitals was the slow, increasing
dreadful acceptance of his absolute
failure with Jennifer. There was truly nothing
could save it now. Oh, surely, there could be
revenge or hurt—but of what use to him?
Would they then heal? A voice within him cried
at his own folly. How, in God's good name,
did he become so suddenly, so wholly,
so wretchedly involved, as though the girl
were key to life itself, as though her love
withheld, the torture of her body
denied him, were to proclaim denial itself
death to all days to come?
                              And this not all,
another torture shook him: the mad desire
to tell Serena, to tell it all, aloud,
to throw himself upon the merciful,
the steady breast of years, to babble pain,
to beg of constancy the profound relief
of this confessional, to purge, on her,

the acids of himself.
                    And yet he sat
quietly in his chair, the words came softly
of minor things, the gentle light surrounded,
the usual contained.
                    But then she said,
"Get me a drink of scotch now, will you, dear?
I'm frightfully tired. I'm going straight to bed
after I've had it."
                    He made the drink for her
and took one for himself. Almost in silence
he watched her drink it. She was quick about it,
the glass was almost empty. In a moment
she'd have gone, left him. This he could not bear.
Be left alone, too full of all he held?
No—something must be said.
                              "Listen," he said.
And, without pausing, he went on to tell
the tale of Lamy and of Jennifer,
the kiss beneath the oak, the passion seen,
the others' witnessing, of Hetty Browne
and Asa Congdon. As he told it to her,
a curious strength returned to him, he felt
powerful and restored. Had he not told her
that this—or something like it—most impended?
He had been right. Oh, had he not been right!
And telling so, there was no need to tell
of the sad rest of it—ah, why distress
faithful Serena?
                    Faithful Serena listened,
unspeaking, still, and kept her eyes cast down
all the long while. When he was done, she said,
"Is that the end of it?"
                    "That's all," he said.
She looked at him. He'd never seen her look
at him like this before.
                    "Oh, generous man!
Oh, generous, foreseeing Rochester,
how clever to have guessed it in advance!
How thoughtful to have told me! How naïve

indeed you must consider me at last,
after these many years!"

"Naïve?" he said,
in pure astonishment.

"Do you truly think
I can't see all the rest of it? Do you think
I don't know what is back of why you tell it?
You purge your disappointment on the wife
you do not want except to keep your house,
consolidate your name and reputation.
The kind, good, faithful wife who always, always
will wear the blinders to prevent her seeing
what is not meant for her. Who curbs her tongue.
Who shuts her door at night." She laughed and said,
"And so to her you tell this pretty tale!
To me, who loves Virginia, so that I
may face her the more easily, give more comfort?
Hide this within me? To me, the very woman
who should have, shall we say, been the replacement
for pretty Jennifer? How kind, how thoughtful!
It makes it all so easy and so clear.
It makes me feel so happy."

Suddenly
she rose, put down her glass. Now when she spoke,
her voice, no longer bitter, had an edge
of anger to it.

"You choose the moment
when I am weariest and most vulnerable
to tell this story. I say I don't believe it.
A kiss, indeed! Even a kiss of passion—
not leading anywhere. Do you then suggest
Jenny has been his mistress too, has slept
together with him while the ailing wife,
the ailing mother is absent? Rubbish, rubbish!
I know the man. And I believe in him.
Yield to a momentary impulse? Yes.
What of it? Do you think I do not know
how much you'd like to have yielded, for yourself?
Thank you for nothing. From the loving wife
who has no marriage—just an old, outworn

habitual formula, and so can be
used as is needed."
                    Without further word
she left the room, rapidly.
                         Listening now,
he heard the door shut on the floor above—
door to her bedroom?
                    If he listened, hard,
would he hear the bolt shoot home?
                              Now the same voice,
the querying one which asked so many questions
without a trace of pity, said, "And now,
where do you go for honey, Rochester?
Serena lost too?"
                    Rather than listen,
he rose abruptly, went up to his room,
undressed and washed, made ready for his bed,
brushed his hair carefully, adjusted
shade to the lamp by the bedside, opened up
package of cigarettes, saw there were matches,
got out his pen, his diary, looked at them,
put them back quickly and relocked the drawer
wherein they lived, hung his coat carefully
on the wood hanger, closed the closet door,
opened the window, let the shade up halfway,
turned out the bathroom light and then . . . and then,
you could go to bed?
                    You can go to bed alone,
the voice said. Isn't that your usual choice?
If the door were not locked shut, even so
you wouldn't open it, would you? Is the word:
could you, the slight change? What? No longer welcome?
Not even by Serena. And Jennifer?
What is she up to?
                    Not alone, he said.
Virginia's home.
                    He heard himself. His words
mocked like the deadly voice.

388

OH, TELL ME, tell me, did you see too much
too soon, too suddenly, beyond your will?
Did lover's want and the betrayal's touch
empty your heart before your heart could fill?
Or did you find complexity too soon,
too much resolved within a single point
as though the sun of passion stood at noon
forever shadowless in love's disjoint?
Can you not rest now? Will not day on day
heap up obscure relief in slow demands
for which such darkness now can better pay
than blazing love built upon lusting sands?
Patience! until the days of true love come
as riches beyond reckoning in sum.

▣▣▣▣▣▣

NIGHT NOW: bedtime. Jennifer closes
door to the room. Chilly. She switches
lamp on by the side of the bed, small pool
of light in the dark room. Stretches. A little
weary. Troubled. So many things to trouble,
too much to sort now?
                           So she undresses:
peels the day, layer by layer, from the young
body—what is the body? Why is it
there at all, weary, the muscles weary, flesh
wanting something, something—the mind,
the spirit, the body. Separate? Same?
Too much to sort now. Room's chilly,
quickly the wrapper, quilted, over
the sensible flesh.
                       The delicious, healing
sound of the water running into the white
shape of the tub, steam rising, heat soon
all surrounding, the liquid ease, bright
flashes of the distorted luminous
flesh in water. Lie so. The warmth
surrounds and supports.
                              The mind only

389

is unsupported.
                    Mother is home again.
Mother is home. Mother is home in bed.
Mother in bed forever. Mother is ill.
Mother is ill forever. But nothing, nothing—
oh, nothing has changed at all!
                    Mother is home again.
Rochester.
          Runnel of light broken flashing
on the long curious legs, the aquamarine light
in the colorless water.
                    Rochester.
Never, I do not want. Or do not want
except as I want. Or the words:
so long as it ain't selfish.
                    He?
He not selfish?
          You.
          Let hands stir
water to change the pattern. Put
big wet and warm face cloth warmly over
breasts against cold air. Keep hair
out of water.
          Never. I do not want.
Or not want now and did not want. So why?
Thing of the moment, gone, not Jennifer,
Jennifer at the moment, another one.
Mother is home again now, all is the same,
nothing is changed.
          No Harlow now.
                    Deep sigh,
and water pushed up by the fountain-maker
of the palm of the small hand. Soft feel
of the warm water.
          Feel the whole house
dark and the doors all shut. Night. Time
for the sleep. The being alone.
                    Doors shut:
my mother's door is shut.
                    Anna Julia Hall:

390

name like the voice in the darkness.
Quintus Lamy. Wanting and not wanting—
what does he want?
                    You.
                         Want or need?
Anna Julia Hall.
               You tried and it didn't
work and was seen. So harm. By you?
Then he wanted: denied.
                         Mother is home again,
everything is unchanged, save harm, save harm,
and the nothing happened. Zero. But then
and before, he wanted.
                         Or you? or putting
your want on him?
                    To live and to be yourself,
to paint, no Mensinger, Rochester.
No.
     Quintus, Quintus. And Mother—
and what is the good of being home, of all
sameness repeated. Whole house
dark with the being alone, the doors shut,
one by one by one. And the harm done?
Nothing was done.
                    Oh, yes. With Rochester.
Nothing at all with Rochester, Rochester Mallin;
not to be devoured up, no.
                         So long
as it ain't selfish.
                    What is the self?
Body or mind or spirit or art or life
or the thing with Harlow, the thing with Rochester—
and Quintus, the nothing?
                         Not to be selfish,
and the harm done, and the wanting, it is
within you, within you.
                    Within what?
Body or mind or spirit?
                    Too much.
                         Rise now.

Towel delicious, the roughness, the feel
of the blood sweet under the skin, the long
cords and tendons relaxed, the neck
arched to freedom. To power.
                              The warmth
of the wrapper's warmth borrowed from heavenly
warmth of the radiator. Power borrowed
from the act of doing. Weakness—borrowed
from the undone, the failed?
                              To bed—oh,
the sharp cool of the sheets and knowing
soon will be warm!
                              Does the wanting
cease forever with have?
                              With had.
                                        With Quintus?
Grew because no have, the thin edge
of the harm only, the touch, the hint
of what have might be?
                              If it ain't selfish.
Light flicked off, the body warms
under the covers.
                              Mother is home again.
Everything is the same?
                              Nothing is ever the
same again.
              Go away, go away.
Go away, float away, fly away, fly off,
off and away, yourself, and alone your own,
and so New York, and the things
happening, electric, flashes of energy,
ideas, your own against
other and other. New York is alone.
                              And Rochester?
Rochester never or never unless needed
and never mind selfish, he too.
Probably never.
                  And Quintus Lamy . . .
and Mother is home, and there will be always
the ailing and the closed doors and the harm

that was not and yet is.
                    The wanting:
not harm: something. But what?
                              Oh, God!
why is the static, the kept-from, the
constant denial, the giving-up, all
of the things left still undone in the power
of wasted doing? Having. The thing you
did not have. Wasted.
                    The thing to give?
Give or take? Or both? Who knows, and
what is the difference, the days go wasting, wasting
like water running, float away, fly away—
and leave not had, not . . .
given?
          Coward!
                    Up with the swift movement,
wrapper on, cool, over the fierce, lovely
heat of the body, no slippers, the chill
of the cold floor, no light, open
the door and the door, and open the door
to child's room. Child sleeps, arm thrown
over the child head. Out again, dark hall
(no light now to pierce, to pierce and reveal),
down to the end, the ear now leaning
noiseless against the wood, hearing
stertorous breath of the deep sedatives. Mother
is home again. Sleep sound.
                    Back on
noiseless feet, chilled now, knowing
emptiness in Lanier's room, holding the
never will be again, oh, glad,
emptiness now, and the soft soundless
progress to the last door.
                    Silence here. Silence
must give consent? No matter, to have,
to grasp and to have, not slip by, wasting
into the unhad harm.
                    To give.
                              Door opens softly,

only the faintest click and the faintest click
as the door closes softly. Darkness, the slit
of night and stars, the almost imperceptible
breathing of sleep here.
                              Wrapper slips
off to the slight rustle on cold floor, body
clad now only in the thin and delicate
cotton of nightdress, feeling the cool waves
of October's air, night's freshness, slips
into the bed too.
                    Darling.
                              Man's form
stirs and moves.
                    And something said, something
indecipherable, word or a groan, or only
the sound of the heart?
                              Lie close, be close, it is
the time of the giving, to have.
                                    And now,
to the mutter ununderstood, to the turning,
hard man's body, say only, softly,
I love you. I must.
                    And in darkness
the cool grown warm, and the warm soon
bathed in heat, oh, the have is
had in the darkness . . . oh, never, never,
oh, never before the whole of the giving given,
the holding, enfolding, God-give-it-us response of
flesh beneath that cries from an aching flesh and
the cry answered, answered.

Oh, God, but I did not know (your whisper says)
it could be like this, I never
knew it could be.
                    Say darling only
and lie still, under. Under the everlasting
weight of love's evanescence.
                              And time is
swallowed up and destroyed in bliss

beyond count or reckoning.

Silence now.

And the door opens, against the hall light,
and the shaky figure, grasping
at the jambs of the door, says, only,
"Quintus? Quintus? I heard . . ."

And the bed, own bed, the single, in the darkness,
and the ears stopped to memory of the words
said and cried out, and the memory sharp
of the hideous cleavage—but now
fly away, fly away, the harm done, truly,
so it ain't selfish, but what is selfish,
the harm and the have are had, and the
incredible, the unimaginable,
the whole fulfilment, the undreamed, never again,
oh never, oh never again?

Fly away, fly:
from harm and the had and the whole
end of fulfilment, the overwhelming
never to be of the giving that was reception
in wonder.

Darling.

Had and the harm
are ended. Only
the acid of memory now, for the long
years on years.

No sleep. The long
linked hours of night to know the being, the knowing
of body and mind and spirit fused into one
great whole of joy and pain, oh, never again,
of the harm and the had!

And Mother
is home again.

Everything's changed.

❑❑❑❑❑❑

A WEEK—it has been measured: it is seven
days, seven nights, the urgent hours knead
the stuff of living that the dark shall leaven
till the unmeasured space of sleep recede.
How soon they're gone! the dragging, the perverse,
the so desired and the unwanted measure
of the clock's power to bless you or to curse,
to mark your agony or your sharpest pleasure!
A week—the endless and the briefest thing,
the span of what you lose and what you gain,
the adulterous love within the marriage ring,
the well-blest love of seven days profane,
the small scale-model of man's huge intent
whose days are lost until its days are spent.

QUINTUS went up the stairs and entered his wife's room
on Thursday after his breakfast. He'd put the letter
from Jennifer in the fire. He put the other,
addressed to his wife, in his pocket.
                                        To his surprise
he found her propped up in her bed, her tray—
and the breakfast eaten—set to the other side
of the double bed.
                    The dazzling light of October
sun poured into the room. In spite of the brightness
Virginia didn't look ill—or not as ill
as he'd expected.
                    He said, "Good morning, Virginia.
Would you like to talk of this now, or rather later?"
She said quite calmly, "I'd rather talk of it now.
And then I'll speak to Jennifer."
                                    "Jennifer's left."
"Left?" she said. "Already? Where did she go?"
"New York," he said. "She's gone to her aunt, Kay Messler.
She's left you a note." He took it out of his pocket
and handed the little blue envelope to Virginia.
Virginia opened it, read it in silence.
                                        "I see.
She plans to stay. I'm glad she has done this, Quintus,

it was a good move. A curious, hard little letter.
Do you know what she says at the end?"

"No, I don't
know."

"She says, 'I am very sorry you found us out.
I'm sorry if it has hurt you.' As if it wouldn't!
She says, 'I felt I was taking nothing away
from you as things stood, only trying to add.'
Incredibly cruel!"

He thought to himself, it's better
to have this out now, fully. He said, "Well, yes,
cruel of course. And somewhat realistic,
if it comes to that."

She said, "I don't understand you."
"Don't you?" said Quintus. "See here, like her I'm sorry.
Sorry it happened, sorry the way it happened.
Damned sorry to hurt you. But I'm a man, Virginia.
I'm forty-three, and healthy. I'm not cut out
to lead a celibate life—or not forever.
I've tried to do it—and done it. Perhaps too long.
That was stupid, doubtless. But I tried it anyway."
"Did you?" Virginia said. "Why should I believe you,
after last night?"

He shrugged his shoulders, said,
"Believe it or don't believe it, it's all one.
It's nothing that I can prove. You either believe
I'll tell the truth, by now, or you don't believe it.
I've nothing to gain by lying."

"And for how long
has this with Jennifer lasted?"

"Only this once."
"You seriously ask me to believe that, Quintus?
And while I was absent?"

"Believe it or don't," he said,
and a trace of anger colored his voice. "I tell you
that was the first. I'm sorry. I've done too much,
let myself get too tired, and tried too hard
to be all things to all men. Stupid. So something popped.
I don't attempt to excuse it or explain it,
beyond that simple statement. I leave it to you

397

to decide what you want to believe, and want to do.
Jennifer's gone. A good thing, for many reasons.
I'll tell you about that too, but presently. Now
we have ourselves to decide about, only that.
If what I have done and been in the past two years
while you were ill is not of sufficient weight
to balance this one act, that is for you to say.
I'll tell you but one thing more, I saw all of this,
all of it, coming. I did try hard to stop it.
I tried too hard, the wrong way. So it happened.
It wasn't all Jennifer's fault."

                    She looked at him,
a questioning look. "You sound so awfully hard."
"Oh, hard," he said. "Perhaps it is just fatigue.
Too many weights to lift, all at the same time.
Well, where do we stand?"

                    She looked down at her hands,
and the slow tears started to come from her large eyes,
and she said, but almost whispering, "I don't know.
Oh, I don't know! What is there to go on for?
What do you want of me? Or what can I do—
except look forward again to a repetition,
another time round. Myself—my sickly self—
what has it got to offer?"

                    "What it has offered.
Or to get well?" he said.

                    "How to get well?
And if I did, what then?"

                    He said, abruptly,
"Too fast, too far ahead. It's too soon for that.
Take the first steps first—if you really want to take them.
What do you want, Virginia? Are you content
to be as you are? With me, or else without me?
What is this thing that happened? What does it mean—
have you thought that out?"

                    She said, but still in a
        whisper,
"Are you in love with her?"

                    "I am not," he said.
"I am not in love with anyone. I'm a man—

398

with a man's appetites, that is all. And all the usual
weaknesses of my kind."   ·

                                   "Is she in love?"
"With me?"

                   "With you."

                              "Jennifer is in love
with Jennifer Messler, whose life is just beginning.
I think she tried to combine self-love with something
a little outside herself, respond to a need
she saw for the first time clearly in someone else.
That's what I think. That's all."

                                   "I see," she said.
There was a long pause then. She said, "I might
go up to Boston and see Dr. McManus."
"He's the psychiatrist?"

                              "Yes. It might do me good
to talk to him, anyway."

                              "Has a good name," said Quintus.
"As you know, I've wanted that."

                              "Yes," she said. "I know.
I've just got a hatred of them. I'll think about it.
Talk to you later."

                              "Yes," he said. "All right.
I ought to be off now. I've a hell of a day.
The meeting's tonight. I'm going to call up Serena
and ask her to look in on you. It's up to you
how much you tell her. I know that she won't talk,
except to Rochester. I had greatly rather
Rochester didn't know."

                              "Oh, no," she said.
"Not ever to Rochester. Will you really try
to hold the meeting tonight?"

                              "I must," he said.
"Not many will come. I ought to tell you this.
On Sunday, when we went over to Harlow's place,
Jenny got me to kiss her. It came too quickly
for me to stop myself. That was the beginning.
I stopped her after it. Hard. But as I told you,
I did it badly, with anger. I should, instead,
have laughed at it, laughed it all off into nothing.

399

By sheer bad luck, there were several people saw us—
Hetty Browne was one, and also Asa Congdon,
and I guess they'll talk if they haven't talked already.
And Rochester saw it too. He was riding by.
He took the trouble to tell me he had seen it,
he gave me advice—to send Jenny off to the city.
As he is Rochester, one doesn't truly know
ever what moves him. But the fact remains
it's good that Jenny has gone. And because of this,
if they have talked—not Rochester, but the others—
it'll hurt the meeting. The whole damned thing is mine
in spite of young Westen's help."
                                        "Oh, God," she said.
"How horrible, horrible! I'll be a laughing stock!"
"No," Quintus said, and his voice was very dry.
"Oh, no, you'll be the object of much sympathy.
Anyway, it is done. I shall hold my meeting,
face it out and, indeed, I'll face them down.
The kiss was nothing. The rest they do not know.
And Jennifer's gone."
                                "Thank God, she's gone!"
                                                    He said,
"Yes. It is good, of course. She took a hell of a
lot of the weight of the house off me, at that.
Well, that'll take care of itself. I've taken Eddie
off to his bus. I shall get back in time
to pick him up, too. No one else to do it.
Well, I am off. I'll say, as I said at first,
I'm damned sorry that it happened—and that you know—
and that it's hurt you. I shall simply hope
good may come out of it in the long end. Good-bye.
You'll be able to care for yourself till Serena comes?"
"I will," she said. "Do you want to kiss me, Q?"
"Of course," he said, and he walked around the bed
and kissed her quickly, and straightened up at once
and he left the room.
                        All right, he said to himself,
now for the bloody long day.

SO NOW on the soft and cumbrous, the ambitioned
wing of words we have flown over the mortal progress
of all these people. These pinions, many-syllabled, can
beat between us and them, we have flown often
alone, the singular, the everlastingly
separate life, the inviolate, the inviolable
aloneness of living.
                    What are they to us?
                                        Why
did we descend the heart—we must descend again—
in the dread compassion, the magical, the betraying
cause of admixture until spirit at long last's
caught in the toils of other?
                            Not safe this, not
safe now: the flight above,
this is the safety: the ants in their agony
or the ants in toil or confusion or malice, these
are not us.
        This Rhode Island village
is miniature in persons, lonely. But loneliness
is a garment you must wear.
                        We fly above for a little: we are
near to the end of flight.

And Jennifer Messler? Will she
be part of the whole rhythm of life?

It is not known, not knowable. It is the future
covered in a dark mercy. It is composed
only of want and of will. It is perhaps. It's the illusory
promise, so infinitely repeated!
                            And what view now
from such sweet heights (all heights being sweet)? Unknown,
unknowable, it is the future covered
in the mercy of darkness: fruitful,
or just the repetition of the stale
and the windy known.

And Harlow? Will he be flung again
in the unconscious' storm, the
ego's hurricane?

401

He, too,
is the dark of the days to be, the creature
of want and of will. He has found reason
who finds a reason, he is not displaced
who has found place at last. This
was the knife, it was
thrust into his life. But wounds heal,
leave but a scar to ache when the tall
glass tumbles down to coming of fruitful rain
and the immaculate
passion of storm.

We hover. They fly off
to the future of being wherein their sun
stands not forever vertical in
time's disjoint.

Another: Hetty Browne. She does not
think long or often of love. She thinks now
briefly of Lamy. Adulterer, betrayer
of the vows of marriage, the ring.
                    She moves,
ring on the finger, the gold band.
                    She did not
betray the ring: there was not
desire for this. So surely (within the mind)
the mind and the spirit ordered, there is
such a thing as control.
                She has confused
the will with the unknown want.
                    But now
simple the thinking in a pleasant
complexity of her calculation. Paper,
pencil, the neat, the accustomed
figures of acres, price, the cost of the
roads driven. Capital. Cottrellton National
Bank and a mortgage, sixty percent of
fair valuation, good. Sufficient.
                  Westen?
A yes and a no. Purpose now

partly served? There is no longer
need for Lamy, it is all done. So Westen?
Bright and efficient. Honest: that's both the
good and the bad. But Harlow Standeven, there
is a link to be forged. Good. Keep him.
Certainly better than Gross and always better
than any of all the rest, local.
                                    Not Sueton,
not on the new scheme. Good.
                                    The lamplight
falls on the white page, the neat, dark
figures of living.
                    She is not thinking
about the meeting: dismissed. Nor Lamy now,
used and no longer
wanted or needed. Perhaps as an architect? No.
Builder only, repairs and alterations. So many
thousand dollars? It takes
some figuring, don't it?
                          Maybe, maybe
the Standeven boy, to see it, to be persuaded
because of the Lamy thing? Sort of
a way to get back at, the selling?
                                    But not Jerome:
do it yourself.
                Or too much capital needed—
mortgage and so much, and something coming
in from the Sweet land, shouldn't
take too long, and always
Anna Julia.
            Old. Easy to handle.
Not here, truly, living now
all in the past. Easy.
                      Live in the present,
that was the thing. Plenty to keep you busy,
occupied.
          Not the conception
of happy: busy. Something yet to be done,
something contrived.
                      You weave together

the pertinent threads. Only.
                                        Well, tomorrow,
hear from Ledbetter. But no
worry about that now.
                                        A pity. We could
have picked up money real fast for the original
scheme of Ted Gross. Stupid. Ought to have
paid no mind to him, hearing in October, too soon,
January, or better February, then
everyone scattered. Well. It was over. No use
to cry over spilt milk.
                                        Put the paper
down now, take off
lavender glasses, eyes can
look to the future better so. Poor thing,
poor Mrs. Lamy! Hope she gives him
what he has coming. The adulterous
love in the marriage ring.
                                        Turn and turn
the barren gold hoop on finger.

We are still safe here: the untouchables, viewing
in high detachment the incredible
other progress of other.
                                        Turn of the mind is
the rare, the wonderful thing.

She sits
heavy, immobile, one lamp only,
Anna Julia Hall in the deep, strong
morris-chair of her father: cripple: strong will
wanting his moon.
                                        The plates of dinner
and lunch and breakfast, the fry-pan, cutlery,
coffee-pot, saucepan, glasses,
lie unwashed in the sink in the big dark
kitchen where now the bitch in season
whines and moves restless as the four
dogs scratch at the closed door, gouging
paint and wood.

404

She does not hear their noise
nor attend their impulse.
Come away!
We cannot hear now the deep, beautiful
tones of the voice in thought.
                        We have no place
to witness the fusion of recollected
youth into Jennifer, Lamy
to Benjamin Sweet and the tall rye
bending beneath the wide spread
arms of the secret oak that yielded
secrecy to a world of eyes.
                        Or, if you know—
if you will commit yourself to the torn
compassion of her long, her unwilled
rich virginity, then descend, and fuse,
and suffer her thinking: the immutable, mutable
past reseen as age begets its youth again
under the one lamp as the loud
whines of eager flesh echo and grow
unheard in the night of thought. Oh,
come away! will you witness
one reach an ending that she might begin?

This is our road. It runs
in such a narrow way there is no turning
to anticipate: we see it
down-looking, steep.

Here's Jacob Ledbetter. And with him
the two bright men, mercurial. Listen to them,
they speak themselves: they fill
the evening hours of such and such a date—
oh, Thursday, October fourteenth, if you must—
with all their thoughts: not meaning to betray
self in their reticences. It's the unsaid
traps and betrays.
                        A week—it has been measured
on the Clerk's calendar. It is seven
days, seven nights.

Jacob says, "Guess you've heard about all there is to it,
that's where it stands. I talked to Cullen Ryan.
He's got in touch now, talked to the whole shebang,
all the petitioners. As I told you first off,
I talked to Hetty Browne and to Sueton Kellam, and
I called up Mitchell Crane, just to make sure.
Seems kind of silly to meet, and wouldn't have asked you,
it hadn't been for the rest that's on the docket.
And none of them's difficult. Can't see why the Board
should refuse the exception now, the way they ask it.
What do you think?"

        "I guess you're right," says Parry.
"Seems they all want it so."

         "That's it," says Cross.
"Tell you the truth, I felt sort of sorry for Sueton.
Wants that store. I guess we'd a had to refuse it,
way it was asked for first off. I reckon Sueton
don't know Hetty too well."

        "No, didn't know her,"
Parry says. "But I guess he knows more now.
Go more slowly, next time, he aims to hook up
in one of her deals."

       Jacob but nods his head.
Parry continues, "How do we work it now?
To be sure and safe?"

       Jacob says, "Well, we'd better
tell him we'll grant the exception, well, provisional,
and make it solid after the papers is all drawn
and the parties signed—providing, of course, the agreement's
agreeable to the Board. How does that seem?"
"Good," says Willoughby Cross.

       And, "Good," says Parry.
"Well, it's so ordered. Willoughby, you just note it
so on the minutes, will you?"

       "I will," says Cross.
Jacob leans back and he strokes his cropped moustache.
"How you men fixed up for tomorrow night—
could you meet then, let the rest of this go till then?"
"No," says Parry. "I got to up to Warwick,
can't say I want to, but can't get out of it now,
  406

wife's mother and father, fiftieth anniversary.
Hell, if I skipped it. What you got on for tonight?"
"Nothing, nothing," says Jacob. "Jest wished I could go
down to the Chogs Cove meeting is all."
                                        "That one of Lamy's?"
"Yes, that's the one. I'd like to hear what they say."
"Lamy," says Parry. "Seems there's some talk about him.
Dunno as I'd want to go."
                          "What talk?" says Cross.
"Ain't neither one of you heard?"
                                  Ledbetter and Cross
shake their heads.
                  "Guess it ain't only a rumor.
Got it from Asa Congdon, he claims to have seen it.
He ain't too strong on facts, or seems so, usually,
but this'd be hard to make up. Or I guess it would.
Don't know, myself. Just heard it. Seems that Lamy,
Sunday it was, was over to Standeven's place,
and took his daughter, I guess she's rightly not his, she's
daughter to Messler, and, so the story has it, as
Asa tells it, they was sort of carrying on."
"You know what they done?" says Cross.
                                        "Well, no, not exactly.
But I guess they was pretty . . . well, as I got it,
not what they'd ought to be up to, man and his daughter,
step-daughter even."
                    "Wife is sick too, ain't she?"
Cross says this, his eyes bright.
                                 "So it seems. Yes.
Dunno how long it's been going on. Don't think
I'd want to get mixed up into no organization
he was the head of it. Course, I mean, if it's true."
"My," says Cross. "That's something!"
                                      Jacob says,
"Lester, you always followed the straight and narrow—
sence you was wedded?"
                       "Well," says Parry. "Well, mostly."
"Mostly?" says Jacob. "Your wife ain't ill any, is she?
Agnes, she able to take care of you, ain't she?"
"Well," says Parry. He cracks his knuckles loudly.

407

"It's just what I heard, from Asa."

"Yes," says Jacob,
dryly. "You find it hard to set down with me
on the Zoning Board of Review?"

"Why, no," says Parry.
"Never said that."

"I been around myself, some,"
Jacob says. "Tough to be called to account for it.
Of course, I'm old now. But I got around plenty, plenty,
when I was younger. Well, let's get at the docket,
seeing as you ain't free. He's a good man, Lamy.
Guess he's human. What's the first case, Willoughby?"

The papers shuffle, under
the touch of Willoughby Cross; the three men
bend to examine them, the merciful
occupation of eyes, not seeing the flush
on the neck of Parry. One thing
divides from another.

What! there's no separation? Must
living mean always dilemma?

Come away, now. You have seen
the last of Jacob Ledbetter, solid,
in the light of his sins, his acts.

Now
is the small meeting. From on high, on high,
the miles are nothing.

Small meeting.
The large room, bare
except for the dusty and the fly-specked bunting
of an occasion long past,
and the walls covered in the stacked books,
it is too large
for this gathering. You can
count them all on the fingers of both your
hands that bear no stigmata other
than just your own.

Let us count them: they are

enclosed for us in the room and the night.

We shall not count Quintus Lamy. No.
Stands large, good-looking, man in his prime,
you would not see his fatigue,
it is hidden. You cannot see
what he is thinking, feeling. It is
hidden under the act of the moment, the thing
to be done, assumed.

There is Jerome Westen. One. There is
his wife, Millicent Westen. Two.
Jerome is thinking about the meeting, and
thinking of Quintus Lamy, noticing
the invisible-magic of
surface exhibited.
                Millicent
is thinking of Jerry, and of the baby
she hopes to have, one day, and of Harlow
and of the sadness
of so few people now, Jennifer. She breathes in
daily air for the body, hers, no
thought for the body, thoughts soon
all fruit of love devour.

There is here too Mrs. John d'Arcy Gosford.
Three. She is sitting
upright as always, next to her daughter
and her son-in-law. Family.
Stick together. Blood
is thicker than water. Family. She is
unaware of the doings, happenings, rumors,
sins and acts. She is thinking
poorly of this small village. She feels
she can afford contempt. Is she
herself not here? At
the age of seventy-three?

There is Serena Mallin. Four. She sits
impassive but pleasant. Empty:

409

aware of emptiness (was it not
the terrible voiding of
anger?) which she does not know
how soon to let fill up. Nor truly,
with what to fill it.

Beside her, not slouched now, but aping
the pose of his mother-in-law—the unconscious
pose of defense—sits
Rochester Mallin. Five.
He is not empty.
He is full of his own reasons for being
here, at any such thing. His reasons
compose of self-anger, self-hate, a measure
of tearing self-pity, of confusion, of the
sense of his own lost way, the destruction
of his own placement. His mind
is closed but to self now. It cries
too loud to let other sounds, words, thoughts
be heard or received.

There is Henry Dexter. Six. Shopkeeper,
one-armed, managing
balance without the other.
He is a little
angry because his daughter Rose
chose to cleave to her husband.
                              And next him,
tall and gaunt and so very neatly
dressed for the moment sits
Mrs. Henry Dexter. Seven. She came
because Henry came and asked her. It is
enough of a reason: has been
these many, these many years, in spite of
pain or the rheumatism.
                              She thinks
of Quintus Lamy, whose wife
must lie forever at home or
lies there forever. If kindness

could warm and transport by the
sending of mind, the man
would be warmed.

There is Walter Hoxsie. Eight. He wears
what he wore at the Hearing before
the Zoning Board of Review. He is
wholly unchanged.
                He is here
from curiosity: there was nothing
to keep him at home.
                      Oh, once, long ago,
there was his cousin, Sarah, housekeeper,
and to stay at home. But that
was a long time back, the years, the accreting
years. Age modifies. It chastens,
what once was, is not.
                Rumor
is but a chaff to him, the wind
of the years blows it away, away, it is lost
in the depths of the sea-water.

There is Loretta Messler. Nine.
She has come because, in a vague,
bird-minded way she is interested in
the cause of the meeting or at least feels
she would like to be interested, it would fill
some of the vacuum of her life;
and because she has heard that Jennifer
turned up this afternoon, suddenly, at
her sister-in-law's house in New York, and Loretta
wants to see how Quintus looks;
and because it is always pleasant to her,
a little exciting, to be near
to Jerome Westen who is the only man
among her many lovers who took her
and didn't become involved, not even remotely, and so
remains the most vivid and the most exciting.
                          She looks

411

at Millicent with surprise, a little wonder,
a pleasant touch of envy, not
understanding this marriage.

There is Dorothy Telford, spinster, librarian. Ten.
She is here because she is essentially kind
and wishes the village well, and because
she hopes Mr. Mallin will be there, he is
her hero, the accomplished, the successful
writer; and because, at forty-five,
she is still capable of being secretly
and wonderfully excited by anything
even remotely romantic and in particular,
faintly illicit, and all the story
of Lamy and Jennifer is much of both. She is
hoping and hoping Jennifer too will come.
A kind woman, half-way
educated, a virgin only
because she is plain to look at, in
all possible ways.

We shall not count now young Gordon Johnson, he
is there from East Olney, he came
to operate the projector, show
a moving picture only: it is
his profession.

Ten persons. They serve
(to the eye of Lamy) to point up
all who are not there. They are
the exclamation points to the obvious
reason for empty chairs.
            But the clock
is not regulated to wait for any
such reason as this. The meeting
begins, a few words, graceful, as though
the place was quite full of eager
and friendly villagers, the lights are turned off,
Gordon Johnson performs his
task and the movie shows now, bleakly, terrible

412

record of war, destruction, the physical and
the human, foot after foot of man's
madness and insolent folly toward
man.
   It's the trick that the lens plays, making—
or hoping to make—the eye
at least percipient.
     But the reels end,
the lights go on again, and the ten
of the various motives become
the apparent audience.
      Quintus Lamy rises
(he has sat down in the darkness, grateful
for the illusion of no-light save
the images shown, transporting); he will speak
as though to a hundred. He speaks. Oh,
we shall not have to hear all of it. He is making
an outline of history, skilful, condensed: the statements
follow a pattern, small blows of the hammer
of human logic, forming
the eternal, repeated questions:
        What treaty, treaties,
what leagues, or covenants, what balances
of power groupings, what motivations
even of any church, of any religion,
stopped the incessant wars, the recurrent, the endless
wars of man against man, the slaughter, the pillage,
the civilizations, bright once and so hopeful, tumbled
into the dark of cruelty, the blackness
of man's inhumanity? When will they do so, while
nations retain the thing called sovereignty which is,
in the last resort, to abandon reason, set
force and bloodshed, violence in its place?
Country by country, epoch by long epoch: it is
swiftly traced, the deadly, the shameful
record of history.
    But now
the thought of the car, the drive home (Jennifer
is forgotten now or buried beneath a passion
other and outer, beyond self), this:

I beg you (he says) to answer the single question:
what is man's progress? Or, if you choose, then say:
has there been a progress? Myself, I believe there has—
slow, small and groping, but progress. It's all contained
in the one phrase, "Love thy neighbor as thyself."
Oh, this not only Christian, it has occurred
in one form or another in all religions
over the centuries. But only with Jesus Christ
did it form the cap, the keystone, the one essential:
love thy neighbor.
                  Where does it show? In war?
No—save for individuals caught up roughly
beyond their will and beyond belief in the thing
they are forced to fight for. Where then, where does it show?
Do we not practise cruelty and destruction,
do we not practise slavery and subjection,
do we not use intolerance as a weapon
to hold down races, minorities, and groups?
Yes. But not praising this. No longer
justified in the public mouth, but always
with the cynical shrug, the hideous, stupid phrase
of "Let's be realistic"—behind the door that's
locked against public eyes, and the hideous torture
denied and suppressed and denied again and again—
in spite of its truth.
               This is a progress. I give it
to you now.
          I give you also the hospital,
the charity and the clinic, the church and school,
the concept of government as the forever servant,
the Magna Carta, the wonderful Declaration
of Independence, the Bill of Rights—all these,
and the keystone, always, "You shall love your neighbor
as you love yourself."
              This is the inch
of progress forward. It grows. It grows in democracy.
It grows where the state and state give up the right
to kill and battle, and merge to a greater whole
and so find a lasting peace: the only one.
What are we asking now? we are asking only

414

that man take the last, the only logical step
forward along that single road of progress,
nation on nation to make, of the whole wide world,
one greater entity saying, but with one voice,
we are one because, before God, we love our neighbor
as we love ourselves.

He ceases. Silence now. Dorothy
Telford and even Loretta Messler have stopped
their private thinking. The ten—
the poor, small ten—are caught up
in the web of words, the emotion
generated by this so genuine
emotion, has seized them.
                                There is
not a ripple or movement, there is
no applause.
                    He thanks them. He knows
there is nothing more to do now.
                                The big piles
of literature on a card table; the many
cups and saucers, the array
of cakes, of plates, the glasses,
the coffee urn and the bottles of coca-cola,
the boxes of paper napkins—these
mock further effort—Millicent's effort:
wasted now. And Jerome Westen's effort,
gone now.
                Still standing, still
in the hush and the pause, the moment
of over but not yet
begun again, Quintus Lamy
thinks, "For a kiss." It is not
a bitter thought, it is only
a facing of some reality.

Now it is over. The stir. The movement.
Nice things said, a little more than polite,
the edge of emotion sharpens
the ordinary words. Not everything's

wasted entirely: coffee and cake and laughter—
and a seed planted, in odd
and small soil.
              Thank you, and very moving,
and interesting, and questions, some
most intelligent, some stupid, some
personal and outside the frame of
the sovereign evening.
                        And then—
it is all over, the lights
go out to stay out, the darkness
hides the room of the meeting, and all
the partings sound in the clear
cool air of October night: again: they sounded
the same with a difference Friday, now
it is different. It is over.
                        But not yet
entirely over.
              Borne on the sounds
of Sanskrit and Greek and Latin, of
Angle and Saxon, of all
the fused things of the word, we fly
high above Quintus Lamy, he goes
to his home and his wife.

He entered the house and he went at once to the kitchen,
poured himself out a glass of milk and drank it,
seated upon the kitchen table. No thought—
thought was turned off now—simply being, drinking
a glass of milk.
              Then he rose suddenly
and as suddenly awkward, his feet too big and heavy,
legs like great stems of lead, an aching stiffness
in the back of his neck, turned off one by one
all the lights on the ground floor and went up
the stairs to Virginia's room, the habitual act
(how strong do habits grow!).
                        She was reading a book,

looked up from it as he entered.

He said, "How are you?"
"I'm all right, Quintus," she said. "I'm quite all right.
How did the meeting go?"

"Oh, very well, thank you.
But small. Ten people. But that was as I expected.
Pity more didn't come."

"You will try it later?
Try it another time?"

"Don't know," he said.
"Too tired to try to decide that now. We'll see.
If you're all right, I think I'll go straight to bed.
I'm pretty bushed. But if you have need to talk,
I'll stay for a short while."

"No, you go to bed.
There's nothing to talk of. I'd only like to tell you,
I've decided to go to Dr. McManus. Soon."
"Oh, yes," said Quintus. "Good. I hope he may help.
You've had a long siege, too long. Hope he helps
if you do go."

"I shall go. I've decided."
"Good," he said. "It's always good to decide."
He saw the tears begin to come from her eyes.
"Oh, God, don't cry," he said.

She made an effort,
smiled rather wanly, took out a piece of tissue
from the box beside her bed and dried her eyes.
Looking at her, he saw that her lips were painted
brightly, rouge on her cheeks. It had been long
since she'd worn these in bed.

He said, "That's better.
It'll all come out in the wash. Look, this is it:
I haven't got one damn thing to give to anyone—
not now. It's not you, and it isn't us, it's
the whole damn business and all the work, and all
the things have happened. Tomorrow will be better.
I just need sleep. Do you understand, Virginia?"
She said, "Yes, I understand. And sleep well, Q.
Do you want a sleeping pill?"

"No," he said. "Don't need one.

417

I can hardly stay awake. I hope you'll sleep, too.
Good night, Virginia."
                        "Good night," she said.
                                        He left her,
closing the door behind him very gently.
He went to his own room and went straight to bed.
The bed felt good. He turned off the light. The darkness
wrapped him, the wanted, the so grateful darkness.
He thought, with a half-smile, well, there's one thing, truly,
I'm grateful to Jenny, I don't want one damn thing,
not one, but sleep.
                    And then the images came:
the week walked by his mind: the Friday hearing,
the hates and the animosities, the partings
under October stars, the sweet drive home,
the hopeful thought for the meeting, the glass of whiskey,
the light and the terrible transparency, anger
covering, covering, and the boy who fled
back to his own, at night, in night, and Rochester
and the hospital and the drawings, and the soft, lovely
brilliance of Sunday, paradox, brilliance in softness,
softness in sharpness, Jennifer, the alone,
Serena-Virginia and the alone, and Jennifer,
and the images blurred and changed and became the symbols
of a huge dream, unwilled, hard-held
in the long depths of a sleep that said tomorrow,
tomorrow and tomorrow.

Let him sleep.
            He is a good man held
in the frame of the everlasting, perishing
thick of the sensible flesh.
                        Our flight
is over Rochester Mallin, who wears
the garment of loneliness.
                        Rochester: man

418

of an earned distinction.
                                    He too is alone
in the bedroom of his own choice.

Undressing, Rochester was conscious only
of one thing—odd, it was so usual—
the shut door leading to Serena's room.
He put it from his mind. He tried to think
about the meeting. He could not recall
what had been said, only the single fact
(garnered by chance then at the very end
in casual talk) that Jennifer had gone.
Gone to New York. Fled? And if fled, why not
joy to his thought?
                              No joy.
                                    The time was gone
when you could fool yourself. You knew, so deeply
it hurt, made empty, that it was all over,
done, done and over. It had been; was gone.
Dead, and brought death?
                                    Death was the emptiness,
the void that would not fill. And if unfilled,
what then?
                  The closed door.
                                    Did you close the door
yourself? You, Rochester?
                                    Now, dressed for bed,
he stood unslippered on the chilly floor
and felt confusion mount.
                                    Whose fault, at last,
had closed the door? Was the door not fast closed
by icy parting for the night, the hard,
too simple phrase, good night? The too direct
look of the eyes that scanned him overtly
as though but now first seeing.
                                    And this door,
this miserable symbol made of wood

419

that could not bar the mind, was it but closed,
or was it locked?

Then suddenly, in relief,
his anger came and he bred fantasies
to feed its flaming.

Ah, so closed and locked?
With whose permission and within whose house?
Was it not his? Was he not master here?
If not his wife, then he would soon discover
what she proposed to be. The meeting: hah!
One World, we gave our sovereignties away,
we dwelt in never-never land, at last
we practised Christianity, loved our neighbor—
but locked our doors?

By God! he said, not here,
not in this house. I am no Quintus Lamy
to kiss the daughter, cater to the wife.
You'll take me as I am, but yet you'll take me,
or let me wholly go.

The anger now,
fresh, moving, welcome, rose another notch.
Lock the damn door?

Swiftly he went to it,
seized on the knob hard, turned it, put his weight
fiercely against the door his mind had bolted,
and it flew open.

And opening, panic seized him:
what would he say to her, why had he come
(what words to cover, what to save his face)?
Oh, God, what now?

The lights were brightly on,
two on the pretty dresser, one beside
the big bed with the two habitual
neatly turned triangles that said for two
(if there were two) to enter in; the chair
whose back bore silken underclothes.

But the room
was wholly empty. He could hear Serena
within the bathroom, back of the closed door,
the splash of water.

Anger'd been supplanted
by panic. Now the panic yielded place
to hideous disappointment, emptiness.
Softly he closed the door as he withdrew
into his room.
                    Here too was emptiness.
He went uncertainly to his bed and sat
on the bed's edge.
                    Male female, female man?
Or just the everlasting, futile struggle
to be yourself? But first, to find yourself:
perhaps immutably alone. There was
no road except the road of pain to lead
to something more than just your own desire—
and yet contain desire?
                    He thought, I cannot
think, it's too hard. It is all much too hard,
I am too tired, I am too much alone,
there's none to help me.
                    Almost unthinking now
he sat in darkness, the light turned off, not daring
the harsh finality of his single bed,
and the uncounted, slippery, the betraying
minutes rushed past upon their dragging feet
like peopled past of dreams.
                    Alone, alone?
The one word echoed till his heart constricted,
and tears—unshed these many adult years—
flowed from his eyes, and the man's body shook
with a sobbing, silent.
                    This too much. He rose,
impulsive and compulsive movement then,
walked to the little barrier of door
that was so great and strong, and opened it,
smelled the rich, the exotic smell of perfume
over the soft and timid smell of cold cream,
crossed the big room in darkness, found the bed,
and entered it, still sobbing.
                    A small voice
said, whispering, "You are having a bad time?"

421

He said, "Oh, God, I'm so alone, Serena."
"Then rest," the voice said. "It will all be gone
when morning comes. Sleep now."
                                        The other body,
warm in the bed, it had not moved or stirred—
only the voice came, softly, gently, kind.
No more than this?
                                There lay a wall of glass
unbreakable between: there was no power
within him to pass through it. He was bound
to ape her stillness.
                                Sleep? But not alone?
Sleep by your wife's side—and the terrible
thin door still stood at closed, and the long night
stretched on ahead, to reach to what, attained
by will, by want? By self?
                                        There was no answer.
Her breathing, audible, was the counterpoint
to deeper loneliness.

Rise now, once more, but
leaving behind as much
of the heart as can be spared. Not meet
to rest here, or become a part
where two become division.
                                        Oh, not yours
the garment to replace, perhaps with praise,
the spirit's heaviness.

Southerly, southerly, over
the short deep of salt water. Will you not
taste beauty who have tasted
that which the fire
burnt to its dust of lye?
Lye. The pun again

is but a sum of living.
                    Millicent
lies in a bed, too. There is here
no loneliness, but only
the very brief of opposite.

Whisper says but, "Millie. Remember, Millie?"
Whisper replies, "Oh, yes. Oh, yes. But not
now, darling, not now. Too tired. You too. Only
untired, to make perfect."
Whisper says, "Yes. Too sad, tonight. Except
for you, you always. Later, but
not forget."
Whisper says, "Never. Never forget. Sleep well, sleep."
and the answer, "Sleep."
                    And the whispers
drown in the wealth of sleep.
                    And sleep
contains, embraces, two, untouching, separate,
free, infinitely bound: by want, by will,
by love compounded: the anointed
with oil of joy.

Epilogue

SO FLY UP NOW, up. Let the harsh-sounding, loud
mechanism lift you, above, above, high,
we are past the soft, the many-syllabled words,
we are past descent of the heart to become part of,
to partake the bread of compassion, to drink the cup
of the wine that is bitter-sweet.
                                    Soon from on high
we see it differently, the topographical
pattern of road, of house, of land and water,
laid out below us, distant. The deep red
foliage of the great oak now can hide from us
lovers seen at ground-level.
                                    Oh, so soon
inland from everlasting mirror of infinite
sea-water—the great waves that great wind angrily
blew to an anger are but the small discernible
etching of surface now—there's a rosy field
dropping to dark of marsh grass, deepest green.
There'll be a store there soon, where on a time
rested a store. Or did not.
                                    Gentlemen of the jury,
this is for your determination only:
you must decide the truth.
                                    All wrongs, all rights,
all justness of all hates, all depths of love,
all self-desires, all charitable acts,
all false or true compassionate or sudden
compulsions, all that's mean, or only cruel,
these are for you: the truth, or not the truth,

427

the just or the unjust, the acceptable things,
impoverishment of life or its enrichment,
these for your minds; your hearts.
                              Seen from this height,
down-looking, steep, you fit them to the pattern:
your pattern, percipient now.
                              Flying away
at this vast speed that is not felt as speed,
back to the usual, the personal day
that's your geography (that holds the pattern
you are too close to see), remember them—
but not as ants that crawled painful and small
down infinite steeps of grass, not as the germs
that brilliance and clever glass made manifest,
but as the echo (the marble harp, the drop
of dripping water to the music bowl,
the taste of bitter leaf mold in the sweet
freshness of water-run) of the thing you lent
when, in participation, you descended
to witness and to know.
                              This is the end.